Reed College

Physics Lounge

Gift of

Robert E. Reynolds

David W. Brauer Professor

QUANTUM MECHANICS

Holden-Day Series in Physics

QUANTUM MECHANICS

by

PHILIP STEHLE

University of Pittsburgh

HOLDEN-DAY, INC., 1966

San Francisco · London · Amsterdam

Library of Congress Catalog Card Number: 66–17893
Printed in the United States of America

PREFACE

Many books on quantum mechanics exist, so that some reasons should probably be given for adding another one to the list. The primary reasons I had for writing this book were to try to reflect the way that quantum mechanics is used in present-day physics and to take advantage of the change in the preparation of students entering graduate school. Both of these seem to me to justify a treatment of quantum mechanics based on the transformation theory so elegantly formulated by Dirac in his classic book* rather than on the wave equation in coordinate space. There is no substitute for the wave equation in treating the motion of a particle in a prescribed potential. This problem, however, is not the only one of interest in present day physics, and for other problems the use of momentum, angular momentum, or occupation number representations is of great help. It appears proper, then, to formulate quantum mechanics from the start in a way which puts these various methods on an equal footing. This I have tried to do. The average graduate student has studied wave mechanics to a considerable extent, so that he is prepared to study the general structure of the theory and to appreciate how the various methods are related to each other through the transformation theory.

The treatment is meant to be of a practical kind. The interesting and difficult mathematical problems associated with the entities use in quantum mechanics are assumed to have solutions with the desired properties, or reasonable facsimiles of them. This has generally been true in the past, though

*P. A. M. Dirac, *The Principles of Quantum Mechanics*, 4th Edition, Oxford University Press, 1958.

some surprises may be in store here. I have tried to be explicit at all times about things like phase conventions and normalizations so that results arrived at or quoted can be used by the reader.

The applications of quantum mechanics made have been chosen because of their wide importance, their value in illustrating the use of different methods, and their simplicity. It has not been my purpose to discuss problems which involve much detailed analysis, but rather to show how problems can be attacked. In many fields, the complexity of the systems studied forces the investigator to use numerical methods or very complicated computational procedures. These have been omitted deliberately as belonging rather in specialized treatments of the topics involved.

I am much indebted to present and former colleagues who have made me aware of developments in many fields of physics, especially to R. Drisko and T. Holstein. The former read most of an early draft of the manuscript and did much to improve it. I am also indebted to the Austro–American Educational Commission and to the University of Innsbruck for giving me the opportunity to complete the manuscript while holding a Fulbright professorship.

Philip Stehle

TABLE OF CONTENTS

I: THE FORMULATION OF QUANTUM MECHANICS

II: BASIC APPLICATIONS OF QUANTUM MECHANICS

III: CENTRAL SYSTEMS

IV: ANGULAR MOMENTUM AND SYMMETRY

I

The formulation of quantum mechanics

1. PRELIMINARY REMARKS

The historical development of quantum theory was far from being a logical progression from one step to the next. The first suggestion of quantum theory arose in the statistical mechanics of the radiation field when Planck overcame the difficulties associated with black body radiation. Classical statistical mechanics leads to the law of equipartition of energy among all possible degrees of freedom. Applied to the radiation field, which has an infinite number of degrees of freedom, it leads to an infinite energy content of this field at any finite temperature and to an infinite specific heat.

A somewhat similar paradox existed in the theory of the specific heats of gases and solids. The specific heat of a gas at low temperature was adequately described by classical statistical mechanics via the equipartition principle as long as the gas molecules were treated as rigid. Furthermore, a linear molecule like CO_2 must have no degree of freedom corresponding to rotation about its own axis. A molecule has internal degrees of freedom, and their failure to contribute to the specific heat is not classically explained. The electrons in a solid do not contribute their share to the specific heat, which, according to the law of Dulong and Petit, is accounted for entirely by the atoms considered as rigid particles.

The classical law of equipartition of energy arises by considering the transfer of energy between elements of the system which is in thermal equilibrium. Classically this interaction can transfer arbitrarily small amounts of energy, and an element of the system possessing high energy at some time probably acquired this excess energy in very many small increments. If, for some reason, arbitrarily small increments are not possible, then the probability of finding parts of the system at high energy is reduced and equipartition is invalid.

Since light does not scatter light to an extent sufficient to produce thermal equilibrium in a reasonable time, the equipartition of energy in the radiation field is arrived at through the interaction of light with the walls of the cavity in which the thermal equilibrium exists. The impossibility of exchanging arbitrarily small amounts of energy with the walls suffices to rule out equipartition. (If light scattered light, the radiation field could achieve equipartition without the help of the walls and a limitation on the exchange between radiation field and wall would not suffice. In a material gas the Maxwell–Boltzmann velocity distribution can be arrived at without the help of the walls, which can be considered as rigid. This is because gas molecules scatter among themselves.)

Planck's hypothesis was that energy could be exchanged only in quanta, the size of the quantum being proportional to the frequency of the radiation involved. Thus, if the walls are considered to be a set of harmonic oscillators, and if these oscillators can have energies given by

$$E = E_0 + nh\nu ,$$

where E_0 is a constant, $h\nu$ is the size of the quantum, and n is an integer, then the desired limitation on energy exchange is achieved. The proportionality between the frequency and the size of the quantum of energy transfer gives quantitative agreement with the frequency distribution observed in cavity radiation.

An essential point in the argument used by Planck is the shift of attention from the radiation to the oscillators composing the wall. Because the oscillators are quantized, equipartition of energy in the radiation field fails. At this stage one does not have to give up the classical description of radiation. Later this must be done, but only much later, when very different realms of physics are considered. For a great many applications one can restrict attention to the quantum features of the matter involved in phenomena, treating light classically. In this way the quantum properties of atoms can describe the light emitted by these atoms. It is only when one tries to describe fine points, like the width and shape of a spectral line, that it is necessary to treat light by the principles of quantum mechanics.

It is worth noting that all the experiments one does in atomic physics, as in nuclear physics, involve the emission, absorption, and scattering of particles in various combinations. Thus the existence of discrete energy states of oscillators and atoms is inferred from what one calls scattering experiments, understanding scattering in a rather general sense. The theory of scattering should, therefore, be the most fundamental theory from which the results of experiments are to be predicted. Indeed, this is very probably the case, but this is not the way the theory developed and is not the way the theory is used in atomic, nuclear, or solid state physics. The physics of high energy particles does require this viewpoint.

This discussion serves as a justification for what is to follow. This book considers the form of quantum mechanics which is adapted to the discussion of the possible states of systems such as atoms and molecules. Only after this is firmly established is the theory of scattering developed. At the very end, the scattering formulation is used to discuss the stationary states of many particle systems. No relativistic systems are discussed. In particular, the quantum mechanics of the radiation field is not developed even though this is what started it all. The quantum nature of light appears only in the discussion of the uncertainty principle.

2. THE UNCERTAINTY PRINCIPLE

The purpose of mechanics is to provide a complete description of systems occurring in nature. This purpose has not been accomplished and presumably never will be. A wide class of systems is very accurately described by non-relativistic classical mechanics, and a still wider one by relativistic classical mechanics. The relativistic theory is necessary when the velocities of parts of the systems being described are not negligible in comparison with the velocity of light, or when strong gravitational fields are involved. The epithet "classical" here is taken to mean that the system can be observed to all relevant accuracy without causing any disturbance of its motion. When the parts of the system become small on a scale to be described below, the assumed observability breaks down and quantum effects become important. This can happen independently of the presence or absence of relativistic effects.

In both classical and quantum mechanics, the description of the system can be divided into two parts. First, the *state* of the system at a given instant of time is given, and the change of this state with time is described. The former involves statements about what can be measured and what must be measured in order to have the basis needed to predict future behavior of the system. The latter involves setting up the *equations of motion* of the system.

The classical description of a system of particles consists of giving the values of the coordinates and momenta of each particle at a certain time, and of giving the differential equations satisfied by these quantities. The values, q_i and p_i, specify the state of the system completely. The equations of motion are Hamilton's equations derived from the Hamiltonian function $H(q, p)$.

$$\dot{q}_i = \frac{\partial H}{\partial p_i}, \qquad \dot{p}_i = -\frac{\partial H}{\partial q_i}. \tag{2.1}$$

It is essential that these equations are of the first order in the time, because only then is a solution uniquely specified by the values of the q's and the p's at the time t_0. The classical description can also be made in terms of the coordinates q_i and the velocities $\dot{q}_i$. The equations of motion are then Lagrange's equations which are half as numerous as Equations (2.1) (there being one equation for each degree of freedom) but which are of second order. This description is less convenient for the purpose at hand.

The Hamiltonian function is the total energy of the system expressed in terms of the q's and the p's. For example consider a particle moving near the surface of the earth. The kinetic energy, T, is given by

$$T = \frac{1}{2m}(p_x^2 + p_y^2 + p_z^2)$$

while the potential energy, V, is

$$V = mgz\,.$$

It is immediately seen that these, together with

$$H = T + V\,,$$

lead to the usual equations for projectile motion.

This kind of description is inadequate when the system to be described is atomic in scale, because the operations needed to specify the state classically cannot be carried out and are therefore meaningless. Consider a system consisting of a charged particle whose only interaction with other systems is electromagnetic. The only practical way to locate the particle is to scatter light from it and to observe the source of the scattered radiation. Now we know that light interacts with matter as though it consisted of quanta of energy* $\hbar\omega$ and momentum $\hbar\omega/c$. The Compton effect, the photoelectric effect, and the black body radiation can be described simply only on this hypothesis. This quantum character must be taken into account in discussing the scattering process.

To locate the charged particle a quantum must be scattered through an angle θ. The momentum of the quantum is therefore changed by an amount s of the order of magnitude

$$s \sim \hbar\omega\theta/c\,.$$

To be able to locate the particle within an uncertainty Δx requires a certain resolving power of the optical system, which entails an angle of acceptance $\Delta\theta$ of the order of magnitude

$$\Delta\theta \sim \frac{\lambda\!\!\!^{-}}{\Delta x}\,.$$

* All frequencies from here on are circular frequencies, and $\hbar = h/2\pi$, where h is Planck's constant.

Elimination of $\Delta\theta$ gives

$$\Delta s \sim \frac{\hbar\omega}{c}\frac{\lambdabar}{\Delta x} = \frac{\hbar}{\Delta x}\,.$$

The uncertainty in the momentum p is at least as great as Δs after the measurement has occurred, so we see that

(2.2) $$\Delta x\,\Delta p \gtrsim \hbar\,.$$

This is a preliminary statement of the *uncertainty principle* first formulated by W. Heisenberg. For macroscopic systems this uncertainty is unimportant because of the large value of the mass which appears in Δp.

The inequality (2.2) is independent of the frequency of the quantum and of the details of the interaction between the quantum and the particle. It depends only on the conservation of momentum and energy, and on the quantum nature of emission and absorption processes. We are thus led to expect that other interactions, such as with sound waves, are also quantized. This assumption is amply supported by observation.

As a second example, let us consider a collimating system consisting of two screens a distance d apart each containing a hole of radius ρ as shown.

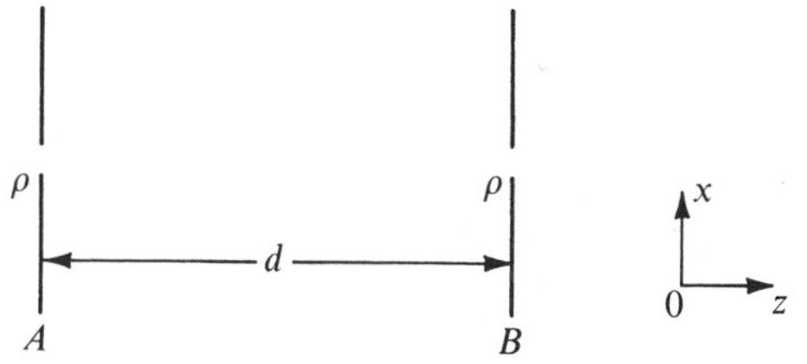

Fig. 2-1

Particles are incident on screen A from the left with a z-component of momentum p_z. Only those whose x-coordinate is defined within $\pm\rho$ (and similarly for y) can get through the hole. For the particle to reach the second hole, the momentum vector must be within a cone of half-angle $p_x/p_z \sim \rho/d$. Thus a particle about to go through the hole in screen B has values of x and of p_x satisfying

(2.3) $$\Delta x\,\Delta p_x \sim \rho^2 p_z/d\,.$$

This can be made as small as desired. This has no predictive value, however, for to know the value of p_x for a particle which has gone through the hole, we must be able to verify that it did not transfer momentum to the screen B. The measurement of the screen's momentum will make the location of the hole uncertain, and we are again left with (1.1). Conservation of momentum guarantees that this uncertainty cannot be reduced. In this system it is possible to know the particle's coordinates and momenta more accurately than (2.2) allows a posteriori, but not a priori. Thus if screen B is fixed and no measurement of its momentum is made, the fact that the particle got through the hole means that (2.3) applied *before* it went through the hole, but not afterwards.

The restriction (2.3) is classical. The quantum restriction (2.2) is only important when it is more stringent than the classical. Thus, quantum effects become important in the two-hole system when

$$\hbar \gtrsim \rho^2 p_z / d ,$$

or when

$$\lambda\!\!\!^{-} = \hbar / p_z \gtrsim \rho^2 / d . \tag{2.4}$$

The quantity ρ^2/d is a length characteristic of the apparatus or of the particle orbit. The quantity $\hbar/p_z$ is characteristic of the quantum nature of the particle. It is the *de Broglie wavelength*. The quantum features of this system become prominent when the de Broglie wavelength becomes comparable to lengths characteristic of the particle orbit. For very small de Broglie wavelengths, i.e., for high momenta, the quantum features are of reduced importance. If the momentum becomes large because of large masses rather than because of large velocities, classical mechanics becomes valid. We shall assume this to be true for all systems which admit of a classical description.

3. PRELIMINARY DISCUSSION OF MEASUREMENT

In classical physics, the means of determining the state of a system at a time t_0 do not require any special discussion. The use of sufficiently delicate probes, or of sufficiently dim light, will enable one to measure the position and momentum of any particle with no limit to the attainable accuracy. The measuring process does not disturb the measured system in any essential way and the measured state can be considered to be that which existed just before, or that which exists just after, the measuring process is carried out. When the measuring instruments themselves are composed of systems of the size of the system to be measured it is perhaps not surprising that new features enter. What is certainly not obvious from the classical viewpoint is the fact that even light shares this discrete structure in some sense and cannot be used to circumvent the atomicity of measuring instruments.

No detailed discussion of measurements and their limitations from the quantum point of view can be given until all of the machinery of quantum mechanics is available. What we want to do here is only to discuss the meaning of the word "measure." When the process of determining the state of a system must affect that state, there is a distinction between preparing a system in a given state and detecting whether the system was in a given state. The two hole apparatus described in Section 2 can be used in either way. If the momentum of screen B is monitored, the apparatus prepares the particle in a certain range of momentum states whose momentum spread is measured by Δp_x. If the momentum of screen A is monitored, the apparatus detects whether the particle was in a certain range of momentum states. The word measure can refer to either of these processes.

The uncertainty principle can be stated as follows. No apparatus can prepare a particle in such a way that a second apparatus is sure to find that its coordinate x and the conjugate momentum p_x are more accurately determined than is allowed by the inequality

$$\Delta x \, \Delta p_x \gtrsim \hbar.$$

The word "sure" is vital to the statement. It is possible to prepare a particle with an arbitrarily small value of Δx and then to detect whether or not it has a momentum in an arbitrarily small range Δp_x. If Δx and Δp_x are smaller than allowed by the uncertainty principle, one cannot say that the particle was in a state with values of x and p_x determined in violation of the uncertainty principle. In the rest of this discussion we use the word measure in the sense of preparation. Thus, if an observable Q associated with a system is measured to have the value Q', we mean that the system is prepared by the apparatus so that immediately after the measurement the quantity Q has the value Q'.

If two variables associated with a system are not constrained by an uncertainty relation between them, then there is an apparatus which will prepare the system so that these two variables take on any desired physically meaningful values. Under these circumstances a detecting apparatus can also be constructed to detect the presence of systems with any values of these variables. There may, of course, be great practical difficulties to be overcome, but there is no difficulty of principle in constructing this apparatus.

Consider a system with which are associated observables $Q_1, Q_2, \ldots, Q_g$. This system can be prepared with a definite value of Q_1, say Q_1'. If Q_2 has no uncertainty relation with Q_1, it too can be given a value, say Q_2'. If, however, there is an uncertainty relation between Q_1 and Q_2, in general no definite value can be assigned to Q_2, or Q_2 cannot be measured without disturbing the value of Q_1, and so we do not measure it. Proceeding in this way, measuring each Q_j that does not disturb previous Q_i''s, and leaving aside all those that do, we make as complete a measurement on the system as is possible. For a finite system there is a finite number of independent variables Q_j so that this process involves only a finite number of steps. We arrive in this way at a *state* of the system. This state is labelled by the values of the variables measured.

If the variables $Q_1, \ldots, Q_g$ had been written in a different order, say starting with the first variable passed over in the previous scheme, we would have arrived at a different state labelled by the values of different variables. We must now decide how to regard these two different states. Should each of them be regarded as a distinct, completely determined state, or should they be regarded as incomplete specifications of the same state? There have been many attempts to carry through the latter interpretation, with the introduction of "hidden variables" whose values cannot be specified by any known apparatus and which must, therefore, be averaged over in some sense. None of these attempts has proved fruitful. The theory resulting from the former interpretation is present-day quantum mechanics which gives a simple and extremely accurate description of what is observed.* We therefore adopt the view that a system on which all mutually compatible independent measurements have been made is in a definite state. This state is labelled with the results of these measurements, and is written symbolically as

$$|Q_1', \ldots, Q_f'\rangle .$$

This symbol is called a *ket*, a notation introduced by Dirac.

Observables whose values can be measured without mutual interference are said to *commute*. The order in which these variables are measured is immaterial. A set of observables whose values determine the state of a system is then called a *complete set of commuting observables*. In general, there is more than one such set associated with a given system. For a single particle, complete sets of commuting observables are p_x, p_y, p_z, and x, y, z, and p_x, p_y, z. The observables x and p_x do not commute as the measurement of one disturbs the value of the other. Thus, both x and p_x cannot be members of a complete set of commuting observables.

A system described by the complete set of commuting observables $Q_1, Q_2, \ldots, Q_f$, can exist in states with various values of these observables, $|Q_1', Q_2', \ldots, Q_f'\rangle$ and $|Q_1'', Q_2'', \ldots, Q_f''\rangle$. These states are distinct if any one of the Q_i'' differs from Q_i'. We must now consider whether all states of the system can be described by kets labelled in this way. If Q_g is an observable which does not commute with $Q_1, Q_2, \ldots, Q_f$, then Q_g cannot have a well-defined value of, say, Q_g', in any state labelled by values $Q_1', Q_2', \ldots, Q_f'$. It is, therefore, conceivable that states labelled with values of Q_g should be completely independent of the states $|Q_1', Q_2', \ldots, Q_f'\rangle$. This would, however, lead to the existence of inconveniently many states, so it is assumed that one kind of labelling is enough to give all the possible states of a system. That is, if $Q_1, Q_2, \ldots, Q_f$ constitute a complete set of commut-

* See "The Development of the Interpretation of the Quantum Theory" by W. Heisenberg in *Niels Bohr and the Development of Physics*, W. Pauli, Ed. McGraw-Hill Book Co., New York, 1955.

ing observables for a system, then the states $|Q_1', Q_2', \ldots, Q_f'\rangle$ with all possible values of the Q_i' suffice to describe any state of the system. The means by which these states are combined to arrive at states labelled with the values of other commuting observables is introduced in the next section.

4. THE PRINCIPLE OF SUPERPOSITION

If $Q_1, Q_2, \ldots, Q_f$ are the elements of a complete set of commuting observables for a system, we assume that the states $|Q_1', Q_2', \ldots, Q_f'\rangle$ can be used to describe any state of the system, say $|P_1', P_2', \ldots, P_g'\rangle$. Here $P_1, P_2, \ldots, P_g$ constitute an alternative complete set of commuting observables for our system. What kind of relation exists between states labelled in these two ways?

In the theory of light, a collimated beam of light travelling in the z-direction can be plane polarized in the x-direction or in the y-direction. These polarization states are most easily described by giving the electric vector as a function of position and time. Thus, for plane polarization in the x-direction, i.e., in the x–z plane, we have

$$\begin{aligned} \mathbf{E}^{(x)} &= \mathbf{e}_x \cos(kz - \omega t) \\ &= \operatorname{Re} \mathbf{e}_x \exp[i(kz - \omega t)] \,. \end{aligned} \tag{4.1}$$

The symbol Re means *real part of*, while $\mathbf{e}_x$ is a unit vector in the x-direction. Similarly,

$$\begin{aligned} \mathbf{E}^{(y)} &= \mathbf{e}_y \cos(kz - \omega t + \delta) \\ &= \operatorname{Re} \mathbf{e}_y \exp[i(kz - \omega t + \delta)] \end{aligned} \tag{4.2}$$

describes a beam plane polarized in the y–z plane and with a phase differing from that in (4.1) by δ.

The two states of plane polarization are not the only ones which can be used to describe a light beam. Two other states which may be used are those of right-circular polarization and left-circular polarization. In a right-circularly polarized beam the electric vector rotates clockwise in time as seen by an observer looking in the direction of propagation. (This convention is opposite to that used in many works on optics. The only useful advice in this connection is, "Reader, beware!") The simplest description of a right circularly polarized beam is

$$\begin{aligned} \mathbf{E}_{\mathrm{RCP}} &= \frac{1}{\sqrt{2}} [\mathbf{e}_x \cos(kz - \omega t) - \mathbf{e}_y \sin(kz - \omega t)] \\ &= \frac{1}{\sqrt{2}} \operatorname{Re} (\mathbf{e}_x + i\mathbf{e}_y) \exp[i(kz - \omega t)] \,. \end{aligned} \tag{4.3}$$

Similarly for a left circularly polarized beam

$$\mathbf{E}_{\mathrm{LCP}} = \frac{1}{\sqrt{2}} \operatorname{Re} (\mathbf{e}_x - i\mathbf{e}_y) \exp [i(kz - \omega t)] . \tag{4.4}$$

The numerical factor $1/\sqrt{2}$ is introduced to make the intensities of the beams the same.

It is now seen that the relationship between plane and circular polarization is a relationship of linear superposition. Two plane-polarized beams of equal amplitude, and appropriate relative phase, constitute circularly polarized light.

$$\mathbf{E}_{\mathrm{RCP}} = \frac{1}{\sqrt{2}} (\mathbf{E}^{(x)} + i\mathbf{E}^{(y)}) , \tag{4.5}$$

where the common exponential factor $\exp[i(kz - \omega t)]$ is omitted, along with the projection on the real axis, Re. The relationship is reciprocal, for $\mathbf{E}^{(x)}$, $\mathbf{E}^{(y)}$ may be expressed as

$$\mathbf{E}^{(x)} = \frac{1}{\sqrt{2}} (\mathbf{E}_{\mathrm{RCP}} + \mathbf{E}_{\mathrm{LCP}}) , \qquad \mathbf{E}^{(y)} = \frac{1}{i\sqrt{2}} (\mathbf{E}_{\mathrm{RCP}} - \mathbf{E}_{\mathrm{LCP}}) . \tag{4.6}$$

A beam which is in a definite state of plane polarization has completely undetermined circular polarization. A beam with elliptical polarization is a linear combination of $\mathbf{E}^{(x)}$, $\mathbf{E}^{(y)}$ with certain amplitudes and phases. It does not represent a completely new state of polarization, as it can be described in terms of plane polarizations.

An unpolarized beam of light does not correspond to any single polarization state. It is not a superposition of two independent polarization states with definite amplitudes and phases. We call such a condition a *mixture* of states. Here it can be thought of as a superposition of $\mathbf{E}^{(x)}$ and $\mathbf{E}^{(y)}$ with equal amplitudes but with randomly varying relative phase. The presence of such a time-dependent phase means that the light cannot be strictly monochromatic.

We use this idea in order to describe the situation when the states of a system are defined by the values of two different complete sets of commuting observables. To make the notation clear, let one set be denoted by $\alpha_1, \ldots, \alpha_f$, the second by $\beta_1, \ldots, \beta_g$. We *assume* that the state $|\beta_1', \ldots, \beta_g'\rangle$ is expressible as a linear combination of states $|\alpha_1', \ldots, \alpha_f'\rangle$ with various values of the α_i' and with certain *complex* coefficients. Thus we write

$$|\beta_1', \ldots, \beta_g'\rangle = \sum_{\alpha'} |\alpha_1', \ldots, \alpha_f'\rangle \langle \alpha_1', \ldots, \alpha_f' | \beta_1', \ldots, \beta_g'\rangle . \tag{4.7}$$

The summation is over all possible combinations of the values $\alpha_1', \ldots, \alpha_f'$. The quantity $\langle \alpha_1', \ldots, \alpha_f' | \beta_1', \ldots, \beta_g'\rangle$ is a complex number. The notation is very convenient because it emphasizes the labels, which are important.

The principle of superposition goes somewhat beyond the statement (4.7). It says also that every linear combination of states is a state. Later we shall see that usually there is a restriction to be put on the coefficients of interesting combinations. Another generalization must be mentioned. It may happen that the possible values of an observable form a continuum. In this case the sum in (4.7) must be interpreted as an integral.

The states $|\alpha_1', \ldots, \alpha_f'\rangle$ are to be taken as linearly independent. That is, no relation

$$\sum_{\alpha''} |\alpha_1'', \ldots, \alpha_f''\rangle c_{\alpha_1'', \ldots, \alpha_f''} = 0$$

exists with non-vanishing coefficients c. The reason for this is physical. If such a relation existed, it could be solved for a particular state $|\alpha_1', \ldots, \alpha_f'\rangle$ in terms of the others. This would mean that a state in which the observables $\alpha_1, \ldots, \alpha_f$ have a particular set of values could be expressed as a linear combination of states in which these same observables have different values. To avoid this interdependence of physically distinct states we *assume* the linear independence of states labelled by distinct values of *any* observable.

5. STATE VECTORS

In the last section, the idea of forming linear combinations of states, which then represent new states, was introduced. Quantities which can be multiplied by numbers and added together to yield new quantities of the same sort are called *vectors*. The three-dimensional vectors of classical mechanics and electrodynamics are the most familiar ones. The property of superposition possessed by the states of a quantum system make these states vectors of a more general kind.

A set of linearly independent vectors spans a vector space. There are as many dimensions in the space as there are linearly independent vectors. In physical space there are three dimensions and every set of four vectors is linearly dependent. In the space of state vectors there is one dimension for each set of possible values of a complete set of commuting observables. For simplicity we assume that all the observables of the system being discussed have discrete sets of possible values. The generalization to continua is made later.

The state of a classical system is specified by giving the values of the coordinates q_i and the momenta p_i of the system at some time t. This way of specifying a state has intuitive appeal as it corresponds directly with our observation of particles in nature. To say that the state of a quantum system is specified by a vector in a multidimensional space lacks this appeal at first. Only when the manipulations with these vectors are familiar does the intuitive acceptance develop. In this section some of these manipulations will be introduced.

The state of a system is specified by a vector labelled by the numerical values of observables. It is therefore necessary to be able to extract numbers from state vectors. In ordinary vector algebra, numbers are extracted by forming scalar products. Thus if $\mathbf{a}$ and $\mathbf{b}$ are two vectors, $\mathbf{a}\cdot\mathbf{b}$ is a number. The length of a vector $\mathbf{a}$ is $(\mathbf{a}\cdot\mathbf{a})^{1/2}$, the cosine of the angle between two unit vectors $\mathbf{e}_1$ and $\mathbf{e}_2$ is $\mathbf{e}_1\cdot\mathbf{e}_2$. Thus, by defining a scalar product we can extract numbers from state vectors. Because we allow complex coefficients to occur in linear combinations, the scalar product is best defined in a somewhat different way from the three-dimensional scalar product. The scalar product of a vector with itself will be interpreted as a probability, and must therefore be a positive real number, no matter what complex coefficient the vector has. This requirement controls the definition of the scalar product.

The first step is to introduce a new type of vector denoted by $\langle\alpha'|$. Here the α' are a set of values of observables just as in the original state vector $|\alpha'\rangle$. The vector $\langle\alpha'|$ is said to be *dual* to $|\alpha'\rangle$ if the same set of labels appears in both. To distinguish the two types, vectors such as $\langle\alpha'|$ are called *bras*, and those such as $|\alpha'\rangle$ are called *kets*. We make the following assumptions about bras and kets:

(i) To each ket $|\alpha'\rangle$ corresponds a unique bra $\langle\alpha'|$ and conversely. They are dual to each other.

(ii) If $\langle\alpha'|$ and $|\alpha'\rangle$ are dual to each other, and $\langle\beta'|$ and $|\beta'\rangle$ are likewise, then so are $\langle\alpha'| + \langle\beta'|$ and $|\alpha'\rangle + |\beta'\rangle$.

(iii) If $\langle\alpha'|$ and $|\alpha'\rangle$ are dual to each other, and if c is a complex number, then $\langle\alpha'|c^*$ and $c|\alpha'\rangle$ are dual to each other. (c^* is the complex conjugate of c.) Postulates (ii) and (iii) together show that $\langle\alpha'|$ is an *antilinear* function of $|\alpha'\rangle$. It would be linear except for the complex conjugation occurring in (iii).

The scalar product is defined only between a bra and a ket. It is denoted by $\langle\beta'|\alpha'\rangle$ and has the properties:

(iv) $\langle\beta'|\alpha'\rangle$ is a complex number which is a linear function of $|\alpha'\rangle$ and an antilinear function of $|\beta'\rangle$. If $|\alpha'\rangle$ is replaced by $c|\alpha'\rangle$, $\langle\beta'|\alpha'\rangle$ is replaced by $c\langle\beta'|\alpha'\rangle$, while if $|\beta'\rangle$ is replaced by $c|\beta'\rangle$, $\langle\beta'|\alpha'\rangle$ is replaced by $c^*\langle\beta'|\alpha'\rangle$.

(v) $\langle\alpha'|\alpha'\rangle$ is real and positive unless $|\alpha'\rangle = 0$ in which case it vanishes.

Because of (iv), postulate (v) remains true when $|\alpha'\rangle$ is replaced by $c|\alpha'\rangle$ for any complex number c. An important consequence of these two postulates is that

$$\langle\beta'|\alpha'\rangle = \langle\alpha'|\beta'\rangle^* . \tag{5.1}$$

This follows from the reality of $(\langle\alpha'| + \langle\beta'|)(|\alpha'\rangle + |\beta'\rangle)$, for

$$(\langle\alpha'| + \langle\beta'|)(|\alpha'\rangle + |\beta'\rangle) = \langle\alpha'|\alpha'\rangle + \langle\beta'|\beta'\rangle + \langle\alpha'|\beta'\rangle + \langle\beta'|\alpha'\rangle$$

and the first two terms on the right are real.

The scalar product of a vector with its dual is called the *norm* of the vector. A vector of unit norm is *normalized.* Two vectors whose scalar product vanishes are called *orthogonal.* This is a generalization of three-dimensional orthogonality. Unless otherwise stated, the vectors representing states are normalized. This still leaves undetermined a numerical factor of modulus unity for each state vector. This is called a *phase factor.* Further, the state vectors labelled by non-identical sets of values of a set of commuting observables are defined to be orthogonal to each other. Thus

$$\langle\alpha_1'', \ldots, \alpha_f''|\alpha_1', \ldots, \alpha_f'\rangle = \delta_{\alpha_1''\alpha_1'}\,\delta_{\alpha_2''\alpha_2'} \ldots \delta_{\alpha_f''\alpha_f'}\,. \tag{5.2}$$

If $\alpha_1, \ldots, \alpha_f$ are a complete set of commuting observables, the vectors $|\alpha_1', \ldots, \alpha_f'\rangle$ span the space of states of the system and any state vector, $|\beta_1', \ldots, \beta_g'\rangle$ can be expanded in terms of the $|\alpha'\rangle$. (α' will frequently denote the set $\alpha_1', \ldots, \alpha_f'$, etc.) This has already been assumed in (4.7), which we may write as

$$|\beta'\rangle = \sum_{\alpha'} |\alpha'\rangle\,\langle\alpha'|\beta'\rangle\,. \tag{5.3}$$

Here the expansion coefficient $\langle\alpha'|\beta'\rangle$ is the scalar product as it has just been defined provided the vectors $|\alpha'\rangle$ are normalized. This is seen by multiplying by $\langle\alpha''|$ and using (5.2).

The scalar products $\langle\alpha'|\beta'\rangle$ for all sets α' and β' constitute a matrix. From (5.3) it is seen that this is the transformation matrix connecting the state vectors $|\beta'\rangle$ with the state vectors $|\alpha'\rangle$. This matrix is of a special kind because it connects two sets of normalized, orthogonal vectors, two *orthonormal* sets. Analogously to (5.3) we may write

$$|\alpha''\rangle = \sum_{\beta'} |\beta'\rangle\,\langle\beta'|\alpha''\rangle\,. \tag{5.4}$$

When (5.3) is substituted into this, there results

$$|\alpha''\rangle = \sum_{\beta'}\sum_{\alpha'} |\alpha'\rangle\,\langle\alpha'|\beta'\rangle\,\langle\beta'|\alpha''\rangle\,,$$

from which it follows that

$$\sum_{\beta'} \langle\alpha'|\beta'\rangle\,\langle\beta'|\alpha''\rangle = \delta_{\alpha'\alpha''}\,. \tag{5.5}$$

This looks more familiar, perhaps, if we introduce $U_{\alpha'\beta'} = \langle\alpha'|\beta'\rangle$. It then becomes

$$\sum_{\beta'} U_{\alpha'\beta'}(U_{\alpha''\beta'})^* = \delta_{\alpha'\alpha''} .$$

This together with

$$\sum_{\beta'} U_{\beta'\alpha'}(U_{\beta'\alpha''})^* = \delta_{\alpha'\alpha''} ,$$

which follows similarly, define $U_{\alpha'\beta'}$ as a *unitary* matrix. The transformations connecting state vectors are unitary transformations.

The mathematical quantities which have been introduced can be given physical meaning. Consider the expansion (5.3). The state $|\beta'\rangle$ is, by definition, one in which a measurement of β_j will result in the value β_j', but in which the measurement of α_k will lead to no sharp value. Repeated measurements of the α' in the state $|\beta'\rangle$ will lead to a distribution of results as the value of α_k is not well defined in this state. All that the theory can be asked to describe is the probability that a particular set of values of the α's will be found. We assume that this probability, P, is given by

(5.6)
$$P = |\langle\alpha'|\beta'\rangle|^2 .$$

P is a positive real number not greater than unity.

If β is measured in the state $|\beta'\rangle$, the probability of finding the result $\beta'' \neq \beta'$ must vanish. This it does because states with different β' are orthogonal. The probability of finding the values β' must be unity. Thus,

(5.7)
$$\langle\beta'|\beta'\rangle = 1 = \sum_{\alpha'} \langle\beta'|\alpha'\rangle \langle\alpha'|\beta'\rangle$$
$$= \sum_{\alpha'} | \langle\alpha'|\beta'\rangle |^2 .$$

The physical meaning of this is simple. If the system is prepared in the state $|\beta'\rangle$, the sum of the probabilities of finding it in the state $|\alpha'\rangle$, summed over all possible values of α', is unity. This implies only that the system cannot disappear from the world, but must give some result when the α are measured.

The statistical interpretation of quantum mechanics was invented by Born. The formulation described here is due to Dirac.*

* P. A. M. Dirac, *Quantum Mechanics*, 4th Edition, Oxford University Press, London, 1958.

6. OBSERVABLES

The idea of the value of an observable in a given state has been introduced in a very basic way. A state is fully described by giving the value of each of a complete set of commuting observables. The observable itself has not been introduced yet. This must be done before the theory acquires any physical content whatever.

In classical mechanics an observable is a function of the coordinates and momenta which specify the system. Thus the angular momentum of a particle about the z-axis of a cartesian coordinate system is the function

$$l_z(q, p) = xp_y - yp_x .$$

The value of l_z is determined in a given state simply by inserting the values of q, p corresponding to that state in this function. In quantum mechanics the state is specified by a state vector $|\alpha'\rangle$. What plays the role of the function of q and p?

Numbers are associated with state vectors by the forming of scalar products. The value of an observable in a given state may be associated with a scalar product involving just that state vector. Let us denote the observable by O. Then O is the quantum analogue of a function of q and p. We write its value in a given state as

$$\langle\alpha'|\mathrm{O}|\alpha'\rangle .$$

This can be interpreted as the scalar product of the bra $\langle\alpha'|$ with a ket $\mathrm{O}|\alpha'\rangle$, or as the scalar product of the bra $\langle\alpha'|\mathrm{O}$ and the ket $|\alpha'\rangle$. We require these two interpretations to be equivalent.

We are considering $\mathrm{O}|\alpha'\rangle$ to be a ket. The quantity O is then called an *operator*. An operator applied to a ket yields a ket. We require this operator to be *linear*, by which we mean

$$\begin{aligned} \mathrm{O}(|\alpha'\rangle + |\beta'\rangle) &= \mathrm{O}|\alpha'\rangle + \mathrm{O}|\beta'\rangle , \\ \mathrm{O}(c|\alpha'\rangle) &= c\mathrm{O}|\alpha'\rangle , \end{aligned} \tag{6.1}$$

where c is a complex number. On occasion it is useful to admit also *antilinear* operators. The only change this makes in (6.1) is that on the right of the second equation c is replaced by c^*. The linearity (or antilinearity) is necessary because of the superposition principle which underlies the statistical interpretation of quantum mechanics.

Let the state $|\alpha'\rangle$ in which O has the value $\langle\alpha'|\mathrm{O}|\alpha'\rangle$ be a superposition of the two states $|\beta'\rangle$ and $|\gamma'\rangle$,

$$|\alpha'\rangle = \lambda_1|\beta'\rangle + \lambda_2|\gamma'\rangle , \ \langle\alpha'| = \langle\beta'|\lambda_1^* + \langle\gamma'|\lambda_2^* , \tag{6.2}$$

where $\lambda_1 = \langle\beta'|\alpha'\rangle$, etc. Then,

$$\langle\alpha'|\mathrm{O}|\alpha'\rangle = |\lambda_1|^2\langle\beta'|\mathrm{O}|\beta'\rangle + |\lambda_2|^2\langle\gamma'|\mathrm{O}|\gamma'\rangle + \lambda_1{}^*\lambda_2\langle\beta'|\mathrm{O}|\gamma'\rangle + \lambda_1\lambda_2{}^*\langle\gamma'|\mathrm{O}|\beta'\rangle\,. \tag{6.3}$$

Now the value of an observable must be a real number. If it were not, then the real part alone could be considered an observable as could the imaginary part alone. The left side of (6.3) must be real. By the same token, the first two terms on the right are real. They are real numbers $|\lambda_j|^2$ times the value of O in the states $|\beta'\rangle$ and $|\gamma'\rangle$, respectively. The sum of the last two terms must also be real. This means that the two terms must be complex conjugates.

$$\lambda_1{}^*\lambda_2\langle\beta'|\mathrm{O}|\gamma'\rangle = [\lambda_1\lambda_2{}^*\langle\gamma'|\mathrm{O}|\beta'\rangle]^* = \lambda_1{}^*\lambda_2\langle\gamma'|\mathrm{O}|\beta'\rangle^*\,.$$

Therefore, for any observable O and any two states $|\beta'\rangle$ and $|\gamma'\rangle$, we must have

$$\langle\beta'|\mathrm{O}|\gamma'\rangle = \langle\gamma'|\mathrm{O}|\beta'\rangle^*\,. \tag{6.4}$$

An operator for which the relation (6.4) holds is called *hermitian*. An observable in quantum mechanics is represented by a hermitian operator. The hermitian quality can be defined in another, equivalent way. Let A be a linear operator so that

$$|\delta'\rangle = A|\gamma'\rangle\,. \tag{6.5}$$

The kets $|\delta'\rangle$ and $A|\gamma'\rangle$ have bras dual to them. These are written

$\langle\delta'|$ [illegible] $\langle\gamma'|A^\dagger$.

Then equation (6.5) has as its dual

$$\langle\delta'| = \langle\gamma'|A^\dagger\,.$$

$A^\dagger$ is the *hermitian adjoint* of A. For a general operator, A, we have

$$\langle\beta'|\delta'\rangle = \langle\beta'|A|\gamma'\rangle\,,$$
$$\langle\delta'|\beta'\rangle = \langle\gamma'|A^\dagger|\beta'\rangle\,.$$

But by (5.1) the two expressions on the left are complex conjugates. Therefore,

$$\langle\beta'|A|\gamma'\rangle = \langle\gamma'|A^\dagger|\beta'\rangle^*\,. \tag{6.6}$$

The condition for an operator to be hermitian is that

$$A = A^\dagger\,.$$

Let A and B be two operators, not necessarily hermitian. If $|\alpha'\rangle$ is a state vector, so is $A|\alpha'\rangle$. The latter can therefore be expanded in terms of the states $|\alpha''\rangle$.

$$A|\alpha'\rangle = \sum_{\alpha''} |\alpha''\rangle\,\langle\alpha''|A|\alpha'\rangle\,. \tag{6.7}$$

The operator B may now be applied, yielding

$$BA|\alpha'\rangle = \sum_{\alpha''} B|\alpha''\rangle \langle\alpha''|A|\alpha'\rangle .$$

Each ket $B|\alpha''\rangle$ may be expanded in turn. Thus

$$BA|\alpha'\rangle = \sum_{\alpha'''}\sum_{\alpha''} |\alpha'''\rangle \langle\alpha'''|B|\alpha''\rangle \langle\alpha''|A|\alpha'\rangle .$$

But the ket $BA|\alpha'\rangle$ may be expanded directly into

$$BA|\alpha'\rangle = \sum_{\alpha'''} |\alpha'''\rangle \langle\alpha'''|BA|\alpha'\rangle .$$

The coefficients of $|\alpha'''\rangle$ may be equated because these states are linearly independent. Hence,

$$\langle\alpha'''|BA|\alpha'\rangle = \sum_{\alpha''} \langle\alpha'''|B|\alpha''\rangle \langle\alpha''|A|\alpha'\rangle . \tag{6.8}$$

This is the law of multiplication of matrices. This gives rise to the expression *matrix element* for quantities like $\langle\alpha''|A|\alpha'\rangle$.

The operator BA is the product of the operator B with the operator A. Applied to kets, A operates first. Applied to bras, B operates first. In general BA is not the same as AB. If $AB = BA$, the two operators *commute*.

On inspecting the equations between (6.7) and (6.8) it will be noticed that the right sides differ only by insertions of sums of the kind $\sum_{\alpha''}|\alpha''\rangle\langle\alpha''|$, which changes nothing, as the left sides are all the same. The operator which makes no alteration in any ket is the *unit operator*, usually denoted simply by 1. We see that

$$\sum_{\alpha''} |\alpha''\rangle \langle\alpha''| = 1 \tag{6.9}$$

whenever the sum is over a complete set of states.

Suppose the operator A is one whose value is used to label a state, say $|A', \alpha'\rangle$. Here the α' are the values of all of the other observables used to label the state. The value of A in the state $|A', \alpha'\rangle$ must be A' exactly. There must be no statistical dispersion in the result of measuring A, so that it is not sufficient to have the mean value of many measurements be A', but each must yield A'. A convenient mathematical criterion to apply to insure this is, that the value measured for A^2 be A'^2. A measure of statistical scatter is the mean square deviation from the mean. In quantum mechanical language, this dispersion is

$$\langle\gamma'|(A - \hat{A})^2|\gamma'\rangle = \langle\gamma'|A^2|\gamma'\rangle - \hat{A}^2 ,$$

where $\hat{A} = \langle\gamma'|A|\gamma'\rangle$. The requirement on $|A', \alpha'\rangle$ is now

$$\langle A', \alpha'|(A - A')^2|A', \alpha'\rangle = 0 .$$

This may be written as

$$\langle A', \alpha'|(A - A')(A - A')|A', \alpha'\rangle = 0 ,$$

which is the statement that the norm of $(A - A')|A', \alpha'\rangle$ vanishes. If the norm of a state vector vanishes, the state vector must vanish as postulated in Section 5. If, therefore, A is to have the value A' in the state $|A', \alpha'\rangle$, it follows that

$$A|A', \alpha'\rangle = A'|A', \alpha'\rangle . \tag{6.10}$$

Equation (6.10) furnishes the desired connection between the hermitian operator A and its sharp value A' used to label a state. The possible sharp values of an observable A are its *eigenvalues* A' as defined by (6.10). A state vector which is merely changed in length but not in direction by an operator is an eigenvector of that operator. The factor by which its length is changed is the eigenvalue of that operator. *A state vector is labelled by the eigenvalues of a complete set of commuting observables.*

It was assumed in Section 5 that the state vectors corresponding to distinct values of any observable were orthogonal. It is easy to verify this under the assumptions that observables are hermitian operators and that the possible results of measurements are eigenvalues of these operators. For, let

$$A|A'\rangle = A'|A'\rangle$$

and

$$A|A''\rangle = A''|A''\rangle ,$$

then

$$\langle A''|A|A'\rangle = A'\langle A''|A'\rangle ,$$
$$\langle A'|A|A''\rangle = A''\langle A'|A''\rangle .$$

Because A is hermitian, the left sides are complex conjugates, therefore

$$(A' - A''^*)\,\langle A''|A'\rangle = 0 . \tag{6.11}$$

If $A'' = A'$, the scalar product does not vanish, so $A' = A'^*$ and A' is real. This is as postulated. If $A'' \neq A'$ (both being real) the scalar product must vanish.

If two observables A and B are to be used to label a state, then the hermitian operators representing these observables must commute. The operators are also denoted by A and B, there being no distinction between an observable A and the corresponding operator. To see this consider a ket $|A', B'\rangle$. We have

$$A|A', B'\rangle = A'|A', B'\rangle ,$$

so that

$$BA|A', B'\rangle = A'B|A', B'\rangle = A'B'|A', B'\rangle\,,$$

and similarly

$$AB|A', B'\rangle = A'B'|A', B'\rangle\,.$$

Now the product AB has the same effect as the product BA on any ket labelled with the eigenvalues of A and B. If the simultaneous eigenstates of A and B form a complete set so that any state can be expanded in terms of them, then A and B must commute. The two senses in which the word commute seems to have been used are really the same. The hermitian operators correlated with commuting observables commute.

If two operators commute, the observables with which they are correlated are simultaneously measurable, and their simultaneous eigenstates form a complete set. Let the observables be A and B, and let

$$AB = BA\,. \tag{6.12}$$

Then if $|A', \alpha'\rangle$ is an eigenstate of A with eigenvalue A', so is $B|A', \alpha'\rangle$, because

$$AB|A', \alpha'\rangle = BA|A', \alpha'\rangle = A'B|A', \alpha'\rangle\,. \tag{6.13}$$

This means that the operator B does not produce linear combinations of eigenvectors of A with different eigenvalues. Thus, the eigenvalue problem for B,

$$B|A', \alpha'\rangle = B'|A', \alpha'\rangle\,, \tag{6.14}$$

can be solved without affecting the eigenvalue A' and the eigenstates of B can be chosen to be eigenstates of A also.

In general, there will be more than one eigenstate of an observable A with eigenvalue A'. These are distinguished, as above, by the values of other observables commuting with A and with each other. These labels are combined in the label α'. A is then said to be *degenerate*. If there corresponds one and only one state to each eigenvalue of A, then the index α' can be omitted. In this case the only observables which can commute with A are those which are constants independent of A', and those which are functions of A. This is a consequence of (6.14), for in the situation where A is nondegenerate $|A'\rangle$ is an eigenstate of B, and so the value of B is determined completely by the eigenvalue of A.

There will be more than one state with a given eigenvalue A' of an observable A, unless A by itself constitutes a complete set of commuting observables. The eigenstates of a complete set of commuting observables $A_1, A_2, \ldots, A_f$, with each combination of eigenvalues $A_1', A_2', \ldots, A_f'$ appearing only in one state vector, constitute a complete set of states in terms of which any state may be expressed. The number of linearly independent state vectors depends on the physical description of the system, on the observables which are to be simultaneously measureable.

7. THE CORRESPONDENCE PRINCIPLE

In classical mechanics, observables are functions of the coordinates and momenta. If the coordinates and momenta of a system are measured, the value of any observable associated with the system can be determined. In quantum mechanics the situation is very different. The coordinate x and its conjugate momentum p_x cannot both be determined with an accuracy exceeding that permitted by the uncertainty principle,

$$\Delta x \, \Delta p_x \gtrsim \hbar \, . \tag{7.1}$$

As the system gets larger, the restriction gets less important because the left side contains the factor m, a mass characteristic of the system. In the classical limit, then, the uncertainty principle becomes empty. It is more convenient to consider the classical limit as that in which $\hbar$ approaches zero, which is mathematically possible even though $\hbar$ is a universal constant.

Two observables which are not simultaneously measurable do not commute. We should, therefore, anticipate that the uncertainty principle is expressible in terms of the commutator of the observables involved. The commutator of two observables, $AB - BA$ is denoted by

$$AB - BA = [A, B] \, . \tag{7.2}$$

The commutator of two observables is $i \, (= \sqrt{-1})$ times an observable. For let

$$AB - BA = iC \, . \tag{7.3}$$

The hermitian conjugate of a product of operators is the product of the hermitian conjugates in reverse order. (The proof of this is asked in Exercise 7.) If A and B are hermitian, the hermitian conjugate of (7.3) is

$$BA - AB = -\, iC^{\dagger} \, ,$$

from which it follows that $C^{\dagger} = C$ and C is hermitian.

A general uncertainty relation can now be derived. Let A, B, and C be related as in (7.3). If any number a is subtracted from A and any number b is subtracted from B, (7.3) is unchanged because a number commutes with any linear operator. Choose a to be the value of A in the state $| \, \rangle$. (No label is inserted as this is an arbitrary state.) Similarly, let b be the value of B in this state. Then introduce

$$\tilde{A} = A - \langle\, |A|\, \rangle\,, \qquad \tilde{B} = B - \langle\, |B|\, \rangle\,. \tag{7.4}$$

This gives

$$[\tilde{A}, \tilde{B}] = iC\,.$$

The advantage lies in the fact that $\tilde{A}$ and $\tilde{B}$ have mean square deviations from the mean in the state $|\,\rangle$, given simply by $\langle\, |\tilde{A}^2|\, \rangle$ and $\langle\, |\tilde{B}^2|\, \rangle$.

We now use the fact that the norm of any state vector is non-negative. Therefore, in particular,

$$\langle\, |(\tilde{A} + i\lambda\tilde{B})^\dagger(\tilde{A} + i\lambda\tilde{B})|\, \rangle \geqslant 0\,. \tag{7.5}$$

Taking the number λ to be real, this may be written as

$$\langle\, |\tilde{A}^2 + \lambda^2\tilde{B}^2 + i\lambda(\tilde{A}\tilde{B} - \tilde{B}\tilde{A})|\, \rangle = \langle\, |\tilde{A}^2 + \lambda^2\tilde{B}^2 - \lambda C|\, \rangle \geqslant 0\,. \tag{7.6}$$

The left side has a minimum value as a function of λ when

$$\lambda = \langle\, |C|\, \rangle / 2\langle\, |\tilde{B}^2|\, \rangle\,. \tag{7.7}$$

Thus, the strongest inequality to be derived from (7.6) is obtained on inserting this value of λ. After rearrangement this yields

$$\langle\, |\tilde{A}^2|\, \rangle\langle\, |\tilde{B}^2|\, \rangle \geqslant \tfrac{1}{4}\langle\, |C\,|\, \rangle^2\,. \tag{7.8}$$

Going back to A and B, and writing

$$\langle\, |(A - \langle\, |A|\, \rangle)^2|\, \rangle = (\Delta A)^2, \tag{7.9}$$

etc., we may write (7.8) as

$$\Delta A\, \Delta B \geqslant \tfrac{1}{2}\, |\langle\, |c|\, \rangle|\,. \tag{7.10}$$

This is a generalized uncertainty principle. It permits two observables to be measured simultaneously in the state $|\,\rangle$ only if the value of their commutator in that state vanishes. If the simultaneous eigenstates of A and B are to form a complete set, then the value of the commutator $[A, B]$ must vanish in every state, i.e., it must be the number zero.

The uncertainty product $\Delta A\, \Delta B$ reaches its minimum value when the equality sign holds in (7.5). This occurs only when

$$(\tilde{A} + i\lambda\tilde{B})\, |\,\rangle = 0\,, \tag{7.11}$$

with the value of λ given by (7.7).

In order to ensure that the uncertainty principle has no effect in the classical limit, it is sufficient to postulate that the commutator of two observables having classical analogues should be proportional to Planck's constant $\hbar$. In the limit $\hbar \to 0$, then, such observables can be assigned arbitrarily precise values. The uncertainty in a coordinate x of a particle and the conjugate momentum p_x is independent of the state of the particle and is a constant. This can be described by assuming the commutation rule for coordinates and momenta

$$[x, p_x] = [y, p_y] = [z, p_z] = i\hbar \; . \tag{7.12}$$

This leads to the uncertainty relation

$$\Delta x \, \Delta p_x \geqslant \tfrac{1}{2}\hbar \; . \tag{7.13}$$

The right side of (7.13) is smaller than might be expected from the earlier discussion of the uncertainty principle. This could be changed by inserting a numerical coefficient in (7.12). It will be seen, however, that (7.12) leads to agreement with experience as it stands. Further, we must assume that all coordinates and momenta of a particle, other than conjugate pairs, commute with each other. Thus

$$\begin{aligned} [x, x] &= \ \ [x, y] = \cdots = 0 \, , \\ [p_x, p_x] &= [p_x, p_x] = \cdots = 0 \, , \\ [x, p_x] &= \ \ [x, p_z] = \cdots = 0 \, . \end{aligned} \tag{7.14}$$

These relations are summed up in

$$\begin{aligned} [x_i, x_j] &= 0 = [p_i, p_j] \, , \\ [x_i, p_j] &= i\hbar\delta_{ij} \, . \end{aligned} \tag{7.15}$$

Equations (7.15) formally resemble the classical equations involving Poisson brackets. Denoting the Poisson bracket of two classical observables $\hat{A}(q, p)$ and $\hat{B}(q, p)$ by

$$(\hat{A}, \hat{B}) \doteq \sum_i \left(\frac{\partial \hat{A}}{\partial q_i} \frac{\partial \hat{B}}{\partial p_i} - \frac{\partial \hat{B}}{\partial q_i} \frac{\partial \hat{A}}{\partial p_i} \right) , \tag{7.16}$$

we recall the relations

$$\begin{aligned} (x_i, x_j) &= 0 = (p_i, p_j) \, , \\ (x_i, p_j) &= \delta_{ij} \, . \end{aligned} \tag{7.17}$$

These follow directly from (7.16). It is tempting, therefore, to generalize on the basis of this similarity and to give a rule for quantizing a classical system. If $\hat{A}$, $\hat{B}$ are classical observables associated with a system of particles, their Poisson bracket is another observable. (This may be a trivial observable such as zero, but no matter.)

$$(\hat{A}, \hat{B}) = \hat{C} \, .$$

The quantum counterparts, A and B, of $\hat{A}$ and $\hat{B}$, have a commutator which is $i\hbar$ times another observable C. The quantization rule is then that C is the quantum counterpart of $\hat{C}$.

This postulate is sufficient to determine the quantum description of any system which has a classical description. There are systems which cannot be described classically, for example the spinning electron. The magnitude of the spin angular momentum needed to describe the magnetic properties of an electron is $\frac{1}{2}\hbar$, and this vanishes in the classical limit. Such variables obey commutation rules which must be determined from experience directly and not via classical mechanics.

We here consider a few particular applications of the postulate given above. (The circumflex denotes classical quantities.)

(i) $$(\hat{f}(\hat{x}), \hat{p}_i) = \frac{\partial \hat{f}(\hat{x})}{\partial \hat{x}_i},$$

hence,

(7.18) $$[f(x), p_i] = i\hbar \frac{\partial f(x)}{\partial x_i}.$$

(ii) $$(\hat{g}(\hat{p}), \hat{x}_i) = -\frac{\partial \hat{g}(\hat{p})}{\partial \hat{p}_i},$$

hence,

(7.19) $$[g(p), x_i] = -i\hbar \frac{\partial g(p)}{\partial p_i}.$$

(iii) If $l_x = yp_z - zp_y$, etc., are the components of angular momentum of a particle,

$$(\hat{l}_x, \hat{l}_y) = \hat{l}_z \quad \text{(cyclic)},$$

then

(7.20) $$[l_x, l_y] = i\hbar l_z \quad \text{(cyclic)}.$$

These examples are unambiguous. Ambiguities arise when both a coordinate and its conjugate momentum appear on the right-hand side. The order of these factors is a matter of indifference classically, but quantum mechanically it makes a difference. We meet with this ambiguity several times in the future.

It should be emphasized that we have in no sense derived the quantum conditions from classical mechanics. The object of keeping a close formal analogy between classical and quantum mechanics is the preservation of classical mechanics as a limiting form of quantum mechanics. The spirit is the same as in relativistic mechanics. Relativistic mechanics must have non-relativistic mechanics as a limit when all velocities are small because experience shows non-relativistic mechanics to be accurate in this limit. It is not obvious that the prescription given really does yield classical mechanics in the limit $\hbar \to 0$. We shall show that this is the case for a particle moving in a potential later in this section.

We are now in a position to formulate the equations of motion of a system in the language of quantum mechanics. Classically the value of an observable $\hat{f}$ in the state specified by the coordinate values q and the momentum values p is $\hat{f}(q, p)$. Its value changes according to the equation

$$\frac{d\hat{f}(q,p)}{dt} = \frac{\partial\hat{f}(q,p)}{\partial t} + \frac{\partial\hat{f}(q,p)}{\partial q}\dot{q} + \frac{\partial\hat{f}(q,p)}{\partial p}\dot{p}\,. \tag{7.21}$$

The time dependence of $\hat{f}(q, p)$ can be ascribed to the time dependence of the functional form of f, (first term), or to the time dependence of the description of the state (second and third terms), or partly to each.

The value of an observable f in quantum mechanics in the state $|\,\rangle$ is the expectation value $\langle\,|f|\,\rangle$. This value changes with time according to the equation

$$\frac{d}{dt}\langle\,|f|\,\rangle = \langle\,|\frac{df}{dt}|\,\rangle + \langle\,|f\left(\frac{d}{dt}|\,\rangle\right) + \left(\frac{d}{dt}\langle\,|\right)f|\,\rangle\,. \tag{7.22}$$

Here, also, the time dependence can be ascribed to the operator f (first term), or to the state (second and third terms), or partly to each.

The first case we examine is that in which the time dependence of the value of f is due entirely to the time dependence of the state. This is called the *Schrödinger picture.* Since d/dt is a linear operator, we write

$$\frac{d}{dt}|\,\rangle = G|\,\rangle\,, \tag{7.23}$$

where G is a linear operator constructed from observables of the system. The state vector has been assumed to be normalized so that

$$\langle\,|\,\rangle = 1\,.$$

Therefore,

$$\langle\,|\left(\frac{d}{dt}|\,\rangle\right) + \left(\frac{d}{dt}\langle\,|\right)|\,\rangle = 0\,.$$

Using (7.23), this becomes

$$\langle\,|(G + G^\dagger)|\,\rangle = 0\,,$$

so that G is antihermitian. We set

$$i\hbar G = H\,,$$

where H is hermitian. The equation of motion (7.23) then becomes

$$i\hbar\frac{d}{dt}|\,\rangle = H|\,\rangle\,. \tag{7.24}$$

This in turn can be used in (7.22) to yield, with $df/dt = 0$,

$$i\hbar \frac{d}{dt}\langle\,|f|\,\rangle = \langle\,|fH|\,\rangle - \langle\,|Hf|\,\rangle = \langle\,|[f, H]|\,\rangle\,. \tag{7.25}$$

This result may be compared with a classical result obtained by using Hamilton's equations of motion in (7.21), assuming there that $\partial\hat{f}/\partial t = 0$.

$$\frac{d\hat{f}(q,p)}{dt} = \frac{\partial\hat{f}}{\partial q}\frac{\partial\hat{H}}{\partial p} - \frac{\partial\hat{f}}{\partial p}\frac{\partial\hat{H}}{\partial q} = (\hat{f},\ \hat{H})_{qp}\,. \tag{7.26}$$

This last is the value of the Poisson bracket of $\hat{f}$ and $\hat{H}$ in the state q, p. We see that for arbitrary f the commutator $[f, H]$ corresponds with $i\hbar$ times the Poisson bracket $(\hat{f}, \hat{H})$. We are therefore justified in calling H the quantum *Hamiltonian*. Equation (7.24) is called the *Schrödinger equation.*

A second form of the quantum equations of motion arises when the time dependence of $\langle\,|f|\,\rangle$ is placed entirely on the observable f. This corresponds to specifying the state of the system by giving it at some fixed time t_0. If we assume that

$$i\hbar \frac{df}{dt} = [f, H]\,, \qquad \frac{d}{dt}|\,\rangle = 0\,, \tag{7.27}$$

then (7.22) becomes

$$i\hbar \frac{d}{dt}\langle\,|f|\,\rangle = \langle\,|[f, H]|\,\rangle\,, \tag{7.28}$$

which is again (7.25). This is necessary since (7.25) is an equation between observed numbers and, hence, must be the same in any picture of the motion. The picture specified by (7.27) is the *Heisenberg picture.*

Still a third picture, the *interaction picture*, is useful in many applications. In this picture the Hamiltonian is written as the sum of two terms, each being hermitian.

$$H = H_0 + V. \tag{7.29}$$

Then observables are assumed to follow Heisenberg equations of motion with H_0 as Hamiltonian, while the state vectors follow the Schrödinger equation with Hamiltonian V.

$$i\hbar \frac{df}{dt} = [f, H_0]\,, \qquad i\hbar \frac{d}{dt}|\,\rangle = V|\,\rangle\,. \tag{7.30}$$

These satisfy (7.25), as may be shown by substitution. This picture is used when H_0 is simple enough to allow the construction of a complete set of its eigenstates, and V is small. It corresponds to the classical method of variation of constants used in celestial mechanics. There, the orbit of a planet in the gravitational field of the Sun is described by the parameters of its Keplerian ellipse. The effect of perturbations on this orbit is then described by allowing these parameters to vary with the time. Thus, the perhelion of Mercury precesses at 573 seconds of arc per century because the potential field of the Sun is not quite Newtonian, and because there are other planets.

From (7.25), the equation for the value of a momentum component may be derived.

$$i\hbar \frac{d}{dt}\langle\, | p_j | \,\rangle = \langle\, | [p_j, H] | \,\rangle \,.$$

Now if the Hamiltonian consists of a function of momenta alone (the kinetic energy) and of a function of the coordinates alone (the potential energy), we have, according to (7.18),

$$[p_j, H] = [p_j, V] = -i\hbar \frac{\partial V}{\partial q_j} \cdot$$

Thus,

$$\frac{d}{dt}\langle\, | p_j | \,\rangle = \langle\, | -\frac{\partial V}{\partial q_j} | \,\rangle \,. \qquad (7.31)$$

This has the form of Newton's second law of motion. It is shown in Section 12 that the state $|\,\rangle$ can consist of a "wave packet" which is localized to a great extent in both position and momentum. In this state, (7.31) really represents the equation of motion of a classical particle. Equation (7.31) is called *Ehrenfest's theorem.*

PROBLEMS

For the purposes of the following problems assume that the vector space of interest has a finite number of dimensions.

1. If $|a\rangle$, $|b\rangle$ are two vectors, show that

$$|\langle b|a\rangle| \leq (\langle a|b\rangle \, \langle b|a\rangle)^{1/2} \,.$$

This is *Schwarz's inequality.*

2. If $|a\rangle + |b\rangle = |c\rangle$, show that

$$(\langle c|c\rangle)^{1/2} \leq (\langle a|a\rangle) + (\langle b|b\rangle)^{1/2} \,.$$

This is the *triangular inequality.*

3. If the assumption of a positive definite metric [assumption (v) of Section 5] is given up, the above inequalities no longer hold. Show this by giving counterexamples in a two-dimensional space spanned by vectors $|1\rangle$, $|2\rangle$ such that

$$\langle 1|1\rangle = +1,\ \langle 2|2\rangle = -1,\ \langle 1|2\rangle = 0\,.$$

In some applications of quantum mechanics (e.g., the Lee model), states with negative norms appear and cause difficulties. They are called ghost states.

4. Given a set of linearly independent vectors $|a_j\rangle$ ($j = 1, 2, \ldots, m$). Show how to construct a set of m orthonormal vectors from linear combinations of this set. Can this recipe be applied routinely if the metric is not positive definite?

5. The components of angular momentum satisfy the commutation relations (7.20). Show that it then follows that if l_z is sharply defined, the expectation values of l_x and of l_y vanish. That is, if

$$(l_z - l_z')|l_z'\rangle = 0$$

then

$$\langle l_z'|l_x|l_z'\rangle = 0 = \langle l_z'|l_y|l_z'\rangle\,.$$

6. A beam of 10 meV protons is considered to be very well defined in direction if it is collimated by two circular apertures of radius 0.1 mm separated by 5 m. In this situation, what are the orders of magnitude of the quantities on the two sides of inequality (2.3)?

7. Show that the adjoint of a product of operators is the product of their adjoints taken in reverse order, and that a similar rule holds for inverses when these exist.

8. If A, B are operators in a finite dimensional vector space, show that if $AB = 1$, then also $BA = 1$.

9. If $|\ \rangle_S$ *and* $|\ \rangle_H$ are the Schrodinger and Heisenberg states of a system, show that

$$|\ \rangle_S = \exp\left[-iHt/h\right]|\ \rangle_H$$

if the two coincide at time $t = 0$, and H is time-independent. Derive the transformation of time-independent operators between the Schrödinger and Heisenberg pictures.

II

Basic applications of quantum mechanics

8. THE HARMONIC OSCILLATOR

The harmonic oscillator was the first system to be quantized. It is the simplest system to treat because its Hamiltonian is symmetrical between coordinate and momentum. We derive the possible energy values, the energy eigenvalues, directly from the commutation relations (7.12).

An oscillator is described by a single coordinate x, and a single momentum p. The energy of the oscillator is the sum of the kinetic and potential energies. Denoting the energy by H,

$$H = \frac{p^2}{2m} + \tfrac{1}{2}\, m\omega^2 x^2 \,. \tag{8.1}$$

Here m is the mass of the oscillating particle and ω is the classical frequency of oscillation. Each term in H is positive so that the eigenvalues of H must be positive. It is impossible for H to take the value zero, because this would mean that both x and p were exactly zero, contradicting the uncertainty principle. A state of the oscillator is completely specified by the energy eigenvalue E,

$$H|E\rangle = E|E\rangle \,. \tag{8.2}$$

It is useful to write H in the following "factored" way:

$$\begin{aligned} H &= \frac{1}{2m}\,\{(ip + m\omega x)(-ip + m\omega x) - m\hbar\omega\} \\ &= \frac{1}{2m}\,\{(-ip + m\omega x)(ip + m\omega x) + m\hbar\omega\} \,. \end{aligned} \tag{8.3}$$

Consider the effect of H on the ket $(ip + m\omega x)\,|E\rangle$ where $|E\rangle$ is an eigenket of H.

$$
\begin{aligned}
H(ip + m\omega x)|E\rangle &= \frac{1}{2m}\{(ip + m\omega x)(-ip + m\omega x) - m\hbar\omega\}(ip + m\omega x)|E\rangle \\
&= \frac{1}{2m}(ip + m\omega x)\{(-ip + m\omega x)(ip + m\omega x) - m\hbar\omega\}|E\rangle \\
&= (ip + m\omega x)\{H - \hbar\omega\}|E\rangle \\
&= (E - \hbar\omega)(ip + m\omega x)|E\rangle\,.
\end{aligned}
\tag{8.4}
$$

Thus, either $(ip + m\omega x)\,|E\rangle$ is an eigenket of H with eigenvalue $E - \hbar\omega$, or it vanishes. Similarly, $(-ip + m\omega x)\,|E\rangle$ is an eigenket of H with eigenvalue $E + \hbar\omega$, or it vanishes.

The operator

$$a = (2m\hbar\omega)^{-1/2}\,(ip + m\omega x) \tag{8.5}$$

is called a *lowering* operator. Its hermitian conjugate,

$$a^\dagger = (2m\hbar\omega)^{-1/2}\,(-ip + m\omega x)\,, \tag{8.6}$$

is a *raising* operator. The numerical factor is so chosen that the commutation relation between them is simply

$$[a, a^\dagger] = 1\,. \tag{8.7}$$

The energy may be written in terms of a and $a^\dagger$. From (8.3), (8.5), and (8.6),

$$H = (a^\dagger a + \tfrac{1}{2})\hbar\omega = (aa^\dagger - \tfrac{1}{2})\hbar\omega\,. \tag{8.8}$$

If a lowers the energy by the amount $\hbar\omega$, a^2 will lower it by $2\hbar\omega$, and a^n will lower it by $n\hbar\omega$. As was pointed out above, however, the energy must be positive so that the lowering process must eventually lead to a vanishing ket. There must be a ket, denoted by $|E_0\rangle$, such that

$$a|E_0\rangle = 0\,. \tag{8.9}$$

Using (8.8),

$$H|E_0\rangle = E_0|E_0\rangle = \tfrac{1}{2}\hbar\omega|E_0\rangle\,. \tag{8.10}$$

E_0 is the ground state energy, or zero point energy, of the oscillator. It is the least energy consistent with the uncertainty principle.

The other eigenvalues of H must differ from E_0 by integer multiples of $\hbar\omega$, because any eigenstate of H must be reduced to $|E_0\rangle$ by applying a an integral number of times. The eigenvalue spectrum of the harmonic oscillator is, therefore, given by

$$E = (n + \tfrac{1}{2})\hbar\omega\,, \tag{8.11}$$

with non-negative integer n. There is no upper limit to the spectrum. If there were an upper limit, it would mean that some ket $|\ \rangle$ is annihilated by $a^\dagger$,

$$a^\dagger|\ \rangle = 0\,.$$

Applying the second expression in (8.8) to this ket,

$$H|\ \rangle = -\tfrac{1}{2}\hbar\omega|\ \rangle\,,$$

which is impossible because H is positive.

The spectrum (8.11) is, aside from the extra $\frac{1}{2}\hbar\omega$, just that postulated by Planck in 1900. It justifies the choice made in (7.12). Experimentally,

$$\begin{aligned}\hbar &= 1.054 \times 10^{-27} \text{ erg seconds}\\ &= 0.658 \times 10^{-15} \text{ electron volt seconds.}\end{aligned}$$

From now on the states of the harmonic oscillator will be labelled by the integer n rather than by E. Thus

$$H|n\rangle = (n + \tfrac{1}{2})\hbar\omega|n\rangle\,. \tag{8.13}$$

The range of n is 0, 1, 2, ... The state $|0\rangle$ is the *ground state* of the oscillator.

The operator

$$N = a^\dagger a \tag{8.14}$$

is called the number operator for the oscillator. Its eigenvalues are the integers starting with zero. This follows directly from the commutation relations (8.7) and the existence of a state $|0\rangle$ which is annihilated by a. We see later that operators a and $a^\dagger$ similar to the present ones can be used to annihilate or create particles or photons. In such a connection they are called annihilation or creation operators.

A complete set of states can be constructed from the ground state by successive applications of the raising operator. Let $|n\rangle$ be an eigenstate of the energy with energy $(n + \frac{1}{2})\hbar\omega$. Then $a^\dagger|n\rangle$ is an eigenstate with one more quantum of energy; it is not properly normalized. We take

$$\langle n|n\rangle = 1$$

for every n. Then,

$$a^\dagger|n\rangle = c_n|n + 1\rangle\,, \tag{8.15}$$

where c_n is a number, in general complex. The phase factor associated with the state vectors $|n + 1\rangle$ can be so chosen, however, that c_n is real and positive. On making this choice, the equation dual to (8.15) becomes

$$\langle n|a = c_n\langle n + 1|$$

so that

$$\langle n|aa^\dagger|n\rangle = c_n^2\langle n+1|n+1\rangle = c_n^2\,.$$

Using the commutation rule (8.7),

$$\langle n|aa^\dagger|n\rangle = \langle n|a^\dagger a + 1|n\rangle = n+1\,.$$

Thus,

$$c_n^2 = n+1\,,\; c_n = +\,(n+1)^{1/2}\,,$$

and we obtain the final result

$$a^\dagger|n\rangle = (n+1)^{1/2}|n+1\rangle\,. \tag{8.16}$$

Similarly, with the same choice of phases,

$$a|n\rangle = n^{1/2}|n-1\rangle\,. \tag{8.17}$$

Equations (8.16) and (8.17) determine all the matrix elements of the operators $a^\dagger$ and a. The only non-vanishing ones are

$$\begin{aligned}\langle n+1|a^\dagger|n\rangle &= (n+1)^{1/2}\,,\\ \langle n-1|a|n\rangle &= n^{1/2}\,.\end{aligned} \tag{8.18}$$

The choice of phase made here is arbitrary, but very convenient. It leads to the simple expression

$$|n\rangle = (n!)^{-1/2}a^{\dagger n}|0\rangle\,. \tag{8.19}$$

The raising and lowering operators are linear combinations of x and p according to (8.5) and (8.6). Solving these equations for x yields

$$x = \left(\frac{\hbar}{2m\omega}\right)^{1/2}(a^\dagger + a)\,. \tag{8.20}$$

The non-vanishing matrix elements of x are, therefore,

$$\begin{aligned}\langle n+1|x|n\rangle &= \left[\frac{(n+1)\hbar}{2m\omega}\right]^{1/2},\\ \langle n-1|x|n\rangle &= \left[\frac{n\hbar}{2m\omega}\right]^{1/2}.\end{aligned} \tag{8.21}$$

Analogous expressions hold for the matrix elements of p. We may now evaluate the average value of x^2 in any state. (Since x has no diagonal matrix elements, the average value of x vanishes.)

$$\begin{aligned}\langle n|x^2|n\rangle &= \sum_m \langle n|x|m\rangle\langle m|x|n\rangle \\ &= \langle n|x|n-1\rangle\langle n-1|x|n\rangle + \langle n|x|n+1\rangle\langle n+1|x|n\rangle \\ &= \frac{n\hbar}{2m\omega} + \frac{(n+1)\hbar}{2m\omega} \\ &= \frac{(2n+1)\hbar}{2m\omega}\,.\end{aligned} \tag{8.22}$$

The average value of the potential energy is $\frac{1}{2}m\omega^2\langle n|x^2|n\rangle$, or

$$\langle n|V|n\rangle = \tfrac{1}{2}(n+\tfrac{1}{2})\hbar\omega = \tfrac{1}{2}E_n\,. \tag{8.23}$$

This is the same as the classical result. On the average, the energy is equally divided between kinetic energy and potential energy.

The harmonic oscillator problem is now completely solved. The states are all known and the matrix elements of all observables can be constructed explicitly. The eigenstates of H do not, however, correspond at all to the classical picture of an oscillator. One reason for this is that classically an oscillator is not in a stationary state unless it is at rest. To construct the quantum analogue of an oscillating particle we must superpose eigenstates of H with different eigenvalues in an appropriate way.

Classically the state of an oscillator can be specified by giving the initial values of x and p. Thus the classical motion is

$$\begin{aligned}x &= x_0\cos\omega t + (p_0/m\omega)\sin\omega t\,,\\ p &= -m\omega x_0\sin\omega t + p_0\cos\omega t\,,\end{aligned}$$

which can be written in complex form

$$(ip + m\omega x) = (ip_0 + m\omega x_0)e^{-i\omega t}\,. \tag{8.24}$$

This way of writing the time dependence calls quantum mechanics to mind and suggests that the quantum analogue of a classical state has a definite value of the complex quantity $(ip + m\omega x)$. This quantity is, aside from the factor $(2m\hbar\omega)^{-1/2}$, just the lowering operator a. We are led, then, to consider eigenstates of a. Since a is not a hermitian operator, its eigenvalues need not be real. Let us denote an eigenvalue of a by z.

The problem being considered is not a stationary one since a does not commute with H. From (8.7) and (8.8) we see that

$$[a, H] = [a, a^\dagger a]\hbar\omega = \hbar\omega a \tag{8.25}$$

so that an eigenstate of a is not in general an eigenstate of H. To describe the time dependence we use the Heisenberg picture. The Heisenberg equation of motion for a is

(8.26)
$$i\hbar \frac{da}{dt} = [a, H] = \hbar\omega a\,,$$

which has the solution

(8.27)
$$a = a_0 e^{-i\omega t}$$

just as in the classical case.

The states of interest are the time-independent Heisenberg states defined by

(8.28)
$$a_0|z_0\rangle = z_0|z_0\rangle\,.$$

Since a differs from a_0 only in the numerical factor $e^{-i\omega t}$, the eigenvalues of a are $z_0 e^{-i\omega t} = z$, so that they are time dependent.

We now multiply (8.28) by $\langle n|$ and obtain

(8.29)
$$\langle n|a_0|z_0\rangle = (n+1)^{1/2}\langle n+1|z_0\rangle = z_0\langle n|z_0\rangle$$

where use has been made of the dual of (8.16). This is a difference equation for $\langle n|z_0\rangle$ whose solution is

(8.30)
$$\langle n|z_0\rangle = \frac{z_0^{\,n}}{(n!)^{1/2}}\langle 0|z_0\rangle$$

as is readily verified by substitution into (8.29). $\langle 0|z_0\rangle$ is a normalization constant. Writing

(8.31)
$$|z_0\rangle = \sum_{n=0}^{\infty} |n\rangle\,\langle n|z_0\rangle = \sum_{n=0}^{\infty} |n\rangle \frac{z_0^{\,n}}{(n!)^{1/2}}\langle 0|z_0\rangle$$

we have

(8.32)
$$\langle z_0|z_0\rangle = \sum_{n=0}^{\infty} \frac{|z_0|^2}{n!}\,|\,\langle 0|z_0\rangle\,|^2 = \exp\,[|z_0|^2]|\,\langle 0|z_0\rangle\,|^2\,.$$

This state is normalized to unity by choosing

(8.33)
$$\langle 0|z_0\rangle = \exp\,[-\tfrac{1}{2}|z_0|^2]\,.$$

Using this in (8.32) shows that the energy eigenstates of the oscillator contribute to the norm of $|z_0\rangle$ or of $|z\rangle$ according to a Poisson distribution.

The quantum state we have constructed is

$$|z\rangle = \exp[-\tfrac{1}{2}|z|^2] \sum_{n=0}^{\infty} |n\rangle \frac{z_0{}^n}{(n!)^{1/2}} \,. \tag{8.34}$$

To verify that this is very analogous to a classical state, we calculate the expectation value of x in this state. x is also a Heisenberg operator and hence time-dependent, but this is explicitly given by (8.20) and the time-dependence of a and $a^\dagger$;

$$\langle z_0|x|z_0\rangle = e^{-|z|^2} \sum_{n',n} \frac{(z_0{}^*)^{n'}}{(n'!)^{1/2}} \langle n'|x|n\rangle \frac{z_0{}^n}{(n!)^{1/2}} \,. \tag{8.35}$$

We now use (8.21) to evaluate $\langle n'|x|n\rangle$, noting the necessary time factors. We get

$$\begin{aligned} \langle z_0|x|z_0\rangle &= e^{-|z|^2} \sum_n \left\{ \frac{(z_0{}^*)^{n+1}}{[(n+1)!]^{1/2}} e^{i\omega t} \left[\frac{(n+1)\hbar}{2m\omega}\right]^{1/2} \frac{z_0{}^n}{(n!)^{1/2}} \right. \\ &\qquad \left. + \frac{(z_0{}^*)^n}{(n!)^{1/2}} \left[\frac{(n+1)\hbar}{2m\omega}\right]^{1/2} e^{-i\omega t} \frac{z_0{}^{n+1}}{[(n+1)!]^{1/2}} \right\} \\ &= e^{-|z|^2} \left(\frac{\hbar}{2m\omega}\right)^{1/2} (z_0{}^* e^{i\omega t} + z_0 e^{-i\omega t}) \sum_n \frac{(z_0{}^* z_0{}^n)}{n!} \\ &= \left(\frac{\hbar}{2m\omega}\right)^{1/2} 2 \operatorname{Re} z_0 e^{-i\omega t} \,. \end{aligned} \tag{8.37}$$

On expressing z_0 in terms of the classical initial values x_0 and p_0, this yields just the classical result. The state $|z_0\rangle$ corresponds to a wave packet whose center executes the classical oscillation. For $z_0 = 0$ the state $|z_0\rangle$ becomes the ground state $|0\rangle$ of the oscillator and the wave packet has the spread in x of the ground state, which is an irreducible minimum imposed by the uncertainty principle. These states may appropriately be called pseudoclassical states. Their description in the coordinate representation is obtained in Section 11.

9. THE FREE PARTICLE

The classical Hamiltonian of a free particle whose mass is m is given by

$$H = \frac{1}{2m}\mathbf{p}^2 = \frac{1}{2m}(p_x{}^2 + p_y{}^2 + p_z{}^2) \,. \tag{9.1}$$

It is a function of three observables which commute with each other. The cartesian momentum components thus furnish a complete set of commuting observables for the system from whose values the value of the energy follows. This was not the situation with the harmonic oscillator.

For the moment we may restrict our attention to one component of $\mathbf{p}$, say p_x, and may omit the subscript. Let $|p'\rangle$ be a state in which p has the eigenvalue p'. If ϵ is a positive real number which approaches zero, we may evaluate $(1 + i\epsilon x)|p'\rangle$ with neglect of terms in ϵ^2 and higher powers. Thus, to first order in ϵ we have

$$(9.2)\quad p(1 + i\epsilon x)|p'\rangle = \{(1 + i\epsilon x)p + \epsilon\hbar\}|p'\rangle = (p' + \epsilon\hbar)(1 + i\epsilon x)|p'\rangle\,,$$

and $(1 + i\epsilon x)|p'\rangle$ is an eigenket of p with eigenvalue $p' + \epsilon\hbar$. The eigenvalues of p constitute a continuum extending from $-\infty$ to $+\infty$. This is true for all three components of $\mathbf{p}$, and so the eigenvalues of H also form a continuum extending from 0 to ∞. By a similar argument, we can see that $(1 - i\epsilon p)|x'\rangle$ is an eigenket of x with eigenvalue $x' + \epsilon\hbar$. Because x does not commute with H, the ket $|x'\rangle$ is not an eigenket of H.

The occurrence of continuous eigenvalue spectra raises a difficulty with the physical interpretation given to the scalar product. The scalar product $\langle\beta'|\alpha'\rangle$ has been interpreted as the probability amplitude for finding the result β', on measuring β when the system has been prepared in the state $|\alpha'\rangle$. If β' is an element of a continuum, it is physically meaningless to ask for one and only one value of β' as the result of a measurement because no physical detector has the infinite resolution required to realize such accuracy. The only physically meaningful requirement is that β' lie in some finite range $\Delta\beta'$ about the value β'. Thus, in the case of the coordinate x, which possesses a continuous spectrum of eigenvalues, what we say is, that

$$|\langle x'|\alpha'\rangle|^2\Delta x'$$

is the probability that x' lies in the range $\Delta x'$ about the value x' when the system is prepared in the state $|\alpha'\rangle$. The situation when α' also has a continuous spectrum of eigenvalues is discussed later in this section.

The continuum of eigenvalues of p is sometimes eliminated by imposing a restriction on the vectors $|p'\rangle$ which are regarded as representing physical states. This restriction is usually that the expansion of $|p'\rangle$ in eigenstates $|x'\rangle$ of x have coefficients $\langle x'|p'\rangle$ which are periodic functions of x' with some very long period L. When this is done, the vector $(1 + i\epsilon x)|p'\rangle$ does not represent a physical state if $|p'\rangle$ does, so that $p' + \epsilon\hbar$ is not a physical eigenvalue of p. The imposition of this periodicity requirement does not affect the description of physical processes which occur in a volume much smaller than L^3, so that by choosing L sufficiently large any process of interest may be described in terms of these states. Clearly no such device can be used to eliminate the continuum of eigenvalues of x, as the kinetic energy of a particle depends on p in a nonperiodic way, so that periodicity of $\langle p'|x'\rangle$ in p' with a large period P cannot be required.

We may choose the phase factors of our states in such a way that

$$|p' + \epsilon\hbar\rangle = (1 + i\epsilon x)|p'\rangle\,. \tag{9.3}$$

The normalization is correct, for to first order in ϵ

$$\langle p' + \epsilon\hbar|p' + \epsilon\hbar\rangle = \langle p'|(1 - i\epsilon x)(1 + i\epsilon x)|p'\rangle = \langle p'|p'\rangle\,. \tag{9.4}$$

We make this choice of phase throughout. Similarly, we choose phases so that as $\epsilon \to 0$

$$|x' + \epsilon\hbar\rangle = (1 - i\epsilon p)|x'\rangle\,. \tag{9.5}$$

Multiplying this equation by $\langle p'|$ yields

$$\langle p'|x' + \epsilon\hbar\rangle = (1 - i\epsilon p')\,\langle p'|x'\rangle\,.$$

With $p' = 0$ we see that

$$\langle p' = 0|x' + \epsilon\hbar\rangle = \langle p' = 0|x'\rangle\,. \tag{9.6}$$

The scalar product of the zero momentum state with a state $|x'\rangle$ is independent of x'.

The state $|p'\rangle$ may be expressed in terms of $|p' = 0\rangle$. In the limit $N \to \infty$ we have

$$|\frac{p'}{N}\rangle = \left(1 + i\frac{p'}{N\hbar}x\right)|p' = 0\rangle\,,$$

so that

$$\begin{aligned} |p'\rangle &= \lim_{N\to\infty}\left(1 + i\,\frac{p'x}{N\hbar}\right)^N |p' = 0\rangle \\ &= \exp\,[ip'x/\hbar]\,|p' = 0\rangle\,. \end{aligned} \tag{9.7}$$

Here the exponential has its usual definition as a power series in the limit $N \to \infty$. The presence of the operator x in the exponent means that the expression is defined only by the power series. There are no difficulties associated with this because there are no non-commuting quantities involved; p' is a number. Now we see that

$$\begin{aligned} \langle x'|p'\rangle &= \exp\,[ip'x'/\hbar]\,\langle x'|p' = 0\rangle \\ &= C\exp\,[ip'x'/\hbar]\,. \end{aligned} \tag{9.8}$$

The quantity $\langle x'|p'\rangle$ will later be called the wave function of the free particle. It is a plane wave in coordinate space. We can conclude from this that the probability of finding a particle with momentum p' in a neighborhood of x' is independent of x'. This also agrees with the uncertainty principle. If $\Delta p \to 0$, then $\Delta x \to \infty$.

The entire development given is easily extended to three dimensions. We merely replace p, x, and ϵ by vectors $\mathbf{p}$, $\mathbf{x}$, and $\boldsymbol{\epsilon}$. Products like ϵx become $\boldsymbol{\epsilon} \cdot \mathbf{x}$, etc.

The normalization of states labelled by eigenvalues belonging to a continuum presents new features. For example, consider the state $|\mathbf{p}'\rangle$, a momentum eigenstate. We have, using (9.8),

$$\langle \mathbf{p}'|\mathbf{p}'\rangle = \int d^3x' \, \langle \mathbf{p}'|\mathbf{x}'\rangle \, \langle \mathbf{x}'|\mathbf{p}'\rangle$$

$$= |C|^2 \int d^3x' \,, \tag{9.9}$$

which is just a constant $|C|^2$ times the volume of all space. This shows why it is convenient to consider "all space" to consist of a cube of edge L. We must then impose periodic boundary conditions on all quantities such as $\langle x'|\alpha'\rangle$ so that particles will not be lost or gained by the system. If a particle should go out through one side of the cube, periodic boundary conditions assure that it will be replaced by a particle coming in the opposite side. The periodic boundary condition applied to (9.8) yields

$$\exp\,[ip_j'L/\hbar] = 1, \quad j = x, y, z\,,$$

so that, for example,

$$p_x'L/\hbar = 2\pi n_x\,,$$

$$p_x' = (2\pi\hbar/L)n_x\,, \tag{9.10}$$

where n_x is an integer. The eigenvalue spectrum is discrete and all difficulties are removed. The constant C is conventionally chosen to be $L^{-3/2}$, so the normalization in the volume L^3 is to unity. This is called *box normalization.* In the end, one must let $L \to \infty$ and express all physically meaningful quantities in a way which is independent of L.

There is an alternative to this *box normalization* which is called *delta function* normalization. We choose

$$\langle \mathbf{x}'|\mathbf{p}'\rangle = \exp[i\, \mathbf{p}' \cdot \mathbf{x}'/\hbar] \tag{9.12}$$

without the factor $L^{-3/2}$. This leads to

$$\langle \mathbf{p}''|\mathbf{p}'\rangle = \int d^3x' \, \langle \mathbf{p}''|\mathbf{x}'\rangle \, \langle \mathbf{x}'|\mathbf{p}'\rangle$$

$$= \int d^3x' \exp\,[i(\mathbf{p}' - \mathbf{p}'') \cdot \mathbf{x}'/\hbar]\,. \tag{9.13}$$

For $\mathbf{p}'' \neq \mathbf{p}'$, the integrand is an oscillating function and the integral can be defined to be zero. If $\mathbf{p}'' = \mathbf{p}'$, the integral is infinite. To give at least a formal meaning to this behavior we look at

(9.14)

$$\int \frac{d^3p''}{(2\pi\hbar)^3} f(\mathbf{p}'') \langle \mathbf{p}''|\mathbf{p}'\rangle = \int \frac{d^3p''}{(2\pi\hbar)^3} \int d^3x' f(\mathbf{p}'') \exp\,[i(\mathbf{p}' - \mathbf{p}'')\cdot \mathbf{x}'/\hbar]\,.$$

Assuming that the order of integration can be changed, we may write this as

$$\begin{aligned} \int d^3x' \int \frac{d^3p''}{(2\pi\hbar)^3} f(\mathbf{p}'') \exp\,[i(\mathbf{p}' - \mathbf{p}'')\cdot \mathbf{x}'/\hbar] \\ = \int d^3x'\,\phi(\mathbf{x}') \exp\,[i\mathbf{p}'\cdot \mathbf{x}'/\hbar] \\ = f(\mathbf{p}')\,, \end{aligned} \tag{9.15}$$

because $\phi(\mathbf{x}')$ is, aside from factors of $\hbar$ which have been carried along, just the Fourier transform of $f(\mathbf{p}')$.

The bracket $\langle \mathbf{p}''|\mathbf{p}'\rangle$ is a *generalized function* or *distribution*. Its establishment as an acceptable mathematical entity was accomplished by Schwarz* long after it was introduced by Dirac. We define the *delta function* by

$$\langle \mathbf{p}''|\mathbf{p}'\rangle = (2\pi\hbar)^3\,\delta(\mathbf{p}'' - \mathbf{p}')\,. \tag{9.16}$$

The three-dimensional delta function is the product of three one-dimensional delta functions. In quantum mechanics, delta functions usually have momenta or functions of momenta as arguments. There is a simple rule which keeps factors of $2\pi\hbar$ in order. All momentum delta functions are written with the coefficient $2\pi\hbar$, and all momentum differentials are divided by $2\pi\hbar$, as in (9.14) above. The physical meaning of this recipe is given in connection with (26.17).

Delta functions can be added and subtracted, differentiated and integrated. They are physically meaningful only after an integration over their arguments has been made. Delta functions of the same argument may not be multiplied together. The delta function may be regarded as the derivative of the unit step function.

There are many useful formal properties of the δ-function. Among these are the following:

$$\begin{aligned} \delta(-\xi) &= \delta(\xi)\,, \\ \delta(a\xi) &= \frac{1}{a}\,\delta(\xi),\ a > 0\,, \\ \delta(g(\xi)) &= \frac{1}{g'(\xi_0)}\,\delta(\xi - \xi_0),\ g(\xi_0) = 0,\ g'(\xi_0) > 0\,, \\ \delta(\xi) &= \frac{1}{2\pi}\int_{-\infty}^{\infty} \exp\,[i\kappa\xi]d\kappa \\ \lim_{\epsilon\to 0} \frac{1}{\xi - i\epsilon} &= \mathcal{P}\frac{1}{\xi} + i\pi\delta(\xi)\,. \end{aligned} \tag{9.17}$$

* L. Schwarz, *Theorie des distributions*, Hermann et Cie, Paris, 1950.

In the last one, $\mathcal{P}$ means "Cauchy principal value." All of these equations make sense only when multiplied by some sufficiently regular function and then integrated over ξ. The "proofs" are left to the reader. The derivative of the δ-function has the property

$$\int_{-\epsilon}^{\epsilon} d\xi\, f(\xi)\delta'(\xi) = f(\xi)\delta(\xi)\Big|_{-\epsilon}^{\epsilon} - \int_{-\epsilon}^{\epsilon} f'(\xi)\delta(\xi)\, d\xi = -f'(0)\,. \tag{9.18}$$

Higher derivatives may be defined also.

It was pointed out earlier in this section that if β has a continuous eigenvalue spectrum, the interpretation of $\langle\beta'|\alpha'\rangle$ is different from that in the presence of only a discrete spectrum. We must also discuss what happens when we consider $\langle\alpha'|\beta'\rangle$ for continuous spectra of β'. This was the amplitude for detecting the value α' (taken to be discrete) when the system was prepared in the discrete state $|\beta'\rangle$. If β' constitutes a continuum, no physical apparatus can prepare a unique state $|\beta'\rangle$; it can only be assured that β' lies in a range $\Delta\beta'$ around the value β'. The total probability of the system having been prepared with some value of α' is then

$$\sum_{\alpha'} |\langle\alpha'|\beta'\rangle|^2\Delta\beta'\,,$$

which may be put equal to unity. If δ-function normalization is used, this becomes ill-defined as $\Delta\beta'$ tends to zero so the sum tends to infinity. The square of the scalar product in this case gives only relative probabilities for detecting various values of α.

When both α and β have continuous spectra, the state prepared and the state detected both are defined only within a spread of eigenvalues. The relevant quantity is then

$$|\langle\alpha'|\beta'\rangle|^2\,\Delta\alpha'\,\Delta\beta'\,.$$

The normalization may be chosen so that the total probability of detecting some value of α is unity; i.e., so that

$$\Delta\beta'\int |\langle\alpha'|\beta'\rangle|^2\, d\alpha' = 1\,.$$

If δ-function normalization is used, this becomes ill-defined because as before now $\Delta\beta' \to 0$ and the integral becomes infinite. In this case again one says that $|\langle\alpha'|\beta'\rangle|^2\Delta\alpha'$ gives only relative probabilities for detecting the system with various values and ranges of α'.

10. THE COORDINATE REPRESENTATION

The Hamiltonian of most classical systems consist of two parts, the kinetic energy and the potential energy. The former is a function solely of the momenta in cartesian coordinates, while the latter is a function of the coordinates. The dependence of the kinetic energy on the momenta is extremely simple. In other coordinate systems and in the presence of magnetic fields this division is no longer so clearcut, but the dependence of the Hamiltonian on the momenta is generally much simpler than its dependence on the coordinates. For this reason it is often advantageous to use a representation in quantum mechanics in which the coordinates are diagonal and, therefore, behave like numbers rather than operators. This avoids dealing with complicated functions of operators explicitly. The coordinate representation also affords a way of picturing the behavior of systems in quantum mechanics. It is a great aid to the intuition and to qualitative reasoning. The form which the quantum mechanical laws assume in the coordinate representation lead it to be called *wave mechanics.*

The eigenvalue equation for H which is to be solved, namely,

$$H|E, \gamma'\rangle = E|E, \gamma'\rangle \,, \tag{10.1}$$

is called the time-independent Schrödinger equation. The operator H is a simple algebraic function of the momenta. Multiplying (10.1) by $\langle x'|$ we obtain

$$\langle x'|H|E, \gamma'\rangle = E\langle x'|E, \gamma'\rangle \,. \tag{10.2}$$

Any coordinate which appears in H can be brought to the left of all the momenta in H by use of the commutation relations. These coordinates acting on $\langle x'|$ give their eigenvalues times $\langle x'|$ and can therefore be taken out as numerical factors. We are left with only matrix elements of products of momenta. We must evaluate a matrix element such as $\langle x'|p^n|\alpha'\rangle$ in terms of $\langle x'|\alpha'\rangle$. If this can be done, (10.2) becomes an equation for the quantity $\langle x'|E, \gamma'\rangle$.

We start from (9.5) which is generalized to the existence of several coordinates $x_1, \ldots, x_f$. It can be written

$$\begin{aligned} &|x_1', \ldots, x_j' + \epsilon\hbar, \ldots x_f'\rangle - |x_1', \ldots, x_j', \ldots, x_f'\rangle \\ &\qquad = -i\epsilon p_j|x_1', \ldots, x_j', \ldots, x_f'\rangle \,. \end{aligned} \tag{10.3}$$

We multiply this by $\langle\alpha'|$ with α' independent of the x's, and divide by $-i\epsilon$.

$$\begin{aligned} i\hbar\, &\frac{\langle\alpha'|x_1', \ldots, x_j' + \epsilon\hbar, \ldots, x_f'\rangle - \langle\alpha'|x_1', \ldots, x_j', \ldots, x_f'\rangle}{\epsilon\hbar} \\ &= \langle\alpha'|p_j|x_1', \ldots, x_j', \ldots, x_f'\rangle \,. \end{aligned}$$

Here, as always in this connection, the limit $\epsilon \to 0$ is understood. Thus,

$$\langle\alpha'|p_j|x'\rangle = i\hbar \frac{\partial}{\partial x_j'} \langle\alpha'|x'\rangle \,. \tag{10.4}$$

The complex conjugate of this is the desired result.

$$\langle x'|p_j|\alpha'\rangle = -i\hbar\frac{\partial}{\partial x_j'}\langle x'|\alpha'\rangle\,. \tag{10.5}$$

From this we may find the matrix element of any product of momenta. For example,

$$\begin{aligned}\langle x'|p_jp_k|\alpha'\rangle &= \sum_{\beta'}\langle x'|p_j|\beta'\rangle\langle\beta'|p_k|\alpha'\rangle \\ &= -i\hbar\frac{\partial}{\partial x_j'}\sum_{\beta'}\langle x'|\beta'\rangle\,\langle\beta'|p_k|\alpha'\rangle \\ &= -i\hbar\frac{\partial}{\partial x_j'}\langle x'|p_k|\alpha'\rangle \\ &= (-i\hbar)^2\frac{\partial^2}{\partial x_j'\partial x_k'}\langle x'|\alpha'\rangle\,.\end{aligned} \tag{10.6}$$

This result leads to a very simple recipe for eigenvalue problems in the coordinate representation. Suppose we want the eigenkets and eigenvalues of the observable $\alpha(x, p)$,

$$\alpha(x, p)\,|\alpha'\rangle = \alpha'|\alpha'\rangle\,. \tag{10.7}$$

The expansion coefficients $\langle x'|\alpha'\rangle$ of this eigenket in eigenkets of the coordinates, $|x'\rangle$, satisfy the differential equation.

$$\alpha\left(x', -i\hbar\frac{\partial}{\partial x'}\right)\langle x'|\alpha'\rangle = \alpha'\langle x'|\alpha'\rangle\,. \tag{10.8}$$

If $\alpha(x, p)$ contains products of conjugate coordinates and momenta, the operator $\alpha(x, -i\hbar\partial/\partial x)$ depends on the order in which these factors are written. In cartesian coordinates the problem is seldom encountered, so that the usual practice is to make the transition from classical function to operator in cartesian coordinates and then to transform to some other coordinates system if this is advantageous. Not all solutions $\langle x'|\alpha'\rangle$ are necessarily acceptable. The boundary conditions to be applied are discussed later.

The most important case of (10.7) is, of course, the eigenvalue problem for the Hamiltonian. Consider a single particle moving in a potential V. The Hamiltonian is

$$H = \frac{\mathbf{p}^2}{2m} + V(\mathbf{x})\,.$$

The eigenvalue equation (10.8) then becomes

$$\left[-\frac{\hbar^2}{2m}\left(\frac{\partial^2}{\partial x'^2}+\frac{\partial^2}{\partial y'^2}+\frac{\partial^2}{\partial z'^2}\right)+V(\mathbf{x}')\right]\langle x'|E, \gamma'\rangle = E\langle x'|E, \gamma'\rangle\,. \tag{10.9}$$

The notation is clumsy for this purpose. We simplify it by noting that the operator x does not appear, so the prime on x' can be omitted without causing ambiguity. The quantity $\langle x'|E', \gamma'\rangle$ is replaced by

$$\langle x'|E', \gamma'\rangle = \psi_{E\gamma}(x)\,. \tag{10.10}$$

ψ is called the *wave function* of the system. Then the differential equation (8.9) can be written

$$\nabla^2\psi_{E\gamma} + \frac{2m}{\hbar^2}(E - V(\mathbf{x}))\psi_{E\gamma} = 0\,. \tag{10.11}$$

This is a standard form of the Schrödinger equation.

Wave functions $\psi(x)$ need not be labelled with an energy eigenvalue. The eigenvalues of any complete set of commuting observables can be used here just as they can be used to label kets.

Matrix elements can be written as integrals involving wave functions. Thus

$$\begin{aligned}\langle\gamma''|\alpha(\mathbf{x}, \mathbf{p})\,|\gamma'\rangle &= \int d^3x'\,\langle\gamma''|\mathbf{x}'\rangle\,\langle\mathbf{x}'|\alpha|\gamma'\rangle\\ &= \int d^3x\;\;\psi_{\gamma''}{}^*(\mathbf{x})\alpha\left(\mathbf{x}, -i\hbar\frac{\partial}{\partial\mathbf{x}}\right)\psi_{\gamma'}(\mathbf{x})\,.\end{aligned} \tag{10.12}$$

This equation shows that the wave function must satisfy certain boundary conditions as well as the differential equation (10.8). Let $\alpha = p_x$, which is conjugate to the coordinate x. Then (10.12) yields

$$\langle\gamma''|p_x|\gamma'\rangle = \int d^3x\,\psi_{\gamma''}{}^*\,(\mathbf{x})\left(-i\hbar\frac{\partial}{\partial x}\psi_{\gamma'}(\mathbf{x})\right). \tag{10.13}$$

But we may also write

$$\begin{aligned}\langle\gamma''|p_x|\gamma'\rangle &= \int d^3x'\,\langle\gamma''|p_x|\mathbf{x}'\rangle\,\langle\mathbf{x}'|\gamma'\rangle\\ &= \int d^3x'\left(i\hbar\frac{\partial}{\partial x'}\langle\gamma'|\mathbf{x}'\rangle\right)\langle\mathbf{x}'|\gamma'\rangle\\ &= \int d^3x\left(i\hbar\frac{\partial\psi_{\gamma''}{}^*}{\partial x}\right)\psi_{\gamma'}\,.\end{aligned} \tag{10.14}$$

Subtracting (10.13) from (10.14) yields

$$\begin{aligned}0 &= \int d^3x\; i\hbar\frac{\partial}{\partial x}(\psi_{\gamma''}{}^*\,\psi_{\gamma'})\\ &= \int dy\,dz\; i\hbar\,[\psi_{\gamma''}{}^*\,\psi_{\gamma'}]_{x_L}^{x_R}\,.\end{aligned} \tag{10.15}$$

The limits have been written as x_L (for left) and x_R (for right). Equation (10.15) thus requires the wave function to satisfy some boundary condition. There are several possibilities.

If x_L and x_R are finite, then (10.15) will be satisfied if $\psi_{\gamma'}(x_L) = 0$, $\psi_{\gamma'}(x_R) = 0$ for all γ'. Similar equations must hold for other coordinates as well. Thus a sufficient condition is

$$\psi_{\gamma'}(x) = 0 \text{ on a boundary surface.} \tag{10.16}$$

This condition is similar to that imposed on sound waves in a rigid box. There it leads to standing wave solutions. We call it the *standing wave boundary condition*. It has a limited application in quantum mechanics.

The condition (10.15) will also be satisfied if, for finite x_L, x_R, the wave function is required to have the same value at the two ends of the internal. This condition is mathematically insufficient unless it is supplemented by the requirement that the derivatives of the wave functions also be equal. These boundary conditions can be applied only to a rectangular box. They are called *periodic boundary conditions* and are very useful in quantum mechanics.

If x_L and x_R are allowed to approach infinity, then the above boundary conditions become meaningless if the wave function oscillates with a finite wavelength for large values of x. Thus, there are no boundary conditions to be applied to oscillating wave functions in the infinite interval. If the wave function does not oscillate at infinity, the above boundary conditions can be applied unambiguously. They are more easily understood, however, when expressed in terms of $\mathbf{p}^2$ rather than of $\mathbf{p}$.

The states $|E, \gamma'\rangle$ constitute a complete set of states. In the coordinate representation, then, the wave functions $\psi_{E\gamma}(\mathbf{x})$ constitute a complete set of functions in terms of which any wave function of the system may be expanded. Therefore, it is sufficient to investigate the boundary conditions to be imposed on $\psi_{E\gamma}(\mathbf{x})$. For simplicity we assume this is an eigenfunction of the Hamiltonian

$$H = \frac{\mathbf{p}^2}{2m} + V(\mathbf{x}) .$$

Thus,

$$H\left(\mathbf{x}, -i\hbar\frac{\partial}{\partial \mathbf{x}}\right)\psi_{E\gamma}(\mathbf{x}) = E\psi_{E\gamma}(\mathbf{x}) .$$

Now let us calculate the expectation value of $\mathbf{p}^2$ in the state whose wave function is $\psi_{E\gamma}(\mathbf{x})$:

$$\langle E\gamma'|\mathbf{p}^2|E\gamma'\rangle = \int d^3x\, \psi_{E\gamma}{}^*\mathbf{p}^2\psi_{E\gamma} = \int d^3x\, \psi_{E\gamma}{}^*2m(E-V)\psi_{E\gamma} . \tag{10.17}$$

The expression $2m\psi_{E\gamma}{}^*\psi_{E\gamma} \geqslant 0$. The sign of the integrand depends on the sign of $E - V$. We assume the integration is over all space.

If $E - V(\mathbf{x}) > 0$ as $|\mathbf{x}| \to \infty$, then the right side of (10.17) is positive and no boundary condition is required. The normalization of the wave function will be of the δ-function type.

If $E - V(\mathbf{x}) < 0$ as $|\mathbf{x}| \to \infty$, then the integral in (10.17) will receive an infinite negative contribution, which will overbalance any positive contribution from a finite region, unless the wave function vanishes at infinity. The condition that $E - V(\mathbf{x}) < 0$ as $|\mathbf{x}| \to \infty$, classically means that the particle cannot get to arbitrarily large coordinate values, but is restricted to a finite region of space. These are *bound states*. They are given this name in quantum mechanics also. The energy eigenvalues associated with bound states are generally discrete. When finite boundaries are used, all energy eigenvalues are discrete and all states are bound states, bound within the box. There may be states which are localized in small regions of the box. These then remain bound states as the box increases without limit.

There exist potentials which behave differently as $|\mathbf{x}| \to \infty$ in different directions. We leave the investigation of the necessary boundary conditions to the reader.

The equation of motion

$$i\hbar \frac{d}{dt} |t\rangle = H|t\rangle$$

may be expressed in the coordinate representation also. Multiplication by $\langle x'|$ leads to

$$i\hbar \frac{d}{dt} \langle x'|t\rangle = \langle x'|H|t\rangle ,$$

or, in coordinate notation,

$$i\hbar \frac{\partial \psi(\mathbf{x}, t)}{\partial t} = H\left(\mathbf{x}, -i\hbar \frac{\partial}{\partial \mathbf{x}}\right) \psi(\mathbf{x}, t) . \tag{10.18}$$

If ψ_E is an eigenfunction of H so that

$$H\psi_E = E\psi_E ,$$

then the time dependence of ψ_E is contained in an exponential factor.

$$\psi_E(\mathbf{x}, t) = \psi_E(\mathbf{x}, 0) \exp[-iEt/\hbar] . \tag{10.19}$$

Equation (10.18) is called the *time-dependent Schrödinger equation*. In deriving it, the assumption has been made that the bra $\langle \mathbf{x}'|$ is time-independent, and, hence, that the operators x are time independent. Equation (10.19) refers, therefore, to the Schrödinger picture. The spatial boundary conditions to be applied to solutions of the time-dependent Schrödinger equation are the same as those for the time-independent case.

Consider a system consisting of a single particle described by the Hamiltonian $H = \mathbf{p}^2/2m + V(\mathbf{x})$. The probability of finding this particle in the volume element d^3x is given by

$$\psi^*\psi \; d^3x = \rho \; d^3x \,, \tag{10.20}$$

so that quantity $\psi^*\psi$ is a probability density. The rate of change of probability of finding the particle in a volume element ΔV should be equal to the flux of a probability current through the boundary of the volume element. Otherwise, the probability of finding a particle one place could decrease and that of finding it another place could increase, while the probability of finding it somewhere between could vanish at all times. The Schrödinger equation has a form which makes this impossible. We show that a probability current $\mathbf{j}$ can be defined so that

$$\partial\rho/\partial t + \nabla \cdot \mathbf{j} = 0 \,. \tag{10.21}$$

This is an *equation of continuity*. Integrated over any finite volume V bounded by the surface S it yields

$$\frac{d}{dt}\int_V d^3x \; \rho = -\int_S dS \; j_n \,, \tag{10.22}$$

where the normal is taken outward.

We construct the current vector for a particle described by a slightly more general Hamiltonian than that given above. We take

$$H = \frac{1}{2m}[\mathbf{p} - \epsilon\mathbf{A}(\mathbf{x})]^2 + V(\mathbf{x}) \,. \tag{10.23}$$

The classical system with this Hamiltonian is a particle of mass m and an electric charge ϵc moving in a magnetic field $\mathbf{B} = \nabla \times \mathbf{A}$ and in the potential V. Now,

$$\begin{aligned} \frac{\partial\rho}{\partial t} &= \frac{\partial\psi^*}{\partial t}\psi + \psi^*\frac{\partial\psi}{\partial t} \\ &= \left(\frac{-1}{i\hbar}H\psi^*\right)\psi + \psi^*\left(\frac{1}{i\hbar}H\psi\right) . \end{aligned} \tag{10.24}$$

It is clear that the terms in V and in $\mathbf{A}^2$ will cancel. The relevant part of H is thus

$$\frac{1}{2m}(\mathbf{p}^2 - \epsilon\mathbf{p}\cdot\mathbf{A} - \epsilon\mathbf{A}\cdot\mathbf{p}) \,.$$

Using the commutation relations (7.18) we see that

(10.25)
$$\mathbf{p}\cdot\mathbf{A}+\mathbf{A}\cdot\mathbf{p} = 2\mathbf{A}\cdot\mathbf{p} - \sum_k [A_k, p_k]$$
$$= 2\mathbf{A}\cdot\mathbf{p} - i\hbar\,\nabla\cdot\mathbf{A}\,.$$

There remains

$$\frac{\partial\rho}{\partial t} = \frac{1}{2im\hbar}\left\{(\hbar^2\,\nabla^2\psi^* - 2i\epsilon\hbar\mathbf{A}\cdot\nabla\psi^*)\psi + \psi^*(-\hbar^2\,\nabla^2\psi - 2i\epsilon\hbar\mathbf{A}\cdot\nabla\psi) + \frac{2i\hbar\epsilon}{m}\,\nabla\cdot\mathbf{A}\psi^*\psi\right\}$$
$$= -\nabla\cdot\left\{\frac{\hbar}{2mi}(\psi^*\,\nabla\psi - \psi\,\nabla\psi^*) - \frac{\epsilon}{m}\,\mathbf{A}\psi^*\psi\right\}.$$

The current may be identified as

(10.26)
$$\mathbf{j} = \frac{\hbar}{2mi}(\psi^*\,\nabla\psi - \psi\,\nabla\psi^*) - \frac{\epsilon}{m}\,\mathbf{A}\psi^*\psi\,.$$

The latter term contributes only for charged particles in a magnetic field. (**A** could be a gradient, hence generating no magnetic field but not vanishing. It can then be transformed away by a gauge transformation. See Section 23.)

In the absence of a magnetic field a real wave function yields zero current. Real wave functions can represent only standing waves, in the absence of magnetic fields.

Let us write the current in (10.26) as $\mathbf{j}\,(\psi^*, \psi)$. If we put

$$\psi = f + g,\ \psi^* = f^* + g^*\,,$$

then

$$\mathbf{j}(\psi^*, \psi) = \mathbf{j}(f^*, f) + \mathbf{j}(g^*, g) + \mathbf{j}(f^*, g) + \mathbf{j}(g^*, f)\,.$$

Now let

$$\phi = f + ig,\ \phi^* = f^* - ig^*,$$

where f and g also satisfy the time-dependent Schrödinger equation.

$$\mathbf{j}(\phi^*, \phi) = \mathbf{j}(f^*, f) + \mathbf{j}(g^*, g) + i\mathbf{j}(f^*, g) - i\mathbf{j}(g^*, f).$$

Similarly ρ is written $\rho(\psi^*, \psi)$, etc. Now the currents and densities of the form $\rho(\psi^*, \psi)$, $\mathbf{j}(\psi^*, \psi)$ satisfy the continuity equation. Therefore,

$$\frac{\partial}{\partial t}(\rho(\psi^*, \psi) + i\rho(\phi^*, \phi)) + \nabla\cdot(\mathbf{j}(\psi^*, \psi) + i\,j(\phi^*, \phi)) = 0\,.$$

This is, however,

(10.27)
$$\frac{\partial}{\partial t}\rho(g^*, f) + \nabla\cdot\mathbf{j}(g^*, f) = 0\,.$$

The current vector regarded as depending on two independent wave functions still satisfies the continuity equation. This fact is very useful in discussing boundary conditions to be imposed on wave functions.

11. THE HARMONIC OSCILLATOR IN THE COORDINATE REPRESENTATION

In Section 8 the energy eigenvalues of the harmonic oscillator were found by algebraic methods. A complete set of states was also constructed and the matrix elements of x and p were evaluated. However, the question of the probability of finding the oscillating particle in the neighborhood of a value x' was not determined, nor is this easy to do by the method used there. All the moments $(x - x')^n$ could be evaluated for any x', and the desired probability distribution could then be inferred, but this is far from direct. The coordinate representation affords a direct and complete answer to this question.

It is possible to write down the time-independent Schrödinger equation and solve it subject to the boundary conditions discussed in the last section. We do this at the end of this section. First, we solve the problem by obtaining the coordinate representation for the raising and lowering operators $a^\dagger$ and a.

From (8.9) we have

$$\begin{aligned} a &= (2m\hbar\omega)^{-1/2}(ip + m\omega x) \\ &= (2m\hbar\omega)^{-1/2}\left(\hbar\frac{\partial}{\partial x} + m\omega x\right). \\ a^\dagger &= (2m\hbar\omega)^{-1/2}(-ip + m\omega x) \\ &= (2m\hbar\omega)^{-1/2}\left(-\hbar\frac{\partial}{\partial x} + m\omega x\right). \end{aligned} \tag{11.1}$$

The latter form of each of these is meaningful only in the coordinate representation and must act to the right on wave functions. These become much simpler on changing the variable x to ξ according to

$$\alpha x = \xi, \quad \alpha^2 = m\omega/\hbar . \tag{11.2}$$

With this coordinate

$$a = \frac{1}{\sqrt{2}}\left(\frac{\partial}{\partial\xi} + \xi\right), \qquad a^\dagger = \frac{1}{\sqrt{2}}\left(-\frac{\partial}{\partial\xi} + \xi\right). \tag{11.3}$$

According to Section 8, the ground state $|0\rangle$ satisfies

$$a|0\rangle = 0 .$$

In the coordinate representation this reads

$$\frac{1}{\sqrt{2}}\left(\frac{\partial}{\partial\xi}+\xi\right)\psi_0(\xi)=0\,. \tag{11.4}$$

The solution of this is

$$\psi_0 = N_0 \exp\left[-\tfrac{1}{2}\xi^2\right]. \tag{11.5}$$

The constant of integration N_0 is determined by the normalization condition

$$\begin{aligned}\langle 0|0\rangle = 1 &= \int_{-\infty}^{\infty} dx\ \psi_0{}^*\psi \\ &= \frac{|N_0|^2}{\alpha}\int_{-\infty}^{\infty} d\xi \exp\left[-\xi^2\right] \\ &= \frac{|N_0|^2}{\alpha}\pi^{1/2}\,.\end{aligned}$$

Choosing N_0 to be real and positive, we have

$$\psi_0 = \left(\frac{\alpha^2}{\pi}\right)^{1/4}\exp\left[-\tfrac{1}{2}\xi^2\right]. \tag{11.6}$$

The wave functions of the excited states are obtained from $\psi_0(\xi)$ by application of $a^\dagger$. According to (8.17),

$$|n\rangle = (n!)^{-1/2}a^{\dagger n}|0\rangle$$

or

$$\psi_n(\xi) = (n!)^{-1/2}(2)^{-n/2}\left(-\frac{\partial}{\partial\xi}+\xi\right)^n\left(\frac{\alpha^2}{\pi}\right)^{1/4}\exp\left[-\tfrac{1}{2}\xi^2\right]. \tag{11.7}$$

Thus, for example,

$$\psi_1(\xi) = \left(\frac{\alpha}{2\pi^{1/2}}\right)^{1/2} 2\xi\exp\left[-\tfrac{1}{2}\xi^2\right]. \tag{11.8}$$

Wave functions of higher states are all polynomials of degree n multiplying the Gaussian.

The polynomials occurring here are called Hermite polynomials. They are defined by

$$\begin{aligned}H_n(\xi) &= (-)^n \exp\left[\frac{\xi^2}{2}\right]\left(\frac{\partial}{\partial\xi}-\xi\right)^n\exp\left[-\frac{\xi^2}{2}\right] \\ &= (-)^n\exp\left[\xi^2\right]\frac{\partial^n}{\partial\xi^n}\exp\left[-\xi^2\right].\end{aligned} \tag{11.9}$$

The latter form is more convenient for purposes of evaluation. $H_n(\xi)$ is a polynomial of degree n. The polynomials of even order are even functions of ξ, those of odd order are odd. In other words the $H_n(\xi)$ have the parity of n. This follows from the even character of $H_0 = 1$ and the fact that the operator $\partial/\partial\xi$ is odd.

Many useful properties of the Hermite polynomials follow easily from their generating function. Let

$$S(\xi, s) = \exp[-s^2 + 2s\xi] = \exp[\xi^2 - (s-\xi)^2].$$

Then

$$\frac{\partial^n}{\partial s^n} S = (-)^n \exp[\xi^2] \frac{\partial^n}{\partial \xi^n} \exp[-(s-\xi)^2].$$

Therefore, according to (11.9)

$$\frac{\partial^n}{\partial s^n} S(\xi, 0) = H_n(\xi). \tag{11.10}$$

But this is $n!$ times the expansion coefficient of $S(\xi, s)$ in powers of s, so that

$$S(\xi, s) = \sum_{n=0}^{\infty} \frac{H_n(\xi)}{n!} s^n. \tag{11.11}$$

Convergence is assured because the power series for exponential functions and Gaussians converge everywhere except at infinity.

Now write the wave function $\psi_n(\xi)$ as

$$\psi_n(\xi) = N_n H_n(\xi) \exp[-\tfrac{1}{2}\xi^2]. \tag{11.12}$$

Then

$$\frac{1}{\alpha}\int_{-\infty}^{\infty} d\xi\, N_m N_n H_m(\xi) H_n(\xi) \exp[-\xi^2] = \delta_{mn}$$

is the normalization and orthogonality condition. We know that the orthogonality condition must be satisfied because of our derivation of the wave functions and the orthogonality of the states $|m\rangle$ and $|n\rangle$. It can be directly verified and the normalization constants can be determined by use of S. We have

$$\int_{-\infty}^{\infty} d\xi\, S(\xi, s) S(\xi, t) \exp[-\xi^2]$$
$$= \int_{-\infty}^{\infty} d\xi \sum_j \sum_k H_j(\xi) H_k(\xi) \exp[-\xi^2]\, s^j t^k / j!k!,$$

so that the coefficient of $s^j t^k$ is $\alpha/(N_m N_n m! n!)$ times the desired integral. However, the above integral is explicitly integrable.

$$\int_{-\infty}^{\infty} d\xi \exp[-s^2 + 2s\xi] \exp[-t^2 + 2t\xi] \exp[-\xi^2]$$
$$= \int_{-\infty}^{\infty} d\xi \exp[-(s + t - \xi)^2] \exp[2st]$$
$$= \pi^{1/2} \exp[2st]$$
$$= \pi^{1/2} \sum_l (2st)^l/l! \, .$$

Comparing coefficients, we see that the wave functions are indeed orthogonal and that

$$\pi^{1/2} \frac{2^n}{n!} = \frac{\alpha}{N_n^2 (n!)^2},$$
$$N_n = \left[\frac{\alpha}{\pi^{1/2} 2^n n!}\right]^{1/2}. \tag{11.13}$$

The generating function $S(\xi, s)$ is useful in obtaining the wave function for the pseudoclassical state $|z_0\rangle$ developed in Section 8. The state obtained in (8.32) was a Heisenberg state, independent of the time. We can find the Schrödinger state which coincides with this Heisenberg state at time $t = 0$ by inserting the time dependence $\exp[-i(n + \frac{1}{2})\omega t]$ of the energy eigenstates on the left of this equation. Inspection shows that this merely replaces z_0 by z and multiplies the entire right side by $\exp[-i\frac{1}{2}\omega t]$. The Schrödinger form of the pseudoclassical state is thus

$$|z\rangle = \exp\left[-\frac{|z|^2}{2} - \frac{i\omega t}{2}\right] \sum_n |n\rangle \frac{z^n}{(n!)^{1/2}}. \tag{11.14}$$

The normalized stationary state wave functions of the oscillator are, according to (11.12) and (11.13),

$$\langle x'|n\rangle = \left[\frac{\alpha}{\pi^{1/2} 2^n n!}\right]^{1/2} H_n(\xi) \exp\left[-\frac{\xi^2}{2}\right]. \tag{11.15}$$

Inserting this into $\langle x'|z\rangle$ then leads to

$$\langle x'|z\rangle = \frac{\alpha^{1/2}}{\pi^{1/4}} \exp\left[-\frac{|z|^2 + \xi^2 + i\omega t}{2}\right] \sum_n \left(\frac{z}{2^{1/2}}\right)^n \frac{H_n(\xi)}{n!}$$
$$= \frac{\alpha^{1/2}}{\pi^{1/4}} \exp\left[-\frac{|z|^2 + \xi^2 + i\omega t}{2}\right] S\left(\xi, \frac{z}{2^{1/2}}\right)$$
$$= \frac{\alpha^{1/2}}{\pi^{1/4}} \exp\left[-\frac{|z|^2 + \xi^2 + z^2 - 2^{3/2} z\xi + i\omega t}{2}\right].$$

On writing out the real and imaginary parts of the exponent, one finally gets

$$\langle x'|z\rangle = \frac{\alpha^{\frac{1}{2}}}{\pi^{\frac{1}{4}}} \exp\left[-\frac{(\xi - 2^{1/2}|z| \cos \omega t)^2}{2}\right] \times \exp\left[-i\left(\frac{\omega t}{2} + |z|^2 \sin 2\omega t - 2^{1/2}|z|\xi \sin \omega t\right)\right]. \tag{11.16}$$

The first exponential gives the magnitude of the wave function. It is a ground state wave function centered on the point $2^{1/2}|z|\cos \omega t$, and oscillating as a whole with the classical frequency and with amplitude $2^{1/2}|z|$. The width of the packet does not depend on the amplitude of the motion, and for large amplitudes becomes negligible relative to the amplitude. This is exactly what the correspondence principle requires.

The method that has been used to find the wavefunctions of the harmonic oscillator is called the *factorization method.* It can be applied to a large number of systems other than the harmonic oscillator, but it is not so simple in these other cases. It depends on being able to find the raising and lowering operators in tractable form. The interested reader is referred to a review article by Infeld and Hull*. For other systems it is usually just as convenient to start from the Schrödinger equation in the form (10.11). We treat the harmonic oscillator on this basis now.

The Schrödinger equation for the harmonic oscillator is

$$\frac{d^2\psi}{dx^2} + \frac{2m}{\hbar^2}(E - \tfrac{1}{2}m\omega^2 x^2)\psi = 0\,. \tag{11.14}$$

The substitutions

$$\xi = \alpha x\,, \qquad \alpha^2 = m\omega/\hbar, \qquad E = \tfrac{1}{2}\lambda\hbar\omega \tag{11.15}$$

reduce this to

$$\left[\frac{d^2}{d\xi^2} + (\lambda - \xi^2)\right]\psi = 0\,. \tag{11.16}$$

A standard attack on such an equation is to satisfy the equation in the neighborhood of each of its singular points first, and then to look for a solution, which is a polynomial times the product of the solutions near the singular points.

Equation (11.16) has singular points at $\xi = \pm\infty$. The equation is even in ξ, so a solution near $\xi = +\infty$ will also be one near $\xi = -\infty$. In the neighborhood of $\xi = \pm\infty$ a solution valid to terms in $1/\xi$ is

$$f(\xi) = \exp\,[-\tfrac{1}{2}\xi^2]\,. \tag{11.17}$$

* L. Infeld and T. E. Hull, Rev. Mod. Phys. **23,** 21 (1951).

Therefore, we set

$$\psi(\xi) = \exp[-\tfrac{1}{2}\xi^2]g(\xi)\,.$$

Inserting this into the original differential equation results in

(11.18) $$g'' - 2\xi g' + (\lambda - 1)g = 0\,.$$

The function $g(\xi)$ is now expanded in a power series.

(11.19) $$g(\xi) = \sum_\nu a_\nu \xi^\nu$$

The differential equation (11.18) clearly changes the degree of a term by two or not at all, so we get a two term recursion relation for the coefficients. The equation becomes

(11.20) $$\sum_\nu a_\nu\{\nu(\nu - 1)\xi^{\nu-2} - 2\nu\xi^2 + (\lambda - 1)\xi^\nu\} = 0\,.$$

This power series must not contain any negative powers because the original equation is regular at the origin. The starting power, ν_0, is obtained by equating the coefficient of the lowest power of ξ to zero in (11.20) assuming that the corresponding $a_\nu \neq 0$. Thus,

$$\nu_0(\nu_0 - 1) = 0\,, \qquad \nu_0 = 0 \text{ or } 1\,.$$

Equating the general coefficient in (11.20) to zero yields

(11.21) $$a_{\nu+2} = a_\nu \frac{2\nu - (\lambda - 1)}{(\nu + 2)(\nu + 1)}\,,$$

which is the anticipated two term recursion relation. The general solution is a sum of an even solution starting with $\nu = 0$ and an odd solution starting with $\nu = 1$. The coefficients a_0 and a_1 are the two constants of integration of the differential equation.

The ratio test shows that the series (11.19) converges.

$$\lim_{\nu\to\infty} \frac{a_{\nu+2}}{a_\nu} = \lim_{\nu\to\infty} \frac{2}{\nu} = 0\,.$$

Convergence is not sufficient, because it must converge to a function which behaves properly for all ξ. The power series expansion of $\exp[\gamma\xi^2]$ is given by

$$\exp[\gamma\xi^2] = \sum_\nu b_\nu \xi^\nu = \sum_\mu \frac{\gamma^\mu \xi^{2\mu}}{\mu!}\,.$$

In this series only the even ν enter. We see that

$$\frac{b_{\nu+2}}{b_\nu} = \frac{2\gamma}{\nu + 2} \xrightarrow[\nu\to\infty]{} \frac{2\gamma}{\nu}\,.$$

For $\gamma < 1$, the b-series is dominated by the a-series. But for $\xi \to \infty, \gamma > \frac{1}{2}$, the sum of the b-series is a function which approaches infinity faster than $\exp[\frac{1}{2}\xi^2]$. Thus, ψ diverges at infinity. This can be prevented only by breaking the a-series off at some ν-value, say n. Thus, we require

$$a_{n+2} = 0\,, \qquad \lambda = 2n + 1\,.$$

This yields the energy eigenvalues

$$E = (n + \tfrac{1}{2})\hbar\omega$$

as before.

The wave functions are now polynomials of degree n and of parity n multiplying the Gaussian. These polynomials are, of course, the Hermite polynomials.

12. FREE PARTICLE WAVE FUNCTIONS

In Section 9 it was shown that the scalar product $\langle \mathbf{x}'|\mathbf{p}'\rangle$ of a state $|\mathbf{x}'\rangle$ labelled by values of coordinates and a state $|\mathbf{p}'\rangle$ labelled by values of momenta is given by

$$\langle \mathbf{x}'|\mathbf{p}'\rangle = \exp[i\mathbf{p}' \cdot \mathbf{x}'/\hbar]\,. \tag{12.1}$$

Using the notation appropriate to the coordinate representation this is written

$$\psi_{\mathbf{p}}(\mathbf{x}) = \exp[i\mathbf{p} \cdot \mathbf{x}/\hbar]\,. \tag{12.2}$$

The amplitude unity gives these wave functions the δ-function normalization.

$$\int d^3x\, \psi_{\mathbf{p}'}{}^*(\mathbf{x})\psi_{\mathbf{p}}(\mathbf{x}) = (2\pi\hbar)^3\, \delta(\mathbf{p}' - \mathbf{p})\,. \tag{12.3}$$

A state, in which $\mathbf{p}$ has a definite value, has a definite value for the energy when the system is a free particle, $E = \mathbf{p}^2/2m$. The converse is not true, but any free particle state of energy E can be written as a superposition of states with the same magnitude of $\mathbf{p}$. A convenient way to write this is

$$\psi_E(\mathbf{x}) = \int \frac{d^3p}{(2\pi\hbar)^3}\, A(\mathbf{p})\, 2\pi\hbar\, \delta\left(\frac{\mathbf{p}^2}{2m} - E\right) \exp[i\mathbf{p} \cdot \mathbf{x}/\hbar]. \tag{12.4}$$

The δ-function insures the correct relation between $\mathbf{p}$ and E. The rule of Section 9 is that every momentum differential is divided by $2\pi\hbar$, and every momentum δ-function is multiplied by $2\pi\hbar$. The evaluation of this integral requires the identity

$$\delta(z^2 - a^2) = \frac{1}{2|a|}\,[\delta(z - |a|) + \delta(z + |a|)]\,, \tag{12.5}$$

which is a special case of (9.17), third equation.

Any state of a single particle system can be written as a superposition of free particle states $|\mathbf{p}'\rangle$, and hence the wave function of any particle is a superposition of plane waves. To see this, note that

$$|\alpha'\rangle = \int \frac{d^3p'}{(2\pi\hbar)^3} |\mathbf{p}'\rangle \langle \mathbf{p}'|\alpha'\rangle ,$$

so that

$$\langle x'|\alpha'\rangle = \int \frac{d^3p'}{(2\pi\hbar)^3} \langle \mathbf{x}'|\mathbf{p}'\rangle \langle \mathbf{p}'|\alpha'\rangle ,$$

or, in terms of wave functions,

(12.6) $$\psi_\alpha(\mathbf{x}) = \int \frac{d^3p}{(2\pi\hbar)^3} \exp [i\mathbf{p} \cdot \mathbf{x}/\hbar]\varphi_\alpha(\mathbf{p}) .$$

This is exactly the definition of a Fourier transform. The amplitude function $\varphi_\alpha(\mathbf{p})$ is obtained by inverting the transformation

(12.7) $$\varphi_\alpha(\mathbf{p}) = \int d^3x \exp [-i\mathbf{p} \cdot \mathbf{x}/\hbar]\psi_\alpha(\mathbf{x}) .$$

$\varphi_\alpha(p)$ is called the *momentum space wave function* of the particle in the state $|\alpha'\rangle$. If $\alpha = \mathbf{p}$, the momentum state wave function is just a δ-function, for if $\psi_\alpha(x) \sim \exp [i\mathbf{p} \cdot \mathbf{x}/\hbar]$, this follows from (12.7).

If $\psi_\alpha(\mathbf{x})$ describes a particle which is not free, then the momentum state wave function $\varphi_\alpha(\mathbf{p})$ will have finite values for $\mathbf{p}$'s not satisfying $E = \mathbf{p}^2/2m$, because this is not the relation between momentum and energy except for free particles. One speaks of $\psi_\alpha(\mathbf{x})$ as a superposition of momentum eigenstates which are "off the energy shell," meaning by this simply that the energy and momentum are not related as they are for free particles.

The position and the momentum of a free particle cannot be specified simultaneously. If the momentum is exactly specified, the wave function is a plane wave and the coordinates are completely undetermined. If a range of momenta of width $\Delta\mathbf{p}$ is all that is specified, the coordinates are in principle determinable within a range $\Delta\mathbf{x}$ as given by the uncertainty principle. We speak then of a *wave packet*. Let $\psi_P(\mathbf{x})$ represent such a packet.

(12.8) $$\psi_P(\mathbf{x}) = \int \frac{d^3p}{(2\pi\hbar)^3} A_P(\mathbf{p}) \exp [i\mathbf{p} \cdot \mathbf{x}/\hbar]$$

and let $\psi_Q(\mathbf{x})$ represent another. Then the scalar product of these two wave packet states is

12.9 $$\begin{aligned}\int d^3x\, \psi_Q{}^*(\mathbf{x})\psi_P(\mathbf{x}) &= (2\pi\hbar)^{-6}\int d^3p\, d^3p'\, d^3x\, A_Q{}^*(\mathbf{p}')A_P(\mathbf{p}) \exp [i(\mathbf{p} - \mathbf{p}') \cdot \mathbf{x}/\hbar] \\ &= (2\pi\hbar)^{-3}\int d^3p\, d^3p'\, A_Q{}^*(\mathbf{p}')A_P(\mathbf{p})\, \delta(\mathbf{p} - \mathbf{p}') \\ &= \int \frac{d^3p}{(2\pi\hbar)^3} A_Q{}^*(\mathbf{p})A_P(\mathbf{p}).\end{aligned}$$

If two wave packets have no momenta in common, then they constitute a pair of orthogonal states. The integral in (12.9) may vanish even if there are momenta in common, but in general it will not. Equation (12.9) shows that the scalar product of two states can also be written as the integral of a product of momentum-space wave functions.

If the function $A_P(\mathbf{p})$ is square integrable, then so is the function $\psi_p(\mathbf{x})$. The difficulties associated with δ-function normalization can thus be avoided by the exclusive use of wave packets. These also correspond more exactly to observation, because momenta (or coordinates) cannot be determined with zero uncertainty. (Any apparatus has a finite resolving power.) The simplicity of plane waves, however, is such an advantage that wave packets are used rather seldom. They are very useful when the plane wave leads to ambiguities as it does in formulation of scattering theory.

A wave packet involving the minimum uncertainty in x for a given uncertainty Δp in p can be constructed. In Section 7 the general uncertainty principle was derived, and it was seen that uncertainty is a minimum when (7.11) is satisfied. Taking $\tilde{A} = x$, $\tilde{B} = p$, $C = \hbar$, so that $\lambda = \hbar/2(\Delta p)^2$, this equation becomes

$$\left(x + \frac{i\hbar}{2(\Delta p)^2} p\right) | \rangle = 0 .$$

In the coordinate representation, then, we obtain

$$\left(x + \frac{h^2}{2(\Delta p)^2} \frac{\partial}{\partial x}\right) \psi = 0 .$$

The solution of this, normalized to unity, is

$$\psi(x) = \left(\frac{2(\Delta p)^2}{\pi\hbar^2}\right)^{1/4} \exp\left[-\frac{(\Delta p)^2 x^2}{\hbar^2}\right]. \tag{12.10}$$

This wave packet is centered at the origin and has zero mean momentum because in its construction $\langle\ |x|\ \rangle$ and $\langle\ |p|\ \rangle$ were equated to zero when $\tilde{A}$ was identified with x and $\tilde{B}$ with p. This is called a *minimal wave packet.*

A minimal free particle wave packet spreads in time. This is most easily seen by expanding in momentum eigenfunctions. From (12.7) we obtain

$$\varphi(p) = \left(\frac{2\pi\hbar^2}{(\Delta p)^2}\right)^{1/4} \exp\left[-\frac{p^2}{4(\Delta p)^2}\right], \tag{12.11}$$

which is also a simple Gaussian. Thus,

$$\psi(x) = \int_{-\infty}^{\infty} \frac{dp}{2\pi\hbar} \varphi(p) \exp\left[\frac{ip_x}{\hbar}\right] \tag{12.12}$$

expresses $\psi(x)$ as a superposition of *free particle energy* eigenfunctions. The time dependence of these is given by (10.19). Taking $\psi(x) = \psi(x, t = 0)$ we have from (10.19), with $E = p^2/2m$,

$$\psi(x, t) = \int_{-\infty}^{\infty} \frac{dp}{2\pi\hbar} \varphi(p) \exp [i(px - Et)/\hbar]$$

$$= \text{const} \int_{-\infty}^{\infty} dp \exp \left[- \frac{p^2}{4(\Delta p)^2} - \frac{ip^2t}{2m\hbar} + \frac{ipx}{\hbar} \right]$$

$$= \text{const} \int_{-\infty}^{\infty} dp \exp [- (\alpha p + \beta)^2 + \beta^2] .$$

The integral over $\exp [-(\alpha p + \beta)^2]$ gives a number independent of β, so that

(12.13) $$\psi(x, t) = \text{const} \exp [+\beta^2] ,$$

where β is given by

(12.14) $$\beta = \frac{ix}{\hbar} \left(\frac{1}{4(\Delta p)^2} + \frac{it}{2m\hbar} \right)^{-1/2} .$$

Thus (12.13) is a Gaussian with a complex width. The real Gaussian $\psi^*\psi$ is what is wanted.

$$\psi^*\psi = \text{const} \exp [\beta^2 + \beta^{*2}] ,$$

(12.15) $$\beta^2 + \beta^{*2} = - \frac{x^2}{2\hbar^2} \left[\frac{1}{4(\Delta p)^2} + \frac{t^2(\Delta p)^2}{2m^2\hbar^2} \right]^{-1} .$$

In terms of its root mean square deviation from the mean, a Gaussian is written $\exp [-x^2/2(\Delta x)^2]$. Thus,

(12.16) $$(\Delta \psi)^2 = \frac{\hbar^2}{4(\Delta p)^2} + \frac{t^2(\Delta p)^2}{2m^2} = (\Delta x)^2_{min} + \left(\frac{\Delta p}{m} \right)^2 \frac{t^2}{2} .$$

Thus, for a given Δp the spread in time of a minimal wave packet decreases as the mass of the system increases. For large values of t the spread can be related to the uncertainty in velocity as in classical mechanics.

The wave function (12.10) is the harmonic oscillator ground state wave function. In the presence of the oscillator potential there is no spreading.

13. ONE-DIMENSIONAL POTENTIAL PROBLEMS

In classical mechanics, a particle may be constrained to remain on a line. Its motion is then completely described by a single coordinate, say x. In quantum mechanics, this is not possible because constraint to remain on a line requires simultaneous vanishing of y and p_y and of z and p_z, taking the line to be the x-axis. We can, however, study systems in which the potential depends on the single coordinate x and can require p_y and p_z to vanish. The system is not localized in the yz plane at all, but since p_y and p_z commute with the Hamiltonian, their vanishing will be permanent. Strictly speaking, the Hamiltonian is still

$$\begin{aligned} H &= \frac{\mathbf{p}^2}{2m} + V(x) \\ &= \frac{1}{2m}(p_x^2 + p_y^2 + p_z^2) + V(x)\,. \end{aligned} \tag{13.1}$$

We may replace p_y and p_z by their values if we study only observables depending on x. In this way we come to the one dimensional problem defined by the Hamiltonian

$$H = \frac{p^2}{2m} + V(x)\,; \tag{13.2}$$

no subscript is needed on the p.

The Schrödinger equation for this system is

$$p^2\psi(x) = 2m[E - V(x)]\psi(x) \tag{13.3}$$

in coordinate language, where $p^2 = -\hbar^2\, d^2/dx^2$. This differential equation is to be solved subject to the boundary conditions discussed in Section 8. These boundary conditions here reduce to the condition that the expectation value of the kinetic energy be non-negative. Thus, if in any infinite interval $x > X_R$ or $x < X_L$ the value of $E - V(x)$ is negative, the wave function must vanish as $x \to +\infty$ or $x \to -\infty$. There are also continuity and differentiability requirements. If $V(x)$ remains finite, then the second derivative of x must also remain finite unless ψ itself becomes infinite. This case does not arise in non-relativistic quantum mechanics. ψ is bounded everywhere. Thus at discontinuities of $V(x)$ we see that ψ and its first derivative must be continuous. If $V(x)$ has an infinite discontinuity the second derivative becomes infinite for finite ψ. There the first derivative need not be continuous, but the wave function itself is. The requirement of non-negative kinetic energy now requires that the wave function vanish on the high potential side of the discontinuity.

The continuity conditions given above result in a continuous probability current j. This could have been used as the basis of the requirements if so desired, but in stationary state problems there is often no current because standing waves can or must be used.

We consider several examples of one-dimensional problems.

(*i*) *Finite Potential Step*. Let $V = 0$, $x < 0$, and $V = V_0$, $x > 0$. The potential is illustrated in Figure 13.1.

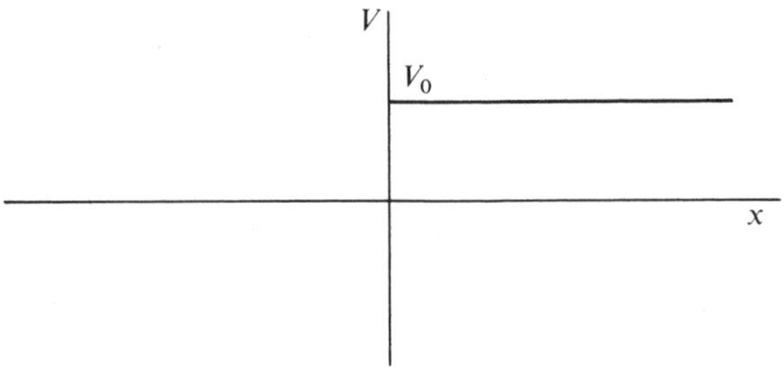

Fig. 13-1

Three cases arise. They are: (a) $E < 0$. There are no solutions because the kinetic energy is negative everywhere. (b) $0 < E < V_0$. The wave function must tend to zero as $x \to \infty$. (c) $V_0 < E$. Here, no boundary conditions are imposed unless the system is put in a one-dimensional box, which we do not do. We construct the solutions explicitly. For $x < 0$, the Schrödinger equation is always

(13.4) $$\psi'' + k^2\psi = 0\,, \qquad x < 0\,, \qquad k^2 = 2mE/\hbar^2\,.$$

This has solutions

(13.5) $$\psi(x) = A \exp[ikx] + B \exp[-ikx]\,.$$

The first term represents a wave travelling in the positive x-direction, the second represents one going the other way. The current associated with this wave function is

(13.6) $$j = (\,|A|^2 - |B|^2)\frac{\hbar k}{m}\,.$$

For $x > 0$, $E < V_0$ the solution must be

(13.7) $$\psi(x) = C \exp[-\kappa x] \qquad \kappa^2 = \frac{2m(V_0 - E)}{\hbar^2}$$

as the other solution with the rising exponential is inadmissible. No current is associated with this wave function. The continuity of ψ and of ψ' now require that

(13.8) $$A + B = C\,, \qquad ik(A - B) = -\kappa C\,.$$

The amplitudes B and C may be expressed in terms of A.

(13.9) $$B = A\frac{k - i\kappa}{k + i\kappa}\,, \qquad C = A\frac{2k}{k + i\kappa}\,.$$

We may take A to be the amplitude of an incident beam of particles coming from the left, and B to be the reflected amplitude. The currents are equal as $|A|^2 = |B|^2$, and reflection is complete. The wave penetrates into the classically forbidden region a distance characterized by $1/\kappa = \hbar[2m(V_0 - E)]^{-1/2}$. This penetration gets larger the closer E is to V_0, and at $E = V_0$ it becomes infinite. This signifies the beginning of transmission.

For $x > 0$, $E > V_0$, the solution is

$$\psi(x) = C\exp[ik'x] + D\exp[-ik'x], \qquad k'^2 = 2m(E - V_0)/\hbar^2, \tag{13.10}$$

which again gives two currents, one, $|C|^2\hbar k'/m$, to the right, and another, $|D|^2\hbar k'/m$, to the left.

The boundary conditions now yield

$$A + B = C + D, \qquad ik(A - B) = ik'(C - D). \tag{13.11}$$

These equations are not sufficient to determine B, C, and D, in terms of A. We may conceive of the situation as that of two mutually independent beams being incident, one from the left and one from the right. Assuming no beam incident from the right means $D = 0$. Then (13.11) gives

$$B = A\frac{k - k'}{k + k'}, \qquad C = A\frac{2k}{k + k'}. \tag{13.12}$$

There is a reflection coefficient R given by

$$R = \left(\frac{k - k'}{k + k'}\right)^2 \tag{13.13}$$

and a transmission coefficient T given by

$$T = \frac{4kk'}{(k + k')^2}. \tag{13.14}$$

Clearly $R + T = 1$. The transmission vanishes as $k' \to 0$ which is as $E \to V_0$ from above. Thus the transmission varies continuously with the energy as E goes through the value V_0. Classically, for $E < V_0$, $R = 1$ (which holds in our present case), and for $E > V_0$, $T = 1$.

We may take $A = 0$ in (13.11). This corresponds to having only a beam incident from the right. This beam then sees a down-step in potential. Now expressing C and B in terms of D, we get

$$C = -D\frac{k - k'}{k + k'}, \qquad B = D\frac{2k'}{k + k'}. \tag{13.15}$$

Note that the phase of the reflected wave differs by π from that given by (13.12). The reflection and transmission coefficients are

$$R = \left(\frac{k - k'}{k + k'}\right)^2,$$

$$T = \frac{4kk'}{(k + k')^2},$$

just as in (13.13) and (13.14). The reflection coefficient vanishes only when $k' = k$, which is at infinite energy. A very slow particle will be reflected from a sharp potential drop almost completely.

The problem being discussed is mathematically identical with the reflection of sound waves from an interface. The wave equation for one-dimensional waves,

$$\frac{\partial^2 \varphi}{\partial x^2} - \frac{1}{v^2}\frac{\partial^2 \varphi}{\partial t^2} = 0\,,$$

where v is the phase velocity of the wave, becomes

$$\frac{d^2\varphi}{dx^2} + k^2\varphi = 0$$

when a harmonic time dependence is assumed. In this case, the value of $k^2 > 0$ and solutions like (13.7) do not occur. Something like it does occur for oblique incidence where total reflection can take place.

(ii) The Square Well. Let $V = -V_0$, $|x| < a$; $V = 0$, $|x| > a$. This potential is illustrated in Figure 13.2.

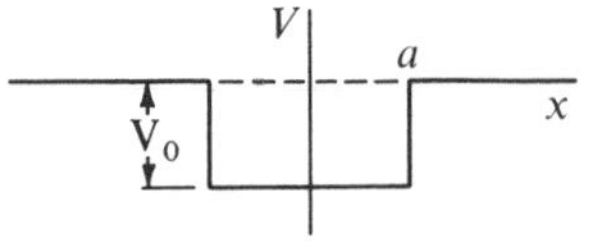

Fig. 13-2

The values of $E < -V_0$ yield no solutions. For $E > -V_0$ the solution in the well can be written

$$\text{(13.16)}\quad \psi(x) = A \exp[iKx] + B \exp[-iKx], \qquad K = +\left(\frac{2m(V_0+E)}{\hbar^2}\right)^{1/2}.$$

For $E < 0$ the solutions in the two regions $|x| > a$ are

$$\text{(13.17)}\quad \begin{aligned} \psi(x) &= C \exp[\kappa x],\ x < -a\,, \\ \psi(x) &= D \exp[-\kappa x],\ x > a, \qquad \kappa = +\left(\frac{-2mE}{\hbar^2}\right)^{1/2}. \end{aligned}$$

The continuity of ψ and ψ' at $x = \pm a$ yields the four equations

$$\text{(13.18)}\quad \begin{aligned} C \exp[-\kappa a] - A \exp[-iKa] - B \exp[iKa] &= 0\,, \\ \kappa C \exp[-\kappa a] - iKA \exp[-iKa] + iKB \exp[iKa] &= 0\,, \\ A \exp[iKa] + B \exp[-iKa] - D \exp[-\kappa a] &= 0\,, \\ iKA \exp[iKa] - iKB \exp[-iKa] + \kappa D \exp[-\kappa a] &= 0\,. \end{aligned}$$

The determinant of the coefficients in these equations must vanish if a solution is to exist. This determinant reduces to

$$\left(1 - i\frac{K}{\kappa}\right)^2 \exp\left[-i2Ka\right] - \left(1 + i\frac{K}{\kappa}\right)^2 \exp\left[i2Ka\right] = 0\,.$$

These quantities are complex conjugate to each other, so the imaginary part alone gives a condition.

$$\tan 2Ka = \frac{-2K/\kappa}{1 - K^2/\kappa^2}\,. \tag{13.19}$$

Recalling that

$$\tan 2\theta = \frac{2\tan\theta}{1 - \tan^2\theta} = \frac{-2\cot\theta}{1 - \cot^2\theta}\,,$$

we see that

$$K \tan Ka = \kappa\,, \qquad \text{even solutions,} \tag{13.20}$$

or

$$K \cot Ka = -\kappa\,, \qquad \text{odd solutions}\,. \tag{13.21}$$

In addition to either of (13.20) or (13.21) there is the relation

$$K^2 + \kappa^2 = 2mV_0/\hbar^2\,. \tag{13.22}$$

These equations are easier to solve if we put $Ka = \xi$, $\kappa a = \eta$. Then,

$$\xi \tan \xi = \eta \tag{13.23}$$

or

$$\xi \cot \xi = -\eta\,, \tag{13.24}$$

and

$$\xi^2 + \eta^2 = 2mV_0a^2/\hbar^2\,. \tag{13.25}$$

The roots can be located graphically by plotting η as a function of ξ according to (13.23)–(13.25). We obtain Fig. 13.3. The tangent-like curves are distorted by the ξ factor in (13.23) and (13.24). The "even" curves are from (13.23), the "odd" curves from (13.24), and the circle from (13.25). Possible eigenstates arise from the intersection of the circle with the other curves. As illustrated there are three stationary states. Only the intersections in the first quadrant are relevant because ξ and η are non-negative.

The wave functions may be chosen as real. They can be complex only to the extent of a complex multiplicative constant because the wave equation is real and the solution in the classically forbidden regions is a real exponential. Those corresponding to intersections with the curves marked even, coming from (13.23), are even functions of x. The others are odd.

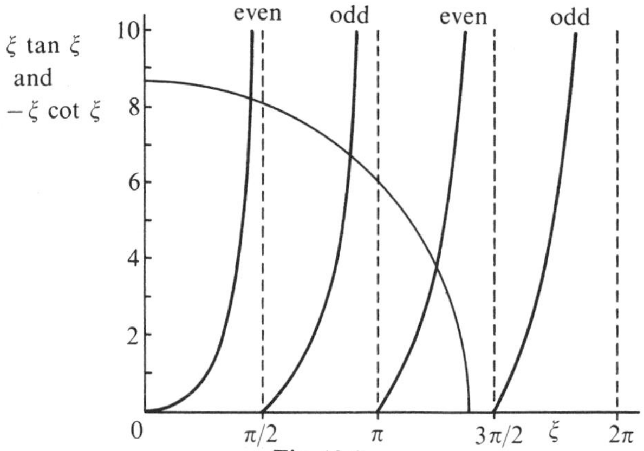

Fig. 13-3

Many features of the spectrum are apparent from Fig. 13.3. There is at least one bound state for any square well no matter how shallow or how narrow it is. The lowest state is even, and there will not be an odd bound state unless $\xi^2 + \eta^2 \geqslant (\frac{1}{2}\pi)^2$, or

$$V_0 a^2 \geqslant \pi^2 \hbar^2 / 8m \,. \tag{13.26}$$

We see later that for a three-dimensional, spherically symmetric well only odd states appear. Hence, a three-dimensional, square well does not necessarily have a bound state. The number of bound states depends only on $V_0 a^2$ (for a given particle mass). As $V_0 a^2 \to \infty$, the states become spaced approximately equally in K, for the circle in Fig. 13.3 cuts the curves near their asymptotes and the ξ values are approximately

$$\xi = \tfrac{1}{2} n \pi \,,$$

or, now measuring E' from the bottom of the well, $E' = E + V_0$,

$$E' = \frac{n^2 \pi^2 \hbar^2}{8ma^2} \,. \tag{13.27}$$

The result (13.27) can be derived by requiring the wave function to vanish at $x = \pm a$. This happens if $2a$ is an integral number of half-wavelengths of the de Broglie wave.

$$2a = \tfrac{1}{2} n \lambda = n\pi / K \,.$$

Then,

$$E' = \frac{p^2}{2m} = \frac{n^2 \pi^2 \hbar^2}{8ma^2} \,.$$

Returning to the square well of finite depth V_0, we look at the states with energies somewhat greater than zero. The only difference from before is in the form of the solution in the region $|x| > a$, outside the well. Instead of the decaying exponentials of (13.17) we must use oscillating functions. For simplicity let us consider only odd states, those for which $\psi(x) = -\psi(-x)$. In Section 23 it is shown that for potentials which are symmetric about the origin, i.e., for which $V(x) = V(-x)$, the states can always be chosen as either even or odd. It is then sufficient to satisfy the boundary conditions at $x = +a$. For $x < a$ we write

$$\psi(x) = A \sin Kx, \qquad K = +\left(\frac{2m(E + V_0)}{\hbar^2}\right)^{1/2}, \tag{13.28}$$

and for $x > a$

$$\psi(x) = B \sin (kx + \delta), \qquad k = +\left(\frac{2mE}{\hbar^2}\right)^{1/2}. \tag{13.29}$$

The continuity of the wave function and its first derivative at $x = a$ requires that

$$\begin{aligned} A \sin Ka &= B \sin (ka + \delta)\,, \\ AK \cos Ka &= Bk \cos (ka + \delta)\,. \end{aligned} \tag{13.30}$$

The determinant of the coefficients of A and B must vanish, so that

$$K \cot Ka = k \cot (ka + \delta)\,. \tag{13.31}$$

By proper choice of δ the right side of this equation can be given any real value when k is real, so that this equation does not give a discrete spectrum of eigenvalues.

The ratio of the amplitudes of the wave function outside and inside the well depends on the energy. We have

$$\begin{aligned} \frac{B^2}{A^2} &= \frac{\sin^2 Ka}{\sin^2 (ka + \delta)} \\ &= \sin^2 Ka + (K^2/k^2) \cos^2 Ka \\ &= 1 + \frac{V_0}{E} \cos^2 Ka\,. \end{aligned} \tag{13.32}$$

For small positive values of E ($E/V_0 \ll 1$), the second term on the right oscillates with a large amplitude as K varies. When $\cos^2 Ka$ is small, the ratio is relatively small and we speak of a *resonance*. It is customary to define the resonant energy as that energy for which $\delta = (n + \frac{1}{2})\pi$. For small ka, that is, for small E, this makes the denominator in the first line of the right side of (13.32) have nearly its maximum value. The behavior of the ratio A^2/B^2 as a function of E near a resonance is schematically shown in Figure 13.4. The full width at half maximum is denoted by Γ. The general character of the curve is the same for a large class of potentials; the spacing and the widths of the resonances depend on the exact form of the potential.

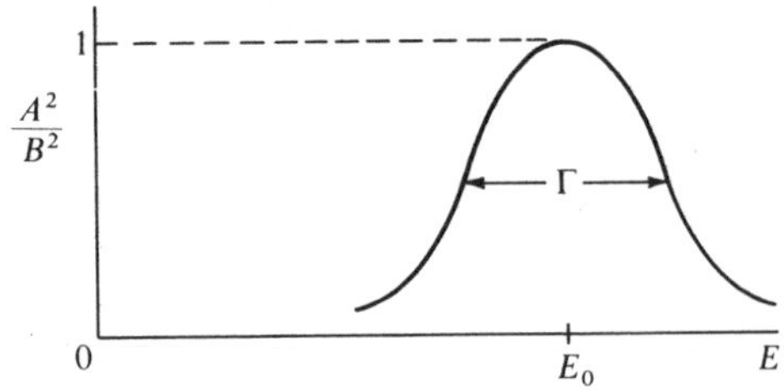

Fig. 13-4

In Section 17 it appears that the odd states discussed here are those appropriate for the discussion of a three-dimensional square well potential, and in Section 35 it is seen that $\sin^2\delta$ is proportional to the cross section for scattering by this potential. Thus, the definition of the resonant energy corresponds closely to a maximum in the scattering cross section. This is agreeable because the probability of scattering by a potential should be large if the scattered particle is likely to be in the neighborhood where the potential is large, and this occurs at the resonant energy.

It is possible to construct a wave packet out of states whose energies lie near the resonant energy, such that the particle is localized within the well. This can be done because δ is a rapidly varying function of E near the resonance, a fact which can be seen in the following way: If $Ka = \pi/2$, the exterior wave function has zero slope at $x = a$, and since the exterior wavelength is assumed long compared to the range a of the potential, the exterior wave function continued in to the origin has essentially zero slope there too, so that $\delta \approx \pi/2$. If $Ka = \pi/2 - \eta$ where η is positive, the exterior wave function has a positive slope and, since its curvature is small, grows to large amplitude as x increases from the value a. The origin is very near a zero of the exterior wave function so that δ is small and positive. If $Ka = \pi/2 + \eta$, the exterior wave function has a negative slope and grows to a large, negative value, the origin being nearly a zero of the exterior function. This makes δ almost π. Thus, as E increases through the resonant energy E_0, the phase shift δ increases rapidly through the value $\pi/2$. This behavior is shown in Figure 13.5.

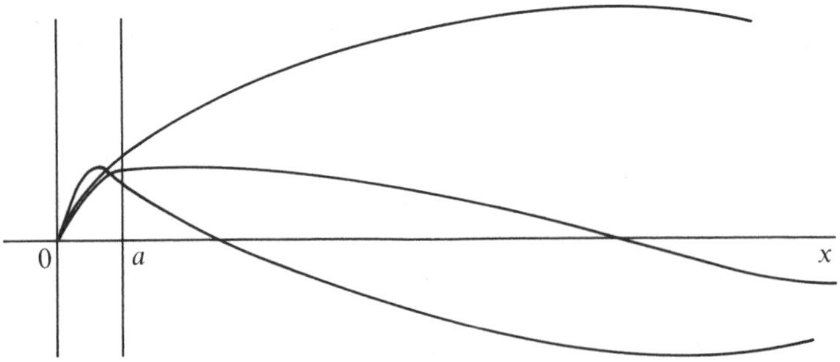

Fig. 13-5

A similar discussion can be given for $Ka = 3\pi/2$, etc. This treatment is repeated in a more general way in Section 35. In this way, destructive interference can be achieved outside the well at the same time that the interference inside the well is constructive.

If the energy range needed to construct a localized wave packet is $\Delta E = \Gamma$, there will be a time dependence of the relative phase of the high and low energy components of the wave packet given by $\Gamma t/\hbar$. When $\Gamma t/\hbar$ becomes of the order of magnitude of unity, the wave packet will have essentially ceased to be localized. We can therefore define a time τ characteristic of the resonance by the condition

$$\Gamma\tau = \hbar\,. \tag{13.33}$$

The narrower the resonance, the longer its characteristic time, or *mean life*. Equation (13.33) looks like an uncertainty principle for energy and time, the mean life representing the "uncertainty" in the time at which the system is localized. This uncertainty principle is connected only indirectly with the uncertainty principle of Section 7, because the time is not an observable of the system to be represented by an operator, but is only a numerical parameter which commutes with all observables.

PROBLEMS

1. Repeat the derivation leading to (12.10) keeping a finite value for $\langle|p|\rangle$. Show that the center of the wave packet moves with speed $\langle|p|\rangle/m$.
2. The spreading of a free particle wave packet is given by (12.10). For large values of t it becomes classical in its relation to the momentum spread Δp of the packet. For what value of t does the classical spread equal the initial quantum mechanical spread $(\Delta x)_{\min}$ of a minimal wave packet? Evaluate this for electrons with energy 5 keV $\pm$ 0.1%. How far has the center of the pulse travelled by this time?
3. Show that (8.9) is a particular case of (7.11), and hence that the harmonic oscillator ground state does provide a minimal packet in coordinate and momentum.
4. Show that in a representation with p diagonal, the conjugate coordinate x can be represented by $i\hbar\,\partial/\partial p$ if the phases of the states are suitably chosen.
5. Construct the momentum space eigenfunctions of the harmonic oscillator (a) starting from the momentum space Schrödinger equation; (b) by taking the Fourier transform of the generating function for the coordinate space wave functions.
6. Suppose that the phases of the coordinate eigenstates $|x'\rangle$ are not chosen as in (9.3), but instead each state is multiplied by a phase factor $\exp[-i\chi(\mathbf{p}')/\hbar]$. Show that this replaces the result (10.5) by

$$\langle \mathbf{x}'|p_j|\alpha'\rangle = \left(-i\hbar\,\frac{\partial}{\partial x_j} + \frac{\partial\chi}{\partial x_j}\right)\langle x'|\alpha'\rangle\,.$$

The transformation $|x'\rangle \rightarrow \exp[-i\ \chi(x')/\hbar]\ |x'\rangle$ is a *gauge transformation of the first kind*, generated by χ.

7. Evaluate the scalar product of two pseudo-classical states of the harmonic oscillator, and thus prove that no two of them are orthogonal.

8. Explain why a state $|z_o\rangle$ defined as an eigenstate of $a^\dagger$ does not have pseudo-classical properties.

9. Show that the peak of the Poisson distribution in (8.30) occurs for an energy closely corresponding to that of a classical oscillator with an amplitude of $\sqrt{2}|z|$.

III

Central systems

14. CENTRAL FORCES

The starting point of any discussion of atomic structure is the two body system with a central potential. This model is subject to many corrections and refinements, but it does provide a description of many features of atoms. It also is surprisingly relevant to nuclear models. The classical Hamiltonian describing such a system is

$$H = \frac{\mathbf{p}_1^{\,2}}{2m_1} + \frac{\mathbf{p}_2^{\,2}}{2m_2} + V(|\mathbf{r}_1 - \mathbf{r}_2|)\,. \tag{14.1}$$

The subscripts 1 and 2 refer to the two particles. Classically, the center of mass motion may be separated from the relative motion. The necessary coordinate transformation is given by

$$\mathbf{R} = \frac{m_1\mathbf{r}_1 + m_2\mathbf{r}_2}{m_1 + m_2} = \mu\left(\frac{\mathbf{r}_1}{m_2} + \frac{\mathbf{r}_2}{m_1}\right), \tag{14.2}$$

$$\mathbf{r} = \mathbf{r}_1 - \mathbf{r}_2\,,$$

together with

$$\mathbf{P} = \mathbf{p}_1 + \mathbf{p}_2\,,$$

$$\mathbf{p} = \frac{m_2\mathbf{p}_1 - m_1\mathbf{p}_2}{m_1 + m_2} = \mu\left(\frac{\mathbf{p}_1}{m_1} - \frac{\mathbf{p}_2}{m_2}\right). \tag{14.3}$$

Here, μ, given by

$$\mu = \frac{m_1 m_2}{m_1 + m_2}\,, \tag{14.4}$$

is the *reduced mass* of the two body system. These transformations may be deduced from the generating function $\Psi(Q, p)$ via

$$P_i = \frac{\partial\Psi}{\partial R_i}\,, \qquad p_i = \frac{\partial\Psi}{\partial r_i}\,,$$

and

$$r_{1i} = \frac{\partial \Psi}{\partial p_{1i}}, \qquad r_{2i} = \frac{\partial \Psi}{\partial p_{2i}},$$

with

$$\Psi = \mathbf{p}_1 \cdot \left(\mathbf{R} + \frac{m_2 \mathbf{r}}{m_1 + m_2}\right) + \mathbf{p}_2 \cdot \left(\mathbf{R} - \frac{m_1 \mathbf{r}}{m_1 + m_2}\right),$$

which establishes their canonical character.

R is the radius vector of the center of mass of the system, while **P** is the total momentum of the system. These variables are canonically conjugate so that

$$[R_i, P_j] = i\hbar\, \delta_{ij} . \tag{14.5}$$

Then **r** is the radius vector of particle 1 with particle 2 as origin, while **p** is the momentum of particle 1 relative to particle 2. If $m_2 \to \infty$ so that particle 2 can be taken as fixed, $p \to p_1$.

The Hamiltonian becomes

$$\begin{aligned} H &= \frac{\mathbf{P}^2}{2\,(m_1 + m_2)} + \frac{\mathbf{p}^2}{2\mu} + V(\,|\mathbf{r}|\,) \\ &= H_{cm} + H_{rel} . \end{aligned} \tag{14.6}$$

This demonstrates the desired separation of the problem. H_{cm} is the Hamiltonian of a free particle, and has a continuous spectrum of eigenvalues stretching from 0 to ∞. Thus, the total Hamiltonian has a continuous spectrum also, starting from the lowest eigenvalue of H_{rel}. This continuous spectrum makes the accurate determination of atomic energy levels more difficult, for it requires the atom as a whole to be prepared in a restricted range of states before the determination can be made. For example, the spectrum of a moving atom is subject to Doppler shifts. We ignore this problem and consider only the Hamiltonian of the relative motion. The subscript "rel" is dropped.

$$H = \frac{\mathbf{p}^2}{2\mu} + V(r), \qquad r = |\mathbf{r}_1 - \mathbf{r}_2| . \tag{14.7}$$

The spherical symmetry of V makes the use of spherical coordinates almost unavoidable. We make the transformation from cartesian coordinates to spherical coordinates in the differential form of the Schrödinger equation. Thus we have

$$\left[\nabla^2 + \frac{2\mu}{\hbar^2}(E - V(r))\right]\psi(r, \theta, \varphi) = 0 , \tag{14.8}$$

with the Laplacian given by*

* In an orthogonal coordinate system with coordinates ξ_i $(i = 1, 2, 3)$, the infinitesimal vectors $(d\xi_1, 0, 0)$, $(0, d\xi_2, 0)$, and $(0, 0, d\xi_3)$ define a rectangular parallelopiped. Denoting

(14.9)
$$\nabla^2 = \frac{1}{r^2}\frac{\partial}{\partial r} r^2 \frac{\partial}{\partial r} + \frac{1}{r^2 \sin\theta}\frac{\partial}{\partial\theta}\sin\theta\frac{\partial}{\partial\theta} + \frac{1}{r^2\sin^2\theta}\frac{\partial^2}{\partial\varphi^2}.$$

A central potential is simple, because it conserves all components of angular momentum. It is readily verified that

(14.10)
$$[l_x, \mathbf{p}^2] = 0, \qquad [l_x, r] = 0$$

with

(14.11)
$$l_x = yp_z - zp_y,$$

and similarly for l_y, l_z. Thus,

(14.12)
$$[l_j, H] = 0$$

and the l_j are constants of the motion. However, it is also readily verified that

(14.13)
$$[l_x, l_y] = i\hbar l_z \qquad \text{(cyclic)}.$$

This follows from the Poisson bracket relations between the components of the angular momentum or directly from (14.11) and the commutation relations between the coordinates and momenta. Thus, unless the expectation values of *all three* components l_j vanish, no two can be given precise values in the same state. It is conventional to choose l_z diagonal.

It is also easy to show that

(14.14)
$$[l_j, \mathbf{l}^2] = 0,$$

and thus $\mathbf{l}^{2\prime}$ can be prescribed in addition to l_z'. A complete set of labels for a state of relative motion is provided by the eigenvalues of H, $\mathbf{l}^2$, and l_z.

These features, which are anticipated on physical grounds, are immediate consequences of (14.8) and (14.9). To see this, it is only necessary to apply the method of separation of variables for the solution of (14.8). We write

(14.15)
$$\psi(r, \theta, \varphi) = R(r)\Theta(\theta)\Phi(\varphi).$$

There results, after dividing by the product $R\Theta\Phi$,

(14.16)
$$\frac{1}{R}\frac{1}{r^2}\frac{d}{dr} r^2 R' + \frac{2\mu}{\hbar^2}(E - V(r)) + \frac{1}{\Theta}\frac{1}{r^2\sin\theta}\frac{d}{d\theta}\sin\theta\Theta' + \frac{1}{\Phi}\frac{1}{r^2\sin^2\theta}\Phi'' = 0.$$

Multiplication of this by $r^2 \sin^2\theta$ splits the equation into two parts, one de-

---

the lengths of the edges of this figure by $dx_i = h_i\, d\xi_i$, we may apply Gauss's theorem to the volume $dx_1\, dx_2\, dx_3$ to obtain the well-known formula:

$$\nabla^2 = \frac{1}{h_1h_2h_3}\left[\frac{\partial}{\partial\xi_1}\left(\frac{h_2h_3}{h_1}\frac{\partial}{\partial\xi_1}\right) + \frac{\partial}{\partial\xi_2}\left(\frac{h_3h_1}{h_2}\frac{\partial}{\partial\xi_2}\right) + \frac{\partial}{\partial\xi_3}\left(\frac{h_1h_2}{h_3}\frac{\partial}{\partial\xi_3}\right)\right].$$

pending on φ alone, the other on r and θ only. The two parts must separately be constant. We write

$$\Phi''/\Phi = -m^2\,, \qquad \Phi'' = -m^2\Phi\,. \tag{14.17}$$

Multiplication by r^2 and use of (14.17) separates it again. Calling the separation constant λ, we obtain

$$\sin\theta\frac{d}{d\theta}\sin\theta\Theta' + (\lambda\sin^2\theta - m^2)\Theta = 0\,, \tag{14.18}$$

$$\frac{1}{r^2}\frac{d}{dr}r^2R' + \frac{2\mu}{\hbar^2}\left(E - \frac{\lambda\hbar^2}{2mr^2} - V(r)\right)R = 0\,. \tag{14.19}$$

The differential equation (14.17) is the eigenvalue equation for l_z^2. With spherical coordinates defined by

$$\begin{aligned} x &= r\sin\theta\cos\varphi\,,\\ y &= r\sin\theta\sin\varphi\,,\\ z &= r\cos\theta\,, \end{aligned} \tag{14.20}$$

it follows that

$$\begin{aligned} l_z &= -i\hbar\left(x\frac{\partial}{\partial y} - y\frac{\partial}{\partial x}\right)\\ &= -i\hbar\frac{\partial}{\partial\varphi}\,. \end{aligned} \tag{14.21}$$

Thus the eigenvalues of l_z are $m\hbar$ with real m.

The differential equation (14.18) is the eigenvalue equation for l^2. This is apparent when we recall that the classical Hamiltonian (14.7) can be written in the form

$$H = \frac{1}{2\mu}\left(p_r^2 + \frac{\mathbf{l}^2}{2\mu r^2} + V(r)\right) \tag{14.22}$$

where $\mathbf{l}^2$ is the square of the angular momentum vector. Thus the eigenvalues of $\mathbf{l}^2$ are $\lambda\hbar^2$. The value of λ depends to a certain extent on m.

Finally, the *radial equation* (14.19) is, for given λ, the eigenvalue equation for H, as it contains E. Therefore, E will depend on λ, and through λ on m. The central potential enters only the radial equation. The angular momentum equations are thus universal equations for all central potential two body systems.

The eigenvalues of l_z, $\mathbf{l}^2$, and of H can be determined only when the boundary conditions to be applied to the wave function have been given. These boundary conditions are not self-evident because the transformation to spherical coordinates is singular at certain places. The single equation $r = 0$ requires $x = y = z = 0$, independent of θ and φ. The equation $\theta = 0$ requires

$x = y = 0$, independent of φ. Thus these places, the origin and the polar axis or z-axis, require some discussion. Here we take up the boundary condition at the origin. The boundary conditions on the polar axis are considered in the next section.

In the radial equation (14.19) let

$$u(r) = rR(r)\,. \tag{14.23}$$

Then the differential equation for $u(r)$ reads

$$u'' + \frac{2\mu}{\hbar^2}\left(E - \frac{\lambda\hbar^2}{2\mu r^2} - V(r)\right)u = 0\,. \tag{14.24}$$

This is exactly the equation for a one-dimensional problem with an effective potential V^* given by

$$V^* = V + \lambda\hbar^2/2\mu r^2\,. \tag{14.25}$$

The additional term is called the *centrifugal potential.* It is positive because $\lambda\hbar^2$ is the eigenvalue of a positive operator $\mathbf{l}^2$, and hence gives a repulsion, the centrifugal force. The equation (14.24), however, is meaningful only for non-negative values of r, while the one-dimensional equation proper is valid for all values of the coordinate from $-\infty$ to $+\infty$. We must investigate the boundary condition to be applied at $r = 0$.

If $f(\mathbf{r})$ and $g(\mathbf{r})$ are two independent solutions of the Schrödinger equation (14.8), we may construct the radial component of the current vector $\mathbf{j}(g^*, f)$ introduced in (8.27).

$$j_r(g^*, f) = \frac{\hbar}{2\mu i}\left(g^*\frac{\partial f}{\partial r} - f\frac{\partial g^*}{\partial r}\right). \tag{14.26}$$

The equation of continuity applied to a spherical volume about the origin then yields

$$\int_V r^2\,dr\,d\Omega\,\frac{\partial}{\partial t}(g^*f) = -\int r^2\,d\Omega\;j_r(g^*, f)\,. \tag{14.27}$$

The integral on the left must vanish in the limit $r \to 0$ whether or not the potential $V(\mathbf{r})$ in the Hamiltonian is singular at the origin. The integral on the right must also vanish in this limit.

Now let $f(\mathbf{r}) = \hat{f}(\mathbf{r})r^{-\alpha}$, $g(\mathbf{r}) = \hat{g}(\mathbf{r})r^{-\alpha}$, where $\hat{f}$ and $\hat{g}$ are regular at the origin. The integral on the right of (14.27) then becomes

$$-r^2\int d\Omega\, r^{-2\alpha}\left(\hat{g}^*\frac{\partial\hat{f}}{\partial r} - \hat{f}\frac{\partial\hat{g}^*}{\partial r}\right).$$

The integrand does not vanish identically. Thus, for the integral to vanish in the limit $r \to 0$,

(14.28) $$2 - 2\alpha > 0, \qquad \alpha < 1 .$$

This gives as a boundary condition at the origin on $u = rR(r)$, that

(14.29) $$u(0) = 0 .$$

This condition is stronger than the requirement of normalizability. It makes the differential operation $-i\hbar\, \partial/\partial r$ hermitian when applied to the wave functions $u_{E'\gamma'}(r)$;

$$\int_0^\infty u_{E'\gamma'}{}^*(r)\left(-i\hbar \frac{\partial}{\partial r} u_{E\gamma}(r)\right) = \int_0^\infty \left(-i\hbar \frac{\partial}{\partial r} u_{E'\gamma'}(r)\right)^* u_{E\gamma}(r) ,$$

provided the limit of $u_{E'\gamma'}{}^*(r)\, u_{E\gamma}(r)$ as $r \to \infty$ vanishes. The wave functions may either vanish or oscillate. In the latter case, we imagine an arbitrarily small damping to be introduced to make the wave function vanish, this damping being allowed to approach zero in the end.

If the potential $V(r)$ is attractive and more singular than the centrifugal potential, then the solutions of the Schrödinger equation are not yet defined. There is a classical analogue to this ambiguity. Classically, if the central potential overcomes the centrifugal potential at the origin, the particle will go to the origin even when it has finite angular momentum. It will not stay there, but will re-emerge. There is no way to connect the orbits before and after the particle has been at the origin because the angular velocity has been infinite, and all information about the azimuth φ of the particle is lost. Theories which lead to attractive potentials diverging faster than r^{-2} are therefore difficult to interpret.

A central potential has a symmetry property in addition to the rotational symmetry which leads to the conservation of angular momentum. This is invariance under spatial reflection. Spatial reflection is described in cartesian coordinates by the transformation

(14.30) $$\mathbf{x} \to \mathbf{x}' = -\mathbf{x} .$$

In spherical coordinates this corresponds to

(14.31) $$\begin{aligned} r &\to r' = r , \\ \theta &\to \theta' = \pi - \theta , \\ \varphi &\to \varphi' = \varphi + \pi . \end{aligned}$$

Reflection in the origin is not an operation that can be carried out physically, but it can be given a physical meaning. If a piece of apparatus is built to prepare a system in a given state $|\alpha'\rangle$, a mirror image piece of apparatus can be built, and it will prepare a system in the state $|\beta'\rangle$. This second state is linearly expressible in terms of states $|\alpha'\rangle$, and is written as

(14.32) $$|\beta'\rangle = P|\alpha'\rangle ,$$

where P is the *parity operator*. Because the reflection of a reflection returns one to the original apparatus,

$$P^2 = 1 \tag{14.33}$$

and the operator P can have eigenvalues ± 1. [Equation (14.33) is not obvious, since two reflections might introduce a common phase factor in all states. This is important when double-valued states are involved, but we ignore these complications here.]

For a particle moving in a central field, the operator P commutes with the Hamiltonian which involves only $\mathbf{p}^2$ and r. Thus, a state can be labelled by the parity as well as by energy and angular momentum. It is readily seen, however, that the parity of a state is a function of the orbital angular momentum, and is, in fact, just $(-)^l$. When the orbital angular momentum is used as a label, then, the parity is determined. When only the total angular momentum of a system including spins is given, the parity is separately specifiable and is a useful quantum number.

15. ORBITAL ANGULAR MOMENTUM

In the previous section we saw that the problem of the motion of a particle in a central potential separates into a part depending on the potential explicitly, the radial part, and a part which is common to all central potential problems. We are dealing here with a system possessing a classical analogue so that the angular momentum may be expressed in terms of canonical coordinates and momenta. Not all angular momenta can be so described; those possessing no classical analogue being called spin angular momenta. They are treated in the next section.

The angular part of the Schrödinger equation does not depend on the potential energy. We may therefore, for the moment, consider our particle to be free. The momentum eigenstates $|\mathbf{p}'\rangle$ then form a complete set of eigenstates, and the corresponding wave functions are single valued. We generalize this and assume that in the presence of a potential depending on r the wave functions are single valued functions of the cartesian coordinates. They must, therefore, be periodic functions of φ with period 2π. This periodicity eliminates the continuum of eigenvalues of l_z which would be expected in analogy with the linear momentum eigenvalues, just as in Section 9 a periodicity requirement removed the continuum for the linear momentum. Periodicity in θ does not arise because of the more restricted range of θ, $0 \leq \theta \leq \pi$. This argument applies only when the coordinates $\mathbf{x}$ and the momenta $\mathbf{p}$ are sufficient for the construction of all observables of the system.

The angular parts of the Schrödinger equation are (14.17) and (14.18), namely,

$$\Phi''(\varphi) = -m^2\Phi(\varphi)\,, \tag{15.1}$$

$$\sin\theta \frac{d}{d\theta} \sin\theta\Theta'(\theta) + (\lambda \sin^2\theta - m^2)\Theta(\theta) = 0\,. \tag{15.2}$$

The first of these has as solutions

$$\Phi = (2\pi)^{-1/2} \exp[im\varphi]\,. \tag{15.3}$$

The constant normalizes the solution to unity. The periodicity requirement now implies that m is an integer, positive, negative, or zero. The eigenvalues of l_z, the z-component of orbital angular momentum, are all integer multiples of $\hbar$, as

$$\begin{aligned} \langle m|p_\varphi|m\rangle &= \int_0^{2\pi} \Phi^* \left(-i\hbar \frac{d}{d\varphi}\Phi\right) \\ &= m\hbar\,. \end{aligned} \tag{15.4}$$

The m which enters the equation for Θ is thus an integer.

Equation (15.2) is the Legendre equation. It takes on a standard form with the new independent variable $\mu = \cos\theta$.

$$(1 - \mu^2)\frac{d^2\Theta}{d\mu^2} - 2\mu\frac{d\Theta}{d\mu} + \left(\lambda - \frac{m^2}{1 - \mu^2}\right)\Theta = 0\,. \tag{15.5}$$

This equation may be solved in a manner similar to the one used for the harmonic oscillator. At $\mu = \pm 1$ the differential equation is singular. Regular solutions at these points must have the form

$$(1 - \mu^2)^{|m|/2} f(\mu)\,,$$

where $f(\mu)$ is regular at $\mu = \pm 1$. The differential equation for $f(\mu)$ is

$$(1 - \mu^2)f'' - 2(|m| + 1)\mu f' + (\lambda - |m|(|m| + 1))f = 0\,.$$

Setting $f = \sum_\nu a_\nu \mu^\nu$ yields

$$\sum_\nu a_\nu\{\nu(\nu - 1)(\mu^{-2} - 1) - 2(\,|m| + 1)\nu + \lambda - |m|\,(\,|m| + 1)\}\mu^{2\nu} = 0\,.$$

The starting power is determined by equating the coefficient of the lowest power of μ to zero. It is 0 or 1, so all exponents are integers. Equating the coefficient of the general power of μ to zero yields

$$\frac{a_{\nu+2}}{a_\nu} = \frac{(\,|m| + \nu)(\,|m| + \nu + 1) - \lambda}{(\nu + 2)(\nu + 1)}\,.$$

Thus the power series diverges for $\mu = 1$ unless the series breaks off. This happens only when

$$\lambda = (|m| + \nu')(|m| + \nu' + 1) \\ = l(l+1),$$

where l is a positive integer or zero. The eigenvalues of $\mathbf{l}^2$ are therefore given by

$$\mathbf{l}^{2\prime} = l(l+1)\hbar^2 , \tag{15.6}$$

where l is an integer. The eigenfunctions of $\mathbf{l}^2$ and of l_z are written as

$$Y_{lm}(\theta, \varphi) = N_{lm}P_{lm}(\theta) \exp [im\varphi] . \tag{15.7}$$

The $P_{lm}(\theta)$ are the associated Legendre functions, which are the solutions of (15.2) whose construction has just been outlined. The $Y_{lm}(\theta\varphi)$ are the *spherical harmonics*. The N_{lm} are normalization constants about which more is said in Section 20.

There is a great deal to be said about angular momentum. Much of it can be said more compactly in an algebraic treatment than in the present one. Most of what has to be said is valid also for spin angular momentum. Therefore, we pause here in the discussion and apply these results to some important special systems. We then return to a discussion of angular momentum in general.

16. THE FREE PARTICLE, ANGULAR MOMENTUM REPRESENTATION

The free particle has already been described in cartesian coordinates, where the simple eigenfunctions are those labelled by the components of the linear momentum and which are plane waves. The state $|\mathbf{p}\rangle$ has energy $E = \mathbf{p}^2/2\mu$. We now wish to discuss the states of this system which arise naturally when spherical coordinates are used. These states are labelled by the angular momentum quantum numbers l and m, and by the energy $E = k^2\hbar^2/2\mu$. This description is basic to the theory of scattering. The angular part of the Schrödinger equation has been solved in Section 15. It remains to investigate the radial equation.

From (14.24) we obtain the radial equation

$$\frac{d^2u_{kl}}{dr^2} + \left(k^2 - \frac{l(l+1)}{r^2}\right) u_{kl} = 0 . \tag{16.1}$$

Division by k^2 shows that u_{kl} depends only on the variable $\rho = kr$. This agrees with the result in cartesian coordinates, where only $\mathbf{k} \cdot \mathbf{x}$ appeared. The differential equation (16.1) is one of the standard forms of Bessel's differential equation.* Its solution is written in terms of the Bessel functions $J_\nu(\rho)$, which are regular at the origin, by

$$u_{kl}(kr) = N(\tfrac{1}{2}\pi kr)^{1/2}J_{l+1/2}(kr) = N\hat{j}_l(kr)\,. \tag{16.2}$$

The function $\hat{j}_l$ is a Ricatti–Bessel function of order l. The normalization factor is found below. The radial function $R_{kl}(r)$ is given by

$$\begin{aligned} R_{kl}(r) &= \frac{u_{kl}(r)}{r} \\ &= Nk\left(\frac{\pi}{2kr}\right)^{1/2} J_{l+1/2}(kr) \\ &= Nk\, j_l(kr)\,. \end{aligned} \tag{16.3}$$

The function $j_l(\rho)$, differing from $\hat{j}_l(\rho)$ only by the factor ρ^{-1}, is a spherical Bessel function of order l.

The real, positive normalization constant N is determined by the requirement that the scalar product of two radial wave functions be given by

$$\begin{aligned} \int_0^\infty u_{k'l}(r)u_{kl}(r)\,dr &= 2\pi\hbar\,\delta(p'-p) \\ &= 2\pi\,\delta(k'-k) \end{aligned} \tag{16.4}$$

in conformity with our usual convention. To obtain N from this, we start from the Fourier–Bessel theorem which states that a function $f(x)$ which satisfies certain integrability and smoothness conditions can be expressed as

$$f(x) = \int_0^\infty g(k)\,J_\nu(kx)k\,dk\,,$$

with

$$g(k) = \int_0^\infty f(x)\,J_\nu(kx)x\,dx$$

for $\nu > -\frac{1}{2}$. Insertion of the former in the latter yields

$$g(k) = \int_0^\infty x\,dx \int_0^\infty k'\,dk'\,g(k')\,J_\nu(k'x)\,J_\nu(kx)\,,$$

which shows that we may write

$$\int_0^\infty x\,dx\,J_\nu(k'x)\,J_\nu(kx) = \frac{1}{k'}\,\delta(k'-k)\,.$$

* G. N. Watson, *A Treatise on the Theory of Bessel Functions*, Cambridge University Press, London, 1944.

Expressing the J's in terms of $\hat{j}$'s then yields

(16.5) $$\int_0^\infty dr\, j_l(k'r)\, j_l(kr) = \frac{\pi}{2}\,\delta(k' - k)\,.$$

Therefore, $N = 2$ and

(16.6) $$u_{kl}(r) = 2\hat{j}_l(kr)\,.$$

Anticipating the result of Section 20, we give the complete, normalized, free particle wave function.

(16.7) $$\psi_{klm}(r, \theta, \phi) = \pm\left[\frac{2l+1}{4\pi}\frac{(l-m)!}{(l+m)!}\right]^{1/2} P_{l|m|}(\cos\theta)\exp[im\phi]\frac{2}{r}\hat{j}_l(kr)\,.$$

The $\pm$ sign is explained in Section 20, being minus for odd positive m and otherwise plus.

The wave function (16.7) satisfies the free particle Schrödinger equation everywhere. In many problems there is a potential in the vicinity of the origin which drops off fast enough with increasing r so that it can be ignored for sufficiently large r. In Section 35, it is shown that if $rV(r) \to 0$ as $r \to \infty$, this can be done. The desired solution of the equation containing the potential is regular at the origin. Where the potential is negligible, this solution is expressible as a linear combination of the two solutions of the free particle equation since this is of second order. We want, therefore, to give here solutions of the free particle radial equation which are singular at the origin. As the singular Bessel function we take the Neumann function

(16.8) $$N_\nu(\rho) = \frac{J_\nu(\rho)\cos\nu\pi - J_{-\nu}(\rho)}{\sin\nu\pi}\,,$$

because its asymptotic behavior is best suited to our purposes. Our notation differs, unfortunately, from Watson's. He calls this function $Y_\nu(\rho)$, which is easily confused with the spherical harmonics $Y_{lm}(\theta, \phi)$. The most usual notation in the physical literature is $N_l(\rho)$. We now define the functions

(16.9) $$\begin{aligned}\hat{n}_l(\rho) &= (\tfrac{1}{2}\pi\rho)^{1/2} N_{l+1/2}(\rho)\\ &= \rho n_l(\rho)\,.\end{aligned}$$

$\hat{n}_l(\rho)$ is the Ricatti–Neumann function and $n_l(\rho)$ the spherical Neumann function.

Some properties of the Ricatti–Bessel functions are given below without proof.

$$\begin{aligned}
\hat{j}_0(\rho) &= \sin\rho\,,\\
\hat{j}_1(\rho) &= \frac{\sin\rho}{\rho} - \cos\rho\,,\\
\hat{j}_2(\rho) &= \left(\frac{3}{\rho^2} - 1\right)\sin\rho - \frac{3}{\rho}\cos\rho\,,\\
&\vdots\\
\hat{n}_0(\rho) &= -\cos\rho\,,\\
\hat{n}_1(\rho) &= -\frac{\cos\rho}{\rho} - \sin\rho\,,\\
\hat{n}_2(\rho) &= -\left(\frac{3}{\rho^2} - 1\right)\cos\rho - \frac{3}{\rho}\sin\rho\,.
\end{aligned} \tag{16.10}$$

For small values of ρ the leading terms in the series expansions are

$$\begin{aligned}
\hat{j}_l(\rho) &\to \frac{\rho^{l+1}}{1\cdot 3\cdot 5\cdots(2l+1)}\,,\\
\hat{n}_l(\rho) &\to \frac{1\cdot 3\cdot 5\cdots(2l-1)}{\rho^l}\,.
\end{aligned} \tag{16.11}$$

For $r \to \infty$,

$$\begin{aligned}
\hat{j}_l(\rho) &\approx \cos(\rho - (l+1)\pi/2) = \sin(\rho - l\pi/2)\,,\\
\hat{n}_l(\rho) &\approx \sin(\rho - (l+1)\pi/2) = -\cos(\rho - l\pi/2)\,.
\end{aligned} \tag{16.12}$$

The above are standing wave solutions. Travelling wave solutions are also of interest, and we give them here for reference. They are necessarily singular at the origin, for an ingoing or outgoing spherical wave must have a sink or a source at the origin. The obvious combinations are

$$\begin{aligned}
h_l^{(1)}(\rho) &= \hat{j}_l(\rho) + i\hat{n}_l(\rho)\\
&\approx (-i)^{l+1}\exp[i\rho]\,,\\
\hat{h}_l^{(2)}(\rho) &= \hat{j}_l(\rho) - i\hat{n}_l(\rho)\\
&\approx (i)^{l+1}\exp[-i\rho]\,.
\end{aligned} \tag{16.13}$$

Combined with a time factor $\exp[-i\omega t]$ these give outgoing and ingoing waves, respectively. These functions are formed from the Hankel functions $H_{l+1/2}{}^{(1)}$, $H_{l+1/2}{}^{(2)}$ just as the functions $\hat{j}_l(\rho)$ are from $J_{l+1/2}(\rho)$.

A useful expression for the Bessel function is the *integral representation*:

$$J_\nu(z) = \frac{(\frac{1}{2}z)^\nu}{\Gamma(\nu+\frac{1}{2})\Gamma(\frac{1}{2})}\int_0^\pi d\theta\,\exp[iz\cos\theta]\sin^{2\nu}\theta\,, \tag{16.14}$$

which is valid for all ν with $\operatorname{Re}\nu > -\frac{1}{2}$. For $\nu = l + \frac{1}{2}$, this becomes

$$(16.15)\quad J_{l+1/2}(z) = \frac{(\frac{1}{2}z)^{l+1/2}}{l!\pi^{1/2}} \int_{-1}^{1} d(\cos\theta) \exp[iz\cos\theta](1-\cos^2\theta)^l .$$

On integrating l times by parts, this yields

$$J_{l+1/2}(z) = \frac{(-)^l(\frac{1}{2}z)^{l+1/2}}{l!\pi^{1/2}(iz)^l} \int_{-1}^{1} d(\cos\theta) \exp[iz\cos\theta] \frac{d^l}{d(\cos\theta)^l} (1-\cos^2\theta)^l .$$

A standard expression for the Legendre polynomial $P_l(\mu)$ is

$$(16.16)\qquad P_l(\mu) = \frac{1}{2^l l!} \frac{d^l}{d\mu^l} (\mu^2 - 1)^l .$$

Thus, we may write

$$(16.17)\quad J_{l+1/2}(z) = (-i)^l \left(\frac{z}{2\pi}\right)^{1/2} \int_0^{\pi} \sin\theta\, d\theta \exp[iz\cos\theta] P_l(\cos\theta) ,$$

or

$$(16.18)\qquad \hat{j}_l(\rho) = (-i)^l\, \frac{\rho}{2} \int_0^{\pi} \sin\theta\, d\theta \exp[i\rho\cos\theta] P_l(\cos\theta) .$$

This last form allows us to expand a plane wave in spherical waves. We write

$$\begin{aligned} \exp[ikz] &= \exp[ikr\cos\theta] \\ &= \sum_{l'=0}^{\infty} A_{l'}(kr) P_{l'}(\cos\theta) , \end{aligned}$$

which is possible since the plane wave is axially symmetric and does not depend on ϕ. Multiplying the expansion by $P_l(\cos\theta)\sin\theta$ and integrating from 0 to π, we obtain

$$\frac{2A_l}{2l+1} = \int_0^{\pi} \sin\theta\, d\theta \exp[ikr\cos\theta] P_l(\cos\theta) .$$

Thus we get the important result

$$(16.19)\qquad \exp[ikz] = \frac{1}{kr} \sum_{l=0}^{\infty} i^l(2l+1)\, \hat{j}_l(kr) P_l(\cos\theta) .$$

For large values of kr this expansion may be written

$$(16.20)\quad \exp[ikz] \approx \frac{1}{2ikr} \sum_{l=0}^{\infty} (2l+1)\{\exp[ikr] - (-)^l \exp[-ikr]\} P_l(\cos\theta) ,$$

which contains the ingoing and outgoing waves explicitly. This assumes an interesting form if we define a δ-function $\delta(\mathbf{n} - \mathbf{n}_0)$ between two unit vectors as

(16.21) $$\delta(\mathbf{n} - \mathbf{n}_0) = \frac{1}{2\pi \sin \theta} \delta(\theta) ,$$

where θ is the angle between the two vectors. This δ-function has the property that

(16.22) $$\int f(\theta, \varphi)\delta(\mathbf{n} - \mathbf{n}_0)\, d\Omega = f(\theta_0, \varphi_0) ,$$

where θ_0 and φ_0 are the angular coordinates of $\mathbf{n}_0$ and the range of integration includes the direction $\mathbf{n}_0$. This δ-function can be expanded about the direction $\mathbf{n}_0$ as a series of Legendre polynomials

(16.23) $$\delta(\mathbf{n} - \mathbf{n}_0) = \sum_{l=0}^{\infty} \frac{2l+1}{4\pi} P_l(\cos \theta) .$$

This is verified by multiplying by $P_{l'}(\cos \theta)$ and integrating over the solid angle 4π. Using this, (16.13) may be written

(16.24) $$\exp[ikz] \approx \frac{2\pi}{ikr} \{\delta(\mathbf{n} - \mathbf{n}_z) \exp[ikr] - \delta(\mathbf{n} + \mathbf{n}_z) \exp[-ikr]\} .$$

The first term of this is an outgoing wave far to the right of the origin, the second an ingoing wave far to the left. This description breaks down near the origin for obvious reasons.

Equation (16.19) has been derived in the coordinate representation. Let us now write it in ket notation. The equation describes a linear momentum eigenstate as a linear superposition of angular momentum eigenstates.

(16.25) $$|\mathbf{p}\rangle = \sum_{p,l} |p, l, 0\rangle \langle p, l, 0|\mathbf{p}\rangle .$$

The summation contains an integration over the variable p, and hence contains the factor $dp/2\pi\hbar$. On multiplying by $\langle \mathbf{x}|$ on both sides, this becomes an equation between normalized wave functions

(16.26) $$\exp[i\mathbf{p} \cdot \mathbf{x}/\hbar] = \sum_l \int \frac{dp}{2\pi\hbar} \psi_{kl0}(r, \theta, \phi)\langle p, l, 0|\mathbf{p}\rangle .$$

The left side is expanded according to (16.19), and (16.7) is used for the wave function on the right. On equating the two series term by term we obtain

(16.27) $$\langle p, l, 0|\mathbf{p}\rangle = 2\pi\hbar\, \delta(p - |\mathbf{p}|)[\pi(2l+1)]^{1/2} \frac{\hbar}{p} i^l$$

as the expansion coefficient.

17. SQUARE WELL IN THREE DIMENSIONS

The three-dimensional square well is a useful model for a very short range force such as that acting between nucleons. It has no pretensions to accuracy as a description of actual potentials in nature. The radial equation for $R_l(r)$ is

$$\text{(17.1)}\qquad \begin{aligned} &R_l'' + \frac{2}{r}R_l' + \frac{2\mu}{\hbar^2}\left(E + V_0 - \frac{l(l+1)\hbar^2}{2\mu r^2}\right)R_l = 0\,, \quad r < a\,, \\ &R_l'' + \frac{2}{r}R_l' + \frac{2\mu}{\hbar^2}\left(E - \frac{l(l+1)\hbar^2}{2\mu r^2}\right)R_l = 0 \qquad r > a\,. \end{aligned}$$

Here V_o is the depth of the potential well and a its radius. The potential is illustrated in Fig. 17–1.

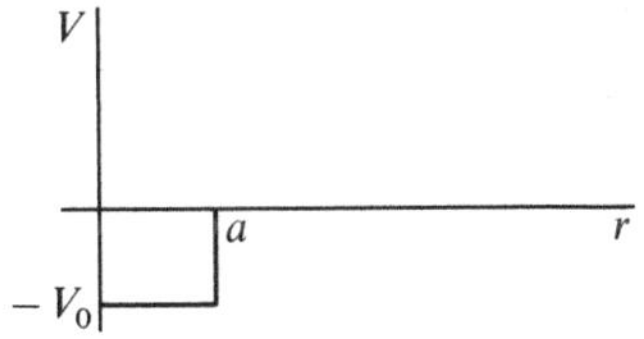

Fig. 17-1

Both equations (17.1) are identical in form with (16.1), the radial equation for a free particle, as would be expected since the potential has zero gradient except at $r = a$ and hence exerts no force on the particle. In the region $r < a$, which contains the origin, the solution must be the spherical Bessel function $j_l(Kr)$, with $K = +[2m(E + V_o)/\hbar^2]^{1/2}$,

$$\text{(17.2)}\qquad R_l(r) = A_l j_l(K_r)\,.$$

For $r > a$ the solution depends on the sign of E.

If $E > 0$, the solution for $r > a$ is a linear combination,

$$\text{(17.3)}\qquad R_l(r) = C_1 j_l(kr) + C_2 n_l(kr)\,, \quad k = +\left(\frac{2mE}{\hbar^2}\right)^{1/2}, \quad r > a\,.$$

The two solutions are connected by the requirement that R and R' be continuous at $r = a$. There is no quantization of the energy because, for any k, the constants C_1 and C_2 can be adjusted to give any value of $R(a)$ and any value of $R'(a)$ desired. It is convenient to write

$$\text{(17.4)}\qquad C_1 = C_l \cos \delta_l, \quad C_2 = -C_l \sin \delta_l$$

because this means that asymptotically the radial wave function is

$$R_l(r) \approx \frac{C_l}{kr} \sin (kr + \delta_l - l\pi/2)\,. \tag{17.5}$$

This differs from the wave function in the absence of the potential only by the phase shift δ_l. This is useful in the description of scattering.

If $E < 0$, the second of (17.1) becomes

$$R_l'' + \frac{2}{r} R_l' - (k^2 + l(l+1))R_l = 0\,, \tag{17.6}$$

which is again transformable into Bessel's equation, but for imaginary argument. If the spherical Hankel functions are taken as the appropriate pair of fundamental solutions, we see that for imaginary argument one grows exponentially as $r \to \infty$ and the other gets small exponentially. Only the latter is acceptable as a physical solution.
Thus,

$$R_l(r) = C_l h_l^{(1)} (ikxr)\,, \qquad r > a\,, \tag{17.7}$$

is the solution needed in the region outside the potential. There is only one constant involved here, so that it is impossible to satisfy two boundary conditions at $r = a$ for general E. The values of E for which they can be satisfied are the energy eigenvalues.

For $l = 0$ the differential equation for $u(r) = rR(r)$ is just the same as that for the one-dimensional wavefunction with the extra boundary condition that $u(0) = 0$. The energy eigenvalues are, therefore, just those corresponding to odd one-dimensional wave functions. For general l, a matching condition at $r = a$ is

$$\frac{j_l'(Ka)}{j_l(Ka)} = \frac{h^{(1)\prime}(ika)}{h^{(1)}(ika)}\,. \tag{17.8}$$

This is an equation for E_l. It may have several real roots, E_{1l}, E_{2l}, ... The index n, which distinguishes these eigenvalues, is called the *radial quantum number*, n_r. The range of n_r depends on l. $n_r - l$ is the number of zeros of the radial wavefunction, not counting those at 0 and ∞.

18. THE THREE-DIMENSIONAL HARMONIC OSCILLATOR

The radial equation for a particle moving in a potential

$$V(r) = \tfrac{1}{2}\mu\omega_0{}^2 r^2 \tag{18.1}$$

is

(18.2) $$u'' + \frac{2\mu}{\hbar^2}\left(E - \tfrac{1}{2}\mu\omega_0{}^2r^2 - \frac{l(l+1)\hbar^2}{2\mu r^2}\right)u = 0\,,$$

where $u(r) = rR(r)$ and $u(0) = 0$. For $l = 0$, this reduces to the one-dimensional harmonic oscillator equation, the odd solutions of which satisfy the boundary condition at the origin. We must investigate the solutions when $l \neq 0$. The eigenvalues are, of course, already known. The oscillator in three dimensions separates in cartesian coordinates into three independent linear oscillators each with eigenvalues $(n + \frac{1}{2})\hbar\omega_0$. Thus

(18.3) $$E = (n_x + n_y + n_z + \tfrac{3}{2})\hbar\omega_0\,,$$

where n_x, n_y, n_z are independent non-negative integers. The wave functions are easily obtained by solving (18.2).

Introducing the variable $\xi = \alpha x$, $\alpha = \mu\omega_0/\hbar$, (18.2) becomes

(18.4) $$u'' + \left(\lambda - \xi^2 - \frac{l(l+1)}{\xi^2}\right)u = 0, \quad \lambda = 2E/\hbar\omega_0\,.$$

This may be solved by the same method as that used for the linear oscillator. The equation has singular points at $\xi = 0, +\infty$. Near the origin

$$\xi^2u'' - l(l+1)u = 0\,,$$

so that $u = \xi^{l+1}$ or ξ^{-l}. The latter is unacceptable. Near ∞

$$u'' = \xi^2u\,,$$

so that $u \approx \exp[-\frac{1}{2}\xi^2]$. Therefore, we write

(18.5) $$u = f\xi^{\,l+1}\exp[-\tfrac{1}{2}\xi^2]$$

and obtain a differential equation for f:

(18.6) $$f'' + 2f'\,\frac{l+1-\xi^2}{\xi} + (\lambda - 2l - 3)f = 0\,.$$

A solution in the form of a power series is tried,

$$f = \sum_\nu a_\nu\xi^\nu\,.$$

Then,

$$\sum_\nu a_\nu\{\nu(\nu-1)\xi^{\nu-2} + 2\nu(l+1)\xi^{\nu-2} - 2\nu\xi^\nu + (\lambda - 2l - 3)\xi^2\} = 0\,.$$

The starting power must be zero. Putting the coefficient of ξ^ν equal to zero yields

$$\frac{a_{\nu+2}}{a_\nu} = \frac{2\nu + 2l + 3 - \lambda}{(\nu + 2)(\nu + 2l + 3)}\,.$$

As for the linear oscillator, this series must break off, so that for $\nu = 2n_r$ (since ν is even)

$$\lambda = 2(2n_r + l) + 3\,, \qquad E = (2n_r + l + \tfrac{3}{2})\hbar\omega_0\,,$$

which reproduces (18.3). The levels are degenerate. To each l there corresponds $2l + 1$ states, and it may be verified that the degree of degeneracy arrived at in this way is the same as that in the cartesian coordinate solution.

The parity of the levels is the parity of l. This also agrees with the cartesian coordinate solution. The parity of a one-dimensional oscillator is the parity of the quantum number n, so the parity of the three-dimensional harmonic oscillator is that of $n_x + n_y + n_z$. In both treatments, therefore, the parity is even if E is an even multiple of $\hbar\omega_0$ above the ground state and is odd if E is an odd multiple of $\hbar\omega_0$ above the ground state.

19. THE HYDROGEN ATOM, FIRST APPROXIMATION

The hydrogen atom is the simplest atomic system existing in nature. Its complete description is extremely complicated and cannot be given in this volume. The atom consists of an electron and a proton interacting through the electromagnetic field. The principal features of the system are already accounted for by considering the electron and proton as point particles and the interaction as that given by Coulomb's law. Missing from this model are effects due to the electron's spin, the proton's spin, the finite radius of the proton's charge distribution, and effects due to quantum fluctuations of the electromagnetic field. All of these have been calculated to some approximation and the results compared with observation. The agreement is extraordinary, being within the very narrow limits of experimental error. In this section, we treat only the simple model. In Section 31, the effect of electron spin and nuclear spin is discussed in a first approximation.

The Hamiltonian describing our model of the hydrogen atom is

$$H = \frac{\mathbf{p}^2}{2\mu} - \frac{Ze^2}{r}\,. \tag{19.1}$$

The center of mass motion has been separated out so that μ is the reduced mass of the electron and proton. The atomic number Z is unity for hydrogen, but is written explicitly so that the results can be used for such things as ionized helium. The potential depends only on r, so that the angular momentum is conserved and all that needs to be discussed is the radial equation. This reads

$$\frac{d^2u}{dr^2} + \frac{2\mu}{\hbar^2}\left(E - \frac{l(l+1)\hbar^2}{2\mu r^2} + \frac{Ze^2}{r}\right)u = 0\,. \tag{19.2}$$

It is convenient to introduce atomic units. These are units of length, mass, and time constructed out of the constants characteristic of atoms, the electron mass m, the electric charge e, and Planck's constant $\hbar$. Combinations of these constants having the dimensions of length, mass, and time are

$$a = \frac{\hbar^2}{me^2}\,, \quad m, \quad \tau = \frac{\hbar^3}{me^4}\,; \tag{19.3}$$

a is the radius of the "first Bohr orbit" in hydrogen according to semiclassical theory. The numerical values of these units are

$$\begin{aligned} a &= 5.2917 \times 10^{-9}\ \text{cm}\,, \\ m &= 9.108 \times 10^{-28}\ \text{g}\,, \\ \tau &= 2.4189 \times 10^{-17}\ \text{sec}\,. \end{aligned} \tag{19.4}$$

Some derived units are

$$\begin{aligned} &\text{energy:} && e^2/a = 4.359 \times 10^{-11}\ \text{erg}\,, \\ &\text{frequency:} && 4\pi R_y = me^4/\hbar^3 = 4.1341 \times 10^{16}\ \text{sec}^{-1}\,. \end{aligned} \tag{19.5}$$

We define the length ρ in atomic units by

$$r = \rho a \tag{19.6}$$

and rewrite the radial equation as

$$\frac{d^2u}{d\rho^2} + \left(2W + \frac{2Z}{\rho} - \frac{l(l+1)}{\rho^2}\right)u = 0\,. \tag{19.7}$$

This equation corresponds to an infinite proton mass because μ has been identified with m, the electron mass. This is done because the device of using the reduced mass works only for one electron atoms. In the case of hydrogen, all results deduced from (19.7) can be corrected for the finite proton mass (or nuclear mass, in the case of ions) by replacing the value of m by the value of μ in all formulae, using the relation

$$\frac{m}{\mu} = \frac{M_Z + m}{M_Z}\,, \tag{19.8}$$

where M_Z is the nuclear mass.

Equation (19.7) has two singular points, $\rho = 0$, and $\rho = \infty$. The former is characterized by the centrifugal potential except when $l = 0$, the latter by the energy eigenvalue. For small ρ,

$$u'' - \frac{l(l+1)}{\rho^2} u = 0 , \tag{19.9}$$
$$u = \rho^{l+1}, \quad \text{or} \quad \rho^{-l} .$$

Only the former satisfies the requirement that $u(0) = 0$, so the radial wave function must contain the factor ρ^{l+1}. For large ρ,

$$u'' + 2Wu = 0 . \tag{19.10}$$

We are primarily interested in bound states of hydrogen for which E, and therefore W, are negative. It is useful to define a quantity ϵ by

$$\epsilon = +(-2W)^{1/2}, \tag{19.11}$$

in terms of which (19.10) becomes

$$u'' - \epsilon^2 u = 0 . \tag{19.12}$$

This has solutions

$$u = \exp[\epsilon\rho] , \qquad \exp[-\epsilon\rho] ,$$

of which only the latter is admissible. Therefore, the radial wave function contains the factor $\exp[-\epsilon\rho]$.

For general ρ we write

$$u(\rho) = \rho^{l+1} \exp[-\epsilon\rho] f(\rho) , \tag{19.13}$$

in which $f(\rho)$ is to be regular in the region $0 \geq \rho < \infty$. At $\rho = \infty, f(\rho)$ is to be dominated by the exponential factor.

Substituting this form for $u(\rho)$ into the radial equation (19.10) leads to a differential equation for $f(\rho)$.

$$f'' + 2\left(\frac{l+1}{\rho} - \epsilon\right) f' + 2\left(\frac{Z - \epsilon(l+1)}{\rho}\right) f = 0 . \tag{19.14}$$

The solution of this may be expressed as a power series.

$$f = \sum_\nu a_\nu \rho^\nu .$$

This yields

$$\sum_\nu a_\nu \{[\nu(\nu-1) + 2\nu(l+1)]\rho^{\nu-2} + 2[Z - \epsilon(l+\nu+1)]\rho^{\nu-1}\} = 0 .$$

A recurrence relation results from equating the coefficient of $\rho^{\nu-2}$ to zero;

$$\frac{a_\nu}{a_{\nu-1}} = 2\frac{(l+\nu)\epsilon - Z}{(l+\nu)(l+\nu+1) - l(l+1)} . \tag{19.15}$$

This must break off when regarded as an equation for $a_{\nu-1}$ in terms of a_ν, as no negative powers are permissible. This happens when

$$(l+\nu)(l+\nu+1) - l(l+1) = 0 ,$$
$$\nu = 0 , \text{ or } -2l - 1 ,$$

of which only the former is possible. (The solution $\nu = -2l - 1$ just gives back $u \sim \rho^{-l}$, which we have already rejected.)

The power series defined by (19.15) converges for all finite ρ according to the ratio test. It dominates the series for exp $[2\epsilon\rho]$, however, and hence spoils the behavior at $\rho = \infty$. To see this, expand exp $[2\epsilon\rho]$:

$$\exp [2\epsilon\rho] = \sum_{\nu=0}^{\infty} \frac{1}{\nu!} (2\epsilon\rho)^\nu$$
$$= \sum_{\nu} b_\nu \rho^\nu .$$

Thus,

$$b_\nu / b_{\nu-1} = 2\epsilon/\nu ,$$

which is $a_\nu/a_{\nu-1}$ as $\nu \to \infty$.

To prevent this catastrophe, the series must terminate at some finite ν. If a_{n_r} is the last non-vanishing coefficient, then according to (19.15), with $n_r = \nu - 1$,

$$(l + n_r + 1)\epsilon - Z = 0 .$$

Therefore,

$$\epsilon = Z/(l + n_r + 1)$$
$$W = -\frac{1}{2}\frac{Z^2}{(l + n_r + 1)^2} = -\frac{1}{2}\frac{Z^2}{n^2} . \tag{19.16}$$

This is the Balmer formula for the energy levels of hydrogen ($Z = 1$) or hydrogen-like ions.

The energy depends on the single integer n, called the *principal quantum number*. It is an "accident" that it does not depend on l except as n depends on l. n_r is called the radial quantum number. It is the number of zeros or nodes of the radial wave function excepting the one at the origin. This accidental degeneracy is removed when the potential is not exactly a Coulomb potential, as in the lithium atom where the outer electron moves in the potential of the nucleus and the two inner electrons. The number of degenerate levels is given by

$$\sum_{l=0}^{n-1} (2l + 1) = n^2 . \tag{19.17}$$

Among the degenerate states are states of both parities. This unusual circumstance makes the hydrogen atom very sensitive to perturbations of odd parity like a uniform electric field, such a perturbation having non-vanishing matrix elements between degenerate states.

The radial wavefunction is the product of a polynomial and ρ^{l+1} $\exp[-(Z/n)\rho]$. The polynomial is known as a *Laguerre polynomial*,* and is denoted by $L_\lambda{}^\mu(\rho)$. The definition of these functions is

$$\begin{aligned} L_\lambda(\rho) &= \exp[\rho] \frac{d^\lambda}{d\rho^\lambda} (\rho^\lambda \exp[-\rho]) , \\ L_\lambda{}^\mu(\rho) &= \frac{d^\mu}{d\rho^\mu} L_\lambda(\rho) . \end{aligned} \tag{19.18}$$

The Laguerre polynomials are related to the confluent hypergeometric function ${}_1F_1(\alpha, \beta; \rho)$.

$${}_1F_1(\alpha, \beta; \rho) = 1 + \frac{\alpha}{\beta \cdot 1} \rho + \frac{\alpha(\alpha + 1)}{\beta(\beta + 1)2!} \rho^2 + \cdots . \tag{19.19}$$

Comparison with the explicit expansion of $L_\lambda{}^\mu(\rho)$ shows that

$$L_\lambda{}^\mu(\rho) = (-)^\mu \lambda! \binom{\lambda}{\mu} {}_1F_1[-(\lambda - \mu), \mu + 1, \rho] . \tag{19.20}$$

In the present case,

$$\lambda = n + l , \qquad \mu = 2l + 1 . \tag{19.21}$$

It is easily seen that ${}_1F_1(\alpha, \beta; \rho)$ is a polynomial of degree $-\alpha$ when α is a negative integer. $L_\lambda{}^\mu$ is therefore of degree $\lambda - \mu = n - l - 1 = n_r$. n_r is the number of zeros of the radial function not located at the origin, as remarked earlier.

* The associated Laguerre polynomial is sometimes defined by

$$L_\lambda{}^\mu(\rho) = (-)^\mu \frac{d^\mu}{d\rho^\mu} L_{\lambda+\mu}(\rho) .$$

We follow the usage of Courant–Hilbert, *Methods of Mathematical Physics*, Interscience, New York, 1953, and of H. A. Bethe and E. E. Salpeter, *Quantum Mechanics of One and Two Electron Atoms*, Academic, New York, 1957.

The normalization is tedious. The result is

(19.22)
$$u_{nl}(\rho) = -\frac{[(n-l-1)!]^{1/2}}{[(n+l)!]^{3/2}(2n)^{1/2}}\left(\frac{2Z}{n}\right)^{1/2}\exp\left[-\frac{Z\rho}{n}\right]\left(\frac{2Z\rho}{n}\right)^{l+1}L_{n+l}^{2l+1}(\rho)\,.$$

The normalization has been defined by

(19.23)
$$\int_0^\infty |u_{nl}(\rho)|^2\,d\rho = 1\,,$$

and must be modified by a square root of the conversion factor when non-atomic units are used. The phase which is chosen makes all the functions start out positive or with positive slope at the origin.

Explicit expressions for the first few radial functions are given, with $Z = 1$.

(19.24)
$$\begin{aligned}
R_{10} &= \frac{u_{10}}{\rho} = 2e^{-\rho}\,,\\
R_{20} &= \frac{u_{20}}{\rho} = 2^{-1/2}e^{-\rho/2}(1 - \tfrac{1}{2}\rho)\,,\\
R_{21} &= \frac{u_{21}}{\rho} = \frac{1}{2\sqrt{6}}e^{-\rho/2}\rho\,;\\
R_{30} &= \frac{u_{30}}{\rho} = \frac{2}{3\sqrt{3}}e^{-\rho/3}(1 - \tfrac{2}{3}\rho + \tfrac{2}{27}\rho^2)\,,\\
R_{31} &= \frac{u_{31}}{\rho} = \frac{8}{27\sqrt{6}}e^{-\rho/3}(1 - \tfrac{1}{6}\rho)\,,\\
R_{32} &= \frac{u_{32}}{\rho} = \frac{4}{81\sqrt{30}}e^{-\rho/3}\rho^2\,.
\end{aligned}$$

The energy eigenvalues and the wave functions found for the simple model of the hydrogen atom form the basis for almost all discussions of more accurate models. The degeneracy found here is not found in the spectrum of hydrogen. There is a *fine structure* of the levels due to the magnetic moment of the electron which, moving through the Coulomb field, is in an effective magnetic field. There is a *hyperfine structure* due to the magnetic moment of the nucleus, the proton. Last but not least, there is the *Lamb shift* which is due primarily to the quantum fluctuations of the electromagnetic field and their interaction with the electron. The first effect will be treated in an elementary approximation after the development of perturbation theory. The last is beyond the scope of this work.*

* See H. A. Bethe and E. E. Salpeter, *op. cit.* p. 103.

PROBLEMS

1. Prove that the center of mass momentum **P** of (14.3) commutes with the relative momentum **p** and the relative coordinate **r**, thus justifying the separation of the two particle system strictly according to quantum mechanics.
2. Verify the statement of Section 18 that the degeneracy of the energy levels of the three-dimensional harmonic oscillator is the same in spherical coordinates as it is in cartesian coordinates.
3. Taking real wave functions for the three-dimensional harmonic oscillator (i.e., taking combinations of states with $l_z' = \pm m\hbar$), sketch the nodal surfaces for the wave functions for each of the first and second excited states. How do these differ from the corresponding surfaces for the hydrogen atom?
4. Find the mean value of the reciprocal radius of the electron in the states of the hydrogen atom with $m = l$. Compare the result with the Bohr theory of hydrogen.
5. An electron and a positron constitute a system much like a hydrogen atom, called *positronium*. Find the analogue of the Balmer formula for positronium. How does the effective size of the positronium atom compare with that of hydrogen? (The size is to be judged in the laboratory coordinate system.)
6. An attractive "shell" potential is given by

$$V(r) = -V_0\,\delta(r - a).$$

Obtain the equation determining the energy eigenvalues. Show that for fixed V_0 and a there is a maximum value of l beyond which no bound states exist.

IV

Angular momentum and symmetry

20. ANGULAR MOMENTUM IN GENERAL

The orbital angular momentum of a particle is defined in quantum mechanics just as it is in classical mechanics, namely by

$$\mathbf{l} = \mathbf{r} \times \mathbf{p}. \tag{20.1}$$

The total orbital angular momentum of a system is the sum of the orbital angular momenta of its constituent particles.

$$\mathbf{L} = \sum_{j=1}^{N} \mathbf{l}_j \, . \tag{20.2}$$

The orbital angular momenta satisfy the commutation relations

$$[l_x, l_y] = i\hbar l_z \qquad \text{(cyclic)} \, . \tag{20.3}$$

There are many advantages to be gained by regarding (20.3) as the defining property of angular momentum rather than the definition (20.1), both in classical and in quantum mechanics. These advantages come from the close connection between the relations (20.3) and the group of rotations in three dimensions, a connection we discuss in Sec. 21.

The components of angular momentum, j_x, j_y, and j_z, of any system, whether or not it possesses a classical analogue, are assumed to satisfy the same commutation rules as the l's.

$$[j_x, j_y] = i\hbar j_z \, . \tag{20.4}$$

They are, of course, to be hermitian operators. We want to show that (20.4) alone determine a set of states labelled by the eigenvalues of two operators, conventionally chosen to be j_z and $\mathbf{j}^2$, the square of the angular momentum vector.

(20.5) $$\mathbf{j}^2 = j_x^2 + j_y^2 + j_z^2 .$$

It is readily shown that $\mathbf{j}^2$ and j_z commute.

The procedure is very similar to that used in the algebraic solution of the harmonic oscillator. $\mathbf{j}^2 - j_z^2$ is the sum of two squares, as is the oscillator Hamiltonian. The difference lies in the different commutation relations between x and p and between j_x and j_y. We write

(20.6) $$\begin{aligned} \mathbf{j}^2 - j_z^2 &= (j_x + ij_y)(j_x - ij_y) - \hbar j_z \\ &= (j_x - ij_y)(j_x + ij_y) + \hbar j_z . \end{aligned}$$

Let $|m\rangle$ be a state in which j_z has the eigenvalue $m\hbar$,

(20.7) $$j_z|m\rangle = m\hbar|m\rangle .$$

Then,

(20.8) $$\begin{aligned} j_z(j_x + ij_y)\,|m\rangle &= (j_x + ij_y)(j_z + \hbar)\,|m\rangle \\ &= (m + 1)\hbar(j_x + ij_y)\,|m\rangle . \end{aligned}$$

The operator $j_x + ij_y$ increases the eigenvalue of j_z by $\hbar$. It is called a raising operator and is denoted by j_+. Similarly, $(j_x - ij_y)$ is a lowering operator denoted by j_-

(20.9) $$\begin{aligned} j_+ &= j_x + ij_y , \\ j_- &= j_x - ij_y = j_+{}^\dagger . \end{aligned}$$

We may now write

(20.10) $$\begin{aligned} \mathbf{j}^2 - j_z^2 &= j_+j_- - \hbar j_z \\ &= j_-j_+ + \hbar j_z . \end{aligned}$$

Consider a state which is an eigenstate of $\mathbf{j}^2$, j_z, with $j_z' = m\hbar > 0$. Application of j_+ to this state increases the value of j_z', and therefore decreases the value of the left side of (20.10) because $\mathbf{j}^{2\prime}$ is not affected. There must be a limit to the number of times this can be done because the left side of (20.10) is positive, being $j_x^2 + j_y^2$. There must, therefore, be a state $|\mathbf{j}^{2\prime}j\rangle$ such that

(20.11) $$j_+|\mathbf{j}^{2\prime}j\rangle = 0 ,$$

so that j is the maximum eigenvalue of j_z consistent with the value $\mathbf{j}^{2\prime}$. According to (20.10) and (20.11)

$$(\mathbf{j}^2 - j_z^2)\,|\mathbf{j}^{2\prime}j\rangle = (j_-j_+ + \hbar j_z)\,|\mathbf{j}^{2\prime}j\rangle ,$$

or

(20.12) $$\begin{aligned} \mathbf{j}^2|\mathbf{j}^{2\prime}j\rangle &= j_z(j_z + \hbar)\,|\mathbf{j}^{2\prime}j\rangle \\ &= j(j + 1)\hbar^2|\mathbf{j}^{2\prime}j\rangle . \end{aligned}$$

The eigenvalue of $\mathbf{j}^2$ is thus connected to the maximum eigenvalue of j_z through

$$\mathbf{j}^{2\prime} = j(j+1)\hbar^2 . \tag{20.13}$$

For a given value of $\mathbf{j}^2$ the eigenvalues of j_z are separated by integral multiples of $\hbar$. Let $m\hbar$ and $\mu\hbar$ be two eigenvalues of j_z for the same $\mathbf{j}^{2\prime}$. Then some integer power of j_+ must annihilate $|\mathbf{j}^{2\prime}m\rangle$, and some other integer power must annihilate $|\mathbf{j}^{2\prime}\mu\rangle$. Thus $m +$ integer $= j = \mu +$ integer, and μ differs from m by an integer.

The operator j_- decreases the eigenvalue of j_z by $\hbar$. If applied often enough it will therefore increase the value of j_z^2 and decrease the value of the left side of (20.10). These must, therefore, be a value $k\hbar$ of j_z such that

$$j_-|\mathbf{j}^{2\prime}k\rangle = 0 . \tag{20.14}$$

This together with (20.10) then gives

$$(\mathbf{j}^2 - j_z^2)\,|\mathbf{j}^{2\prime}k\rangle = (j_+j_- - \hbar j_z)\,|\mathbf{j}^{2\prime}R\rangle$$

or

$$\mathbf{j}^2|\mathbf{j}^{2\prime}k\rangle = k(k-1)\hbar^2|\mathbf{j}^2k\rangle . \tag{20.15}$$

The eigenvalue of $\mathbf{j}^2$ can thus be expressed in terms of k. We have, therefore,

$$j(j+1) = k(k-1) ,$$

or

$$k = -j, \text{ or } j+1 .$$

The latter solution is unacceptable as it makes the minimum of j_z' greater than the maximum. Thus the minimum value of j_z is $-j$.

We have seen that the difference between any two eigenvalues of j_z must be an integer multiple of $\hbar$. This applies to the difference between the maximum and the minimum values, which is $2j\hbar$. Thus

$$2j = \text{integer} \tag{20.16}$$

and j can be an integer or a "half integer." (Half integer means half of an *odd* integer.) Only the former were found when orbital angular momentum was discussed. If j is an integer, so is m; and if j is a half integer, m is also.

The eigenstates of $\mathbf{j}^2$, j_z are labelled by the numbers j, m rather than by $\mathbf{j}^{2\prime}$, m as has been done so far. From now on we write

$$|\mathbf{j}^{2\prime}, m\rangle \equiv |\,j, m\rangle .$$

If the angular momentum of concern is orbital, we write l instead of j. l is always an integer. For a given value j there are $2j+1$ states which are mutually orthogonal, namely

$$|j,j\rangle, |j,j-1\rangle, \ldots |j,-j+1\rangle, |j,-j\rangle .$$

Any state of given j is a linear combination of these.

At this point one would think that a given system can have total angular momentum quantum numbers $j = 0, \frac{1}{2}, 1, \frac{3}{2}, \ldots$. That this is not so is a new feature whose deeper meaning will be shown in Section 21. A given system of particles has either integral j or half integral j, and linear combinations of states $|j = \text{integer}\rangle$ and states $|j = \text{half integer}\rangle$ do not occur. This is known as a *superselection rule*. Another way of stating this is that *no observable has a non-vanishing matrix element between a state with integral j and a state with half integral j*. In this latter form, the superselection rule also is valid in quantum field theory.

The matrix elements of j_+ and j_- may now be determined, and hence those of j_x and j_y. Let us choose the phases of the states so that

$$j_+|j,m\rangle = C|j,m+1\rangle ,$$

with C *real and positive*. Then, writing the equation dual to this,

$$\langle j,m|j_- = C\langle j,m+1| ,$$

so that, assuming the states normalized to unity,

$$\begin{aligned} C^2 &= \langle j,m|j_-j_+|j,m\rangle \\ &= \langle j,m|\mathbf{j}^2 - j_z^2 - \hbar j_z|j,m\rangle \\ &= (j-m)(j+m+1)\hbar^2 . \end{aligned}$$

Thus,

$$\langle j,m+1|j_+|j,m\rangle = +[(j-m)(j+m+1)]^{1/2}\hbar . \tag{20.17}$$

Similarly,

$$\langle j,m-1|j_-|j,m\rangle = +[(j+m)(j-m+1)]^{1/2}\hbar . \tag{20.18}$$

All other matrix elements vanish. The matrix elements of j_x, j_y follow from

$$j_x = \frac{1}{2}(j_+ + j_-), \qquad j_y = \frac{1}{2i}(j_+ - j_-) . \tag{20.19}$$

Let us apply these methods to the problem of orbital angular momentum where the components l_i are differential operators. By definition,

$$-\frac{1}{i\hbar}\mathbf{l} = \mathbf{r} \times \nabla . \tag{20.20}$$

Introducing the unit vectors $\mathbf{e}_r$, $\mathbf{e}_\theta$, $\mathbf{e}_\varphi$ perpendicular to the surfaces $r = \text{const}$, $\theta = \text{const}$, $\varphi = \text{const}$, this becomes

$$r\mathbf{e}_r \times \left[\mathbf{e}_r \frac{\partial}{\partial r} + \mathbf{e}_\theta \frac{1}{r}\frac{\partial}{\partial \theta} + \mathbf{e}_\varphi \frac{1}{r \sin\theta}\frac{\partial}{\partial \varphi} \right]$$
$$= \mathbf{e}_\varphi \frac{\partial}{\partial \theta} - \mathbf{e}_\theta \frac{1}{\sin\theta}\frac{\partial}{\partial\varphi}\,.$$

The unit vectors $\mathbf{e}_r$, etc., may be expressed linearly in the cartesian unit vectors $\mathbf{e}_x$, etc.

$$\mathbf{e}_\varphi = -\sin\varphi\, \mathbf{e}_x + \cos\varphi\, \mathbf{e}_y\,,$$
$$\mathbf{e}_\theta = \cos\theta\cos\varphi\, \mathbf{e}_x + \cos\theta\sin\varphi\, \mathbf{e}_y - \sin\theta\, \mathbf{e}_z\,.$$

Thus, in spherical coordinates

$$l_x = i\hbar\left(\sin\varphi \frac{\partial}{\partial\theta} + \cot\theta\cos\varphi\frac{\partial}{\partial\varphi}\right),$$
$$l_y = i\hbar\left(-\cos\theta \frac{\partial}{\partial\theta} + \cot\theta\sin\varphi\frac{\partial}{\partial\varphi}\right), \tag{20.21}$$
$$l_z = -i\hbar\frac{\partial}{\partial\varphi}\,.$$

From them we obtain

$$l_+ = l_x + il_y = \hbar \exp[i\varphi]\left(\frac{\partial}{\partial\theta} + i\cot\theta\frac{\partial}{\partial\varphi}\right),$$
$$l_- = l_x - il_y = \hbar \exp[-i\varphi]\left(-\frac{\partial}{\partial\theta} + i\cot\theta\frac{\partial}{\partial\varphi}\right). \tag{20.22}$$

When they operate on eigenfunctions of l_z, $i\,\partial/\partial\varphi$ becomes equivalent to $-m$. Thus, effectively,

$$l_+ = \hbar \exp[i\varphi]\left(\frac{\partial}{\partial\theta} - m\cot\theta\right),$$
$$l_- = \hbar \exp[-i\varphi]\left(-\frac{\partial}{\partial\theta} - m\cot\theta\right). \tag{20.23}$$

Denoting the θ-dependent factor in the wave function by $\Theta_{lm}(\theta)$ as in Section 15, (20.11) becomes

$$\left(\frac{\partial}{\partial\theta} - l\cot\theta\right)\Theta_{ll} = 0\,. \tag{20.24}$$

The normalized solution to this is

$$\Theta_{ll} = \left[\frac{2l+1}{2(2l)!}\right]^{1/2} \sin^l\theta\,. \tag{20.25}$$

The eigenfunctions for lower m values are now obtained by application of the lowering operator l_-. Thus, from (20.18)

$$\begin{aligned}\Theta_{l,l-1} &= \frac{l_-\Theta_{ll}}{\langle l, l-1|l_-|l, l\rangle} \\ &= -\left[\frac{2l+1}{2}\frac{1}{(2l-1)!}\right]^{1/2} \sin^{l-1}\theta\cos\theta\,.\end{aligned} \tag{20.26}$$

Except for the numerical coefficients, these functions are just the associated Legendre functions.

The associated Legendre functions are defined by

$$P_{l,m}(\mu) = (1-\mu^2)^{m/2}\frac{d^m}{d\mu^m}P_{l,0}(\mu)\,, \qquad m \geqslant 0\,, \tag{20.27}$$

where $P_{l0}(\mu)$ is the Legendre polynomial of degree l. Increasing m by unity

$$\begin{aligned}P_{l,m+1}(\mu) &= (1-\mu^2)^{(m+1)/2}\frac{d}{d\mu}\frac{d^m}{d\mu^m}P_{l,0}(\mu) \\ &= (1-\mu^2)^{1/2}\left[\frac{d}{d\mu}+\frac{m\mu}{1+\mu^2}\right]P_{l,m}(\mu) \\ &= -l_+P_{l,m}(\mu)\,.\end{aligned} \tag{20.28}$$

This demonstrates, as in Section 13, that the eigenfunctions of the orbital angular momentum are the spherical harmonics.

A word must be said about the phases of these wave functions. In Section 15, this question did not come up as no matrix elements were evaluated. Here, by using the choice of phases made in writing (20.17) and (20.18), a minus sign has appeared in (20.28), thus changing the signs of alternate wave functions when expressed in terms of the P_{lm}. This alternating sign occurs only for positive m. We choose to write the wave functions of the orbital angular momentum as follows

$$\begin{aligned}\Omega_{l,m}(\theta,\varphi) &= \pm Y_{l,m}(\theta,\varphi) \\ &= \pm\left[\frac{2l+1}{4\pi}\frac{(l-m)!}{(l+m)!}\right]^{1/2} P_{l|m|}(\cos\theta)\exp[im\varphi]\,,\end{aligned} \tag{20.29}$$

where the positive sign is taken *except for odd positive m*. This choice is the most commonly made, and will be adhered to throughout the remainder of this work. The normalization factor in (20.29) is compounded out of $(2\pi)^{-1/2}$ from the φ-dependent factor, $[(2l+1)/2]^{1/2}$ from the normalization of P_{l0}, and a factor coming from the matrix element of l_+. The ratio of the factorials for neighboring m values is

$$\frac{(l-m)!}{(l+m)!}\,\frac{(l+m+1)!}{(l-m-1)!} = (l-m)(l+m+1)\,.$$

This method of developing the angular momentum wave function is very like the first method used in Section 11 to find the harmonic oscillator wave functions. It is another example of the factorization method.

The angular momentum states with half integral j remain. Suppose we try to find wave functions for them. The eigenfunction of $j_z' = \hbar/2$ would be

$$\exp\,[\tfrac{1}{2}i\varphi]\,,$$

which is double valued, as an increase of φ by 2π changes the sign of this function. This goes contrary to our assumption of single valuedness. This assumption, however, may be considered as unnecessarily strong. What if it is given up? Then we find a wave function, for example,

$$\Omega_{1/2,1/2} = N \sin^{1/2}\theta \exp\,[\tfrac{1}{2}i\phi]\,,$$

which satisfies the differential equation, which is finite everywhere, though it possesses branch points at the poles $\theta = 0, \pi$. If we apply l_- to this, we obtain

$$l_-\Omega_{1/2,1/2} = -N\hbar \frac{\cos\theta}{\sin^{1/2}\theta} \exp\,[-\tfrac{1}{2}i\varphi]\,,$$

which is infinite at the poles. If we apply l_- once more, instead of zero, we get

$$N\hbar^2\left[\frac{-1}{\sin^{1/2}\theta} - \frac{\cos^2\theta}{\sin^{3/2}\theta}\right] \exp\,[-\tfrac{3}{2}i\varphi]\,.$$

This violates the requirement that $l_x^2 + l_y^2$ be positive. This can be regarded as the fundamental reason for the single valuedness condition.*

No wave function $\langle x'|j, m\rangle$ exists for half integral j. There are still states $|j, m\rangle$, however, whose quantum numbers describe a form of angular momentum possessing no classical analogue. This is called *spin* angular momentum. When a particle is in a state of zero linear momentum, it also has no orbital angular momentum and any angular momentum it has is spin. In this situation the quantum number j is replaced by s. s is a characteristic of an elementary particle, as the total spin of a particle is a constant of motion. Thus in the classical limit $s\hbar \to 0$ and spin effects go away. Orbital angular momentum persists because l can increase without limit.

There are $2s + 1$ *spin states* for a particle of spin s. If s is half integral they cannot be described by an angular wave function, while if s is integral they can be, but are not. The description of "spin" in terms of internal coordinates and momenta is appropriate for compound systems like atoms and nuclei when we are concerned with their internal structure, but is not useful for particles.

* W. Pauli, Helv. Phys. Acta **12,** 147 (1939).

A particle with spin can move in a potential, and the potential is described naturally by coordinates x. It is therefore desirable to have a wave function of some kind. Consider the electron with $s = \frac{1}{2}$. Any state of the electron can be represented as a linear combination of the two spin states with $m_s = +\frac{1}{2}$, $m_s = -\frac{1}{2}$. Thus,

$$|\alpha'\rangle = |\beta', \tfrac{1}{2}\rangle + |\gamma', -\tfrac{1}{2}\rangle \,. \tag{20.30}$$

The β' and γ' describe the state as defined by all variables other than the spin component s_z.

$$\begin{aligned} |\beta', \tfrac{1}{2}\rangle &= (\tfrac{1}{2} + s_z)\,|\alpha'\rangle \,, \\ |\gamma', -\tfrac{1}{2}\rangle &= (\tfrac{1}{2} - s_z)\,|\alpha'\rangle \,. \end{aligned} \tag{20.31}$$

The operators $(\frac{1}{2} \pm s_z)$ are called *projection operators*. They have eigenvalues 1 and 0, and project the state $|\alpha'\rangle$ onto the states with $s_z = \pm\frac{1}{2}$. Each projection can be described by a wave function, $\langle x'|\beta', \frac{1}{2}\rangle$, $\langle x'|\gamma', -\frac{1}{2}\rangle$. The entire state can in this way be described by a *pair* of wave functions, or a *two-component* wave function. This is usually written as a column vector

$$\begin{pmatrix} \psi_1(x) \\ \psi_2(x) \end{pmatrix}$$

with the first row giving the projection on $s_z = +\frac{1}{2}$, the second on $s_z = -\frac{1}{2}$.

This representation requires s_z to be diagonal. All the components of $\mathbf{s}$ can be represented by 2×2 matrices operating on this two-component wave function. The matrices are uniquely determined by (18.17)–(18.19). To avoid fractional matrix elements it is convenient to define the *Pauli spin vector* $\boldsymbol{\sigma}$ by

$$\mathbf{s} = \tfrac{1}{2}\hbar\boldsymbol{\sigma} \,. \tag{20.32}$$

The matrices σ_k are then

$$\sigma_1 = \begin{pmatrix} 0 & 1 \\ 1 & 0 \end{pmatrix}, \quad \sigma_2 = \begin{pmatrix} 0 & -i \\ i & 0 \end{pmatrix}, \quad \sigma_3 = \begin{pmatrix} 1 & 0 \\ 0 & -1 \end{pmatrix}. \tag{20.33}$$

These are called the *Pauli spin matrices*. They obey the relations

$$\sigma_k^2 = 1, \qquad \sigma_1\sigma_2 = -\sigma_2\sigma_1 = i\sigma_3 \qquad \text{(cyclic)} \,. \tag{20.34}$$

As a consequence, the components s_k of the spin obey the angular momentum commutation rules.

In general the angular momentum of a system arises both from orbital angular momentum and from spin. An important problem is the addition of various angular momenta as, in general, only the total angular momentum is conserved. This is the topic of Section 22.

$\sigma_1\sigma_2 + \sigma_2\sigma_1 = 0$ and

$\sigma_1\sigma_2 - \sigma_2\sigma_1 = 2i\sigma_3$

21. ANGULAR MOMENTUM AND ROTATIONS

On the basis of the commutation relations between the components of the angular momentum of a system we have shown that a complete set of angular momentum states is furnished by the eigenstates of $\mathbf{j}^2$ and j_z. The former of these observables is a scalar and does not discriminate between various directions in space, but the latter, being the component of a vector, does. The states of a system may therefore be labelled in a great variety of ways depending on the direction chosen for the z axis, or the axis of quantization. For any given j, the states $|j, m'\rangle$ quantized along the z' axis of a right-handed cartesian coordinate system $x'y'z'$ must be expressible linearly in terms of states $|j, m\rangle$ quantized along the z axis of another right-handed system xyz. Not only the direction of the z axis matters, because we have also agreed to assign phases to the states in such a way that $j_x \pm i j_y$ have real, positive matrix elements.

Let us write the linear dependence as

$$|j, m'\rangle = \sum_m |j, m\rangle U_{mm'}, \tag{21.1}$$

where, of course,

$$U_{mm'} = \langle j, m | j, m'\rangle . \tag{21.2}$$

Throughout this section m' refers to z', and m to z. The simplest case of (21.1) should be that for $j = \frac{1}{2}$, as the matrix $U_{mm'}$ is then a 2×2 unitary matrix. We look for a way to correlate such a matrix with a rotation in three dimensions.

If R is hermitian and U is unitary, then

$$R' = U^{-1} R U \tag{21.3}$$

is also hermitian. Furthermore,

$$\operatorname{tr} R' = \operatorname{tr} R, \qquad \det R' = \det R .$$

Let us take R to be the 2×2 hermitian matrix

$$R = \begin{pmatrix} z & x - iy \\ x + iy & -z \end{pmatrix} = \mathbf{r} \cdot \boldsymbol{\sigma} , \tag{21.4}$$

where $\boldsymbol{\sigma}$ is the Pauli spin vector of (20.33). We see that

$$\operatorname{tr} R = 0, \qquad \det R = -(x^2 + y^2 + z^2) . \tag{21.5}$$

Now the matrix elements of R' are linear functions of those of R, so that we have here a real linear transformation of x, y, and z, which leaves $x^2 + y^2 + z^2$

invariant. It is therefore a rotation, or a rotation combined with a reflection. The latter does not occur.

To a given rotation there correspond infinitely many unitary matrices U, for $\exp[i\chi]\,U$ yields the same rotation as U with any real χ. We restrict this freedom by requiring

$$\det U = 1\,. \tag{21.6}$$

This still leaves two U's per rotation because U and $-U$ give the same result. This cannot be avoided. The most general 2×2 unitary, unimodular matrix is of the form

$$U = \begin{pmatrix} \alpha & \beta \\ -\beta^* & \alpha^* \end{pmatrix}, \qquad \alpha\alpha^* + \beta\beta^* = 1\,. \tag{21.7}$$

Matrices of this form constitute a group known as $SU(2)$.

We need a relationship between the parameters α and β, which are the Cayley–Klein parameters, and the Euler angles describing a rotation. This is established by investigating two special cases. First let $\beta = 0$, $\alpha = \exp[-i\gamma]$. Then (21.3) becomes

$$\begin{pmatrix} z' & x' - iy' \\ x' + iy' & -z' \end{pmatrix} = \begin{pmatrix} \exp[i\gamma] & 0 \\ 0 & \exp[-i\gamma] \end{pmatrix} \begin{pmatrix} z & x - iy \\ x + iy & -z \end{pmatrix} \begin{pmatrix} \exp[-i\gamma] & 0 \\ 0 & \exp[i\gamma] \end{pmatrix},$$

or

$$\begin{aligned} x' &= x \cos 2\gamma + y \sin 2\gamma\,, \\ y' &= -x \sin 2\gamma + y \cos 2\gamma\,, \\ z' &= z\,. \end{aligned} \tag{21.8}$$

This is a rotation about the z axis. The primed coordinate system is obtained from the unprimed by a rotation through 2γ about z. Next let $\alpha = \cos\gamma$, $\beta = -i \sin\gamma$. Equation (21.3) becomes

$$\begin{pmatrix} z' & x' - iy' \\ x' + iy' & -z' \end{pmatrix} = \begin{pmatrix} \cos\gamma & i\sin\gamma \\ i\sin\gamma & \cos\gamma \end{pmatrix} \begin{pmatrix} z & x - iy \\ x + iy & z \end{pmatrix} \begin{pmatrix} \cos\gamma & -i\sin\gamma \\ -i\sin\gamma & \cos\gamma \end{pmatrix},$$

or

$$\begin{aligned} x' &= x\,, \\ y' &= y \cos 2\gamma + z \sin 2\gamma\,, \\ z' &= -y \sin 2\gamma + z \cos 2\gamma\,. \end{aligned} \tag{21.9}$$

This is a rotation about the x axis. The primed coordinate system is obtained from the unprimed by a rotation through 2γ about x.

Now any rotation is describable as a rotation about z through angle φ, a rotation about the new x axis through angle θ, and a rotation about the new z axis through angle ψ. φ, θ, ψ are the Euler angles. We have, therefore,

$$U(\varphi, \theta, \psi) = \begin{pmatrix} \exp[-i\varphi/2] & 0 \\ 0 & \exp[i\varphi/2] \end{pmatrix}$$

$$\begin{pmatrix} \cos(\theta/2) & -i\sin(\theta/2) \\ -i\sin(\theta/2) & \cos(\theta/2) \end{pmatrix} \begin{pmatrix} \exp[-i\psi/2] & 0 \\ 0 & \exp[i\psi/2] \end{pmatrix}, \tag{21.10}$$

where the order of the factors is appropriate, as in (21.3), U is multiplied into R from the right. Explicitly,

(21.11)

$$U(\phi, \theta, \psi) = \begin{pmatrix} \exp\left[-i\dfrac{\phi+\psi}{2}\right]\cos\dfrac{\theta}{2} & -i\exp\left[-i\dfrac{\phi-\psi}{2}\right]\sin\dfrac{\theta}{2} \\ -i\exp\left[i\dfrac{\phi-\psi}{2}\right]\sin\dfrac{\theta}{2} & \exp\left[i\dfrac{\phi+\psi}{2}\right]\cos\dfrac{\theta}{2} \end{pmatrix}.$$

We must now show that the matrix U of (21.10) or (21.3) and that of (21.1) for $j = \frac{1}{2}$ are the same. Consider a rotation of the coordinate axes through ϕ about z. Then the components of angular momentum in the two systems are related through

$$j_x' = j_x \cos\varphi + j_y \sin\varphi, \qquad j_y' = -j_x \sin\varphi + j_y \cos\varphi. \tag{21.12}$$

Assuming the U of (21.3) is that of (21.1) we obtain

$$|\tfrac{1}{2}, \tfrac{1}{2}'\rangle = |\tfrac{1}{2}, \tfrac{1}{2}\rangle\alpha - |\tfrac{1}{2}, -\tfrac{1}{2}\rangle\beta^* = |\tfrac{1}{2}, \tfrac{1}{2}\rangle \exp[-\tfrac{1}{2}i\varphi],$$

$$|\tfrac{1}{2}, -\tfrac{1}{2}'\rangle = |\tfrac{1}{2}, \tfrac{1}{2}\rangle\beta + |\tfrac{1}{2}, -\tfrac{1}{2}\rangle\alpha^* = |\tfrac{1}{2}, -\tfrac{1}{2}\rangle \exp[\tfrac{1}{2}i\varphi]. \tag{21.13}$$

The first row and column of U have been associated with $m = +\frac{1}{2}$, the second with $m = -\frac{1}{2}$. It is now easy to show that

$$\langle\tfrac{1}{2}, \pm\tfrac{1}{2}'|\,\mathbf{j}'|\tfrac{1}{2}, \pm\tfrac{1}{2}'\rangle = \langle\tfrac{1}{2}, \pm\tfrac{1}{2}|\,\mathbf{j}|\tfrac{1}{2}, \pm\tfrac{1}{2}\rangle. \tag{21.14}$$

This shows that the relation between the rotated operators and the rotated states is the same as that between the unrotated operators and the unrotated states, which was our aim. With slightly more algebraic complication the proof for rotations about x can be carried through, and hence the proof for any rotation.

If the rotation of coordinate axes is through an infinitesimal angle, say ϵ, about the x axis, then the matrix U becomes

$$U(0, \epsilon, 0) = \begin{pmatrix} 1 & -i\epsilon/2 \\ -i\epsilon/2 & 1 \end{pmatrix}$$
$$= 1 - i\epsilon s_x$$

where s_x is the x-component of the spin angular momentum. In general, for an infinitesimal rotation through ϵ about the direction of the unit vector $\mathbf{n}$ the corresponding matrix is

$$1 - i\epsilon\mathbf{n} \cdot \mathbf{s} .$$

The components of the spin $\mathbf{s}$ thus can be said to generate infinitesimal rotations of the coordinate system about the various coordinate axes. For arbitrary j the components j_k generate infinitesimal rotations of the coordinate system about the coordinate axes, the matrices being of dimension $2j + 1$ appropriate to the $2j + 1$ states which are mixed by rotations.

From (21.10) we see that

(21.15) $$U(0, 0, 0) = 1 .$$

A rotation about any axis, in particular the z axis, through 2π is physically equivalent to the identity transformation. The matrix $U(2\pi, 0, 0)$ is not unity, however, but is

(21.16) $$U(2\pi, 0, 0) = -1 .$$

This is just a reflection of the fact noted earlier that U and $-U$ give the same rotation. The state vector $|\frac{1}{2}, m\rangle$ therefore goes over continuously into $-|\frac{1}{2}, m\rangle$ when a rotation through 2π is made. The state vector is thus double valued, a property of all states with half integer j as is shown. An observable, A, is not changed by a rotation through 2π about an axis. The matrix element of A between states of integral j, or between states of half integral j, is not changed by such a rotation, for the state vectors either do not change sign or both change sign. A matrix element of A between a state with integral j and one with half integral j, however, changes sign when a rotation through 2π about any axis is carried out. Since this rotation is physically equivalent to the identity, all such matrix elements must vanish.

(21.17) $$\langle j = \text{integer}| A \,| j = \text{half integer}\rangle = 0 .$$

This is the superselection rule mentioned in Section 20.

The 2×2 matrix $U_{mm'}$ gives the transformation of states $|\frac{1}{2}, m\rangle$ when the coordinate system to which the angular momentum vector is referred is rotated. The effect of a rotation of the coordinate system on a state labelled by the total angular momentum quantum number j and the corresponding m is completely specified by j and m. We are led, therefore, to seek the $(2j + 1) \times$

$(2j+1)$ matrix, which describes the effect of a rotation of coordinates on states $|j, m\rangle$. The result is independent of how the states $|j, m\rangle$ are constructed as long as they are labelled by these quantum numbers. Any other quantum numbers used to specify the states must be unaffected by rotations. This will always be the case when j and m refer to the *total* angular momentum. In a system involving both orbital and spin angular momenta, for example, one may also study the effect of rotations referring separately to the orbital and spin variables. This leads to problems associated with the addition of angular momenta which are treated in Section 22.

To get angular momentum j we may combine $2j$ independent systems each with angular momentum $\frac{1}{2}$ in the appropriate way. Let the angular momentum vectors of the individual systems be $\mathbf{j}^{(k)}$. Then

(21.18) $$\mathbf{j} = \sum_{k=1}^{2j} \mathbf{j}^{(k)}\,,$$

so that, in particular,

(21.19) $$j_{\pm} = \sum_{k=1}^{2j} j_{\pm}{}^{(k)}\,.$$

Let us now construct the state in which each subsystem k is in the state $|k, \frac{1}{2}, \frac{1}{2}\rangle$, which we write $|k, \frac{1}{2}\rangle$. The first label $\frac{1}{2}$ never changes and can be suppressed. This state can be represented by a product

(21.20) $$|j, j\rangle = |1, \tfrac{1}{2}\rangle\,|2, \tfrac{1}{2}\rangle \cdots |2j, \tfrac{1}{2}\rangle\,.$$

The labels on the left are correct because application of j_z gives

$$\begin{aligned} j_z|j, j\rangle &= \sum_k j_z{}^{(k)}|1, \tfrac{1}{2}\rangle\,|2, \tfrac{1}{2}\rangle \cdots |2j, \tfrac{1}{2}\rangle \\ &= \sum_k \tfrac{1}{2}\hbar|1, \tfrac{1}{2}\rangle\,|2, \tfrac{1}{2}\rangle \cdots |2j, \tfrac{1}{2}\rangle \\ &= j\hbar|j, j\rangle\,, \end{aligned}$$

and also

$$\begin{aligned} j_+|j, j\rangle &= \sum_k j_+{}^{(k)}|1, \tfrac{1}{2}\rangle\,|2, \tfrac{1}{2}\rangle \cdots |2j, \tfrac{1}{2}\rangle \\ &= 0\,. \end{aligned}$$

The state $|j, j\rangle$ is symmetrical in the subsystems. The operators $\mathbf{j}$ are also symmetric in the $2j$ subsystems so that the results of all operations by $\mathbf{j}$'s on $|j, j\rangle$ are symmetric.

Now we can construct the state $|j, j-r\rangle$ by applying j_- to the state $|j, j\rangle$ r times and dividing by the product of the matrix elements of j_-. This product is

$$\prod_{m=j-r+1}^{j} [(j+m)(j-m+1)]^{1/2} = \left[\frac{(2j)!r!}{(2j-r)!}\right]^{1/2} .$$

Next we look at j_-^r.

$$j_-^r = (j_-^{(1)} + j_-^{(2)} + \cdots + j_-^{(2j)})^r. \tag{21.21}$$

The only terms in the expansion of this which do not annihilate $|j, j\rangle$ are those which contain r different lowering operators. In the expansion of

$$(x_1 + x_2 + \cdots + x_n)^r ,$$

the coefficient of $x_1^{a_1}{}_1 x_2^{a_2} \cdots x_n^{a_n}$ is

$$\frac{r!}{a_1!a_2! \ldots a_n!} \delta_{a_1+a_2+\cdots+a_n,\, r} .$$

In our case all the a's are zero or unity, so the coefficient of each contributing term is $r!$. Therefore,

$$|j, j-r\rangle = \left[\frac{r!(2j-r)!}{(2j)!}\right]^{1/2} \sum_{\text{sym}} |1, \tfrac{1}{2}\rangle \cdots \times |2j-r, \tfrac{1}{2}\rangle\, |2j-r+1, -\tfrac{1}{2}\rangle \cdots |2j, -\tfrac{1}{2}\rangle , \tag{21.22}$$

where the summation is over all distributions of the $+\frac{1}{2}$'s and $-\frac{1}{2}$'s among the $2j$ kets. This is more conveniently written

$$|j, m\rangle = \left[\frac{(j+m)!(j-m)!}{(2j)!}\right]^{1/2} \sum_{\text{sym}} |1, \tfrac{1}{2}\rangle \cdots \times |j+m, \tfrac{1}{2}\rangle\, |j+m+1, -\tfrac{1}{2}\rangle \cdots |2j, -\tfrac{1}{2}\rangle . \tag{21.23}$$

In this way the state $|j, m\rangle$ is related to states $|\pm\frac{1}{2}\rangle$. Because the transformation of the latter under rotations is known, the transformation of the general state can be inferred.

From (21.13)

$$|\tfrac{1}{2}'\rangle = |\tfrac{1}{2}\rangle\alpha - |-\tfrac{1}{2}\rangle\beta^* ,$$
$$|-\tfrac{1}{2}'\rangle = |\tfrac{1}{2}\rangle\beta + |-\tfrac{1}{2}\rangle\alpha^* .$$

When primed coordinates are used (21.23) becomes

$$|j, m'\rangle = \left[\frac{(j+m')!(j-m')!}{(2j)!}\right]^{1/2} \sum_{\text{sym}} |1, \tfrac{1}{2}'\rangle \cdots$$

(21.24)
$$\times\, |j+m', \tfrac{1}{2}'\rangle\, |j+m'+1, -\tfrac{1}{2}'\rangle \cdots |2j, -\tfrac{1}{2}'\rangle$$
$$= \left[\frac{(j+m')!(j-m')!}{(2j)!}\right]^{1/2} \sum_{\text{sym}} (\,|1, \tfrac{1}{2}\rangle\alpha - |1, -\tfrac{1}{2}\rangle\beta^*) \cdots$$
$$\times\, (\,|2j, \tfrac{1}{2}\rangle\beta + |2j, -\tfrac{1}{2}\rangle\alpha^*)\,.$$

But

$$|j, m'\rangle = \sum_m |j, m\rangle\, \langle j, m|\, j, m'\rangle$$

(21.25)
$$= \sum_m \left[\frac{(j+m)!(j-m)!}{(2j)!}\right]^{1/2} \sum_{\text{sym}} |1, \tfrac{1}{2}\rangle \cdots$$
$$\times\, |j+m, \tfrac{1}{2}\rangle \cdots |2j, -\tfrac{1}{2}\rangle\, \langle j, m|\, j, m'\rangle\,.$$

By comparing coefficients between (21.24) and (21.25) we obtain

(21.26)
$$\langle j, m|\, j, m'\rangle \quad \sum_r (-)^r \frac{[(j+m)!(j-m)!(j+m')!(j-m')!]^{1/2}}{r!(j+m'-r)!(j-m-r)!(m-m'+r)!}$$
$$\times\, \alpha^{j+m'-r} \alpha^{*\,j=m=r} \beta^{m-m'+r} \beta^{*r}\,.$$

To see this, it is sufficient to compare terms in which the first $j+m$ terms are states $|+\frac{1}{2}\rangle$, the last $j-m$ are states $|-\frac{1}{2}\rangle$, as all terms in both equations are symmetrized. The effective range of the index r is that which does not yield the factorial of a negative integer in the denominator of (21.26), the factorial of a negative integer being infinite.

If $m' = j$, the angular momentum vector is as well defined as is possible in quantum mechanics. We may then ask for the angle of rotation θ which will give the greatest probability for finding the value $m\hbar$ for j_z in the rotated coordinate system. Let $\alpha = \cos(\theta/2)$, $\beta = -i \sin(\theta/2)$, as is appropriate. With $j = m'$, only the term with $r = j - m$ contributes to the sum. Thus,

$$\langle j, m|\, j, j\rangle = (-)^{j-m} \left[\frac{(2j)!}{(j+m)!(j-m)!}\right]^{1/2} \left(\cos\frac{\theta}{2}\right)^{j+m} \left(i \sin\frac{\theta}{2}\right)^{j-m}.$$

This has its maximum magnitude when

$$\frac{d}{d(\theta/2)}\left(\cos^{j+m}\frac{\theta}{2}\, \sin^{j-m}\frac{\theta}{2}\right) = 0\,,$$

or

(21.27)
$$\cos\theta = m/j\,.$$

This is just what would be expected in the classical limit, but is correct for all j values including $j = \frac{1}{2}$.

For this value of $\cos\theta$ we may ask for the relative probability of finding the values $(m + \Delta)\,\hbar$ for j_z'. This will tell us the width of the distribution of states about $\Delta = 0$. We have

$$|\langle j, m + \Delta | j, j\rangle|^2 = \frac{(2j)!}{(j + m + \Delta)!(j - m - \Delta)!} \times \left(\frac{1 + \cos\theta}{2}\right)^{j+m+\Delta} \left(\frac{1 - \cos\theta}{2}\right)^{j-m-\Delta}.$$

Therefore,

(21.28)
$$P(\Delta) = \frac{|\langle j, m + \Delta | j, j\rangle|^2}{|\langle j, m | j, j\rangle|^2} = \frac{(j + m)!(j - m)!}{(j + m + \Delta)!(j - m - \Delta)!}\left(\frac{j + m}{j - m}\right)^{\Delta}.$$

If all the arguments of the factorials are large, Stirling's approximation may be used. Then

(21.29)
$$\ln P(\Delta) \approx -(j + m + \Delta)\ln\frac{j + m + \Delta}{j + m} - (j - m - \Delta)\ln\frac{j - m - \Delta}{j - m} \approx -\frac{j\Delta^2}{j^2 - m^2}.$$

The probability is thus a Gaussian about the classical value with a width of approximately $j^{1/2}$. The classical limit for a fixed value of $\mathbf{j}^{2\prime} = j(j + 1)\hbar^2$ requires j to vary as $1/\hbar$ as $\hbar \to 0$. The width of the above distribution measured in fixed units of angular momentum rather than in units of $\hbar$ is thus proportional to $j^{1/2}\hbar \sim \hbar^{1/2}$ and tends to zero with $\hbar$ even though the number of states involved tends to infinity.

If we were to start from a state $|j, m\rangle$ with $m < j$, the result would be a wider distribution because the statement that a vector has less than the maximum possible component in the z-direction gives incomplete information about the direction of the vector. Classically this specifies only a cone on which the vector must lie, and what the projection will be after a rotation depends on where on the cone the vector actually is. In quantum mechanics, it has no preferred azimuthal location on this cone.

The transformation matrices $\langle j, m | j, m'\rangle$ are often written as

(21.30)
$$\langle j, m | j, m'\rangle = D_{mm'}^{(j)}(R).$$

They constitute a *representation* of the three-dimensional rotations. This means that the D's combine in the same way that the rotations do, namely, if

$$\mathrm{R} = \mathrm{R}_1\,\mathrm{R}_2$$

then

$$D_{mm}^{(j)}(R) = \sum_{m''} D_{mm''}^{(j)}(R_1)\, D_{m''m'}^{(j)}(R_2)\,. \tag{21.31}$$

These representations are *irreducible*. This means that the $2j + 1$ states $|j, m\rangle$ cannot be divided into two sets which are not mixed with each other by any rotation. Any representation of the three-dimensional rotations can be expressed in terms of the $D^{(j)}$. Let $|\mu\rangle$ be any set of vectors which undergo a linear transformation when a rotation of the cartesian coordinate system is made. The space spanned by the vectors $|\mu\rangle$ can be divided up into subspaces, the vectors in each subspace being labelled by a j and an m. Then, when the rotation is made, each subspace is transformed into itself according to the representation $D_{mm'}{}^{(j)}(R)$, provided only that the basis vectors in each subspace are appropriately chosen. If the basis vectors are transformed by the unitary matrix M:

$$|j, m\rangle \rightarrow |\alpha\rangle = \sum_m |j, m\rangle M_{m\alpha}\,,$$

then the representation matrix is transformed:

$$\sum_m |j, m\rangle\, D_{mm'}{}^{(j)} \rightarrow \sum_{mm'} |j, m\rangle\, D_{mm'}{}^{(j)} M_{m'\alpha}$$

$$= \sum_{\alpha' mm'} |\alpha'\rangle M_{\alpha' m}{}^{*}\, D_{mm'}{}^{(j)} M_{m'\alpha}\,.$$

But

$$|\alpha\rangle = \sum_{\alpha'} |\alpha'\rangle\, \bar{D}_{\alpha'\alpha}{}^{(j)}\,,$$

so that the new representation matrices are related to the original ones by

$$\bar{D}^{(j)} = M^{*}\, D^{(j)}\, M = M^{-1}\, D^{(j)}\, M. \tag{21.32}$$

Representations so related are called *equivalent* to each other.

The statements made in the last paragraph are not self evident. The proof belongs to the theory of group representations and will not be given here.*

22. ADDITION OF ANGULAR MOMENTA

In many physical systems there occur two or more different angular momenta each of which is labelled by a j and an m. It is then desired to describe

* See E. P. Wigner, *Group Theory*, Academic Press, New York, 1959.

the total angular momentum of the system by a pair of quantum numbers J, M. Thus, in a deuteron there is the spin angular momentum of the neutron and of the proton and the relative orbital angular momentum of the two particles, which must be combined into a total angular momentum. In the previous section, we added angular momenta in the especially simple system of $2j$ spins each with $j = \frac{1}{2}$, but there we considered only one value of j, the maximum possible. We start here with just two angular momenta, but take all possibilities into account.

Consider a system made up of two parts. The first part has a complete set of states $|\alpha', j_1, m_1\rangle$, the second, a complete set of states $|\beta', j_2, m_2\rangle$. The entire system has a complete set of states $|\gamma', J, M\rangle$. We omit the labels α', β', γ' from now on as they do not concern us here. The question is, what values of J can occur, and what are the expansion coefficients in the expansion

$$|j_1, j_2, J, M\rangle = \sum_{m_1 m_2} |j_1, m_1\rangle\, |j_2, m_2\rangle\, \langle j_1, m_1, j_2, m_2 | j_1, j_2, J, M\rangle\,. \tag{22.1}$$

It is necessary to indicate the values of j_1, j_2 from which the states J are made as these are not determined by J alone. These coefficients are called *vector addition coefficients*, *Clebsch–Gordan* coefficients, or *Wigner* coefficients.

The total angular momentum is

$$\mathbf{j} = \mathbf{j}_1 + \mathbf{j}_2\,. \tag{22.2}$$

When the z component of $\mathbf{j}_1$ and $\mathbf{j}_2$ is diagonal, so is that of $\mathbf{j}$ and we have the result

$$M = m_1 + m_2\,. \tag{22.3}$$

The maximum value of m_1 is j_1, etc., so that the maximum value of M is $j_1 + j_2$. This is, therefore, the maximum value of J. We may write, making the simplest possible choice of the phase,

$$|j_1 + j_2,\ j_1 + j_2\rangle = |j_1, j_1\rangle |j_2, j_2\rangle \tag{22.4}$$

This is obviously annihilated by $(j_{1+} + j_{2+}) = j_+$.

The state $|j_1 + j_2,\ j_1 + j_2 - 1\rangle$ is easily constructed.

$$\begin{aligned} |j_1 + j_2,\ j_1 + j_2 - 1\rangle &= [2(j_1 + j_2)]^{-1/2}(j_{1-} + j_{2-})|j_1, j_1\rangle |j_2, j_2\rangle \\ &= [2(j_1 + j_2)]^{-1/2}[(2j_1)^{1/2}|j_1,\ j_1 - 1\rangle |j_2,\ j_2\rangle \\ &\qquad + (2j_2)^{1/2}|j_1,\ j_1\rangle |j_2,\ j_2 - 1\rangle]\,. \end{aligned} \tag{22.5}$$

The right side of this equation is a linear combination of two mutually orthogonal states. These may be combined in another way to yield a state orthogonal to (22.5) but with the same value of M, namely $j_1 + j_2 - 1$.

$$\begin{aligned} |j_1 + j_2 - 1,\ j_1 + j_2 - 1\rangle &= [2(j_1 + j_2)]^{-1/2} \\ &\times [(2j_2)^{1/2}|j_1, j_1\rangle |j_2,\ j_2 - 1\rangle - (2j_1)^{1/2}|j_1,\ j_1 - 1\rangle |j_2, j_2\rangle] \end{aligned} \tag{22.6}$$

The value $M = j_1 + j_2 - 1$ is clearly correct. The value $J = j_1 + j_2 - 1$ is verified by applying j_+, which yields zero.

Proceeding on down, we apply j_- to (22.5) to get $|j_1 + j_2, j_1 + j_2 - 2\rangle$. On the right there will now appear three mutually orthogonal states,

$$|j_1, j_1\rangle|j_2, j_2 - 2\rangle, \ |j_1, j_1 - 1\rangle|j_2, j_2 - 1\rangle, \ |j_1, j_1 - 2\rangle|j_2, j_2\rangle,$$

from which three different linear combinations can be built, each with $M = j_1 + j_2 - 2$. One will be the state $|j_1 + j_2, j_1 + j_2 - 2\rangle$; another, the state $|j_1 + j_2 - 1, j_1 + j_2 - 2\rangle$; and a third, the state $|j_1 + j_2 - 2, j_1 + j_2 - 2\rangle$. This will continue to happen, a new state appearing on each application of j_-, until j_- starts to annihilate states which have reached the bottom of their m value range. If j_2 is not greater than j_1, this will happen when j_- is applied for the $(2j_2 + 1)^{st}$ time. This tells us, then, that

$$j_1 + j_2 \geqslant J \geqslant |j_1 - j_2|. \tag{22.7}$$

That we have got all the states is checked by noting that there are $(2j_1 + 1)(2j_2 + 1)$ of the separately labelled states, and that the number of combined states is

$$\sum_{J=|j_1-j_2|}^{j_1+j_2} (2J + 1) = (2j_1 + 1)(2j_2 + 1).$$

The process may be carried out explicitly for $j_1 = l$, $j_2 = \frac{1}{2}$. Here l need not be an integer, but may be a half integer. We use it to avoid the subscript on j_1:

$$\begin{aligned} |l + \tfrac{1}{2}, l + \tfrac{1}{2}\rangle &= |l, l\rangle|\tfrac{1}{2}, \tfrac{1}{2}\rangle, \\ |l + \tfrac{1}{2}, l - \tfrac{1}{2}\rangle &= (2l + 1)^{-1/2} j_-|l, l\rangle|\tfrac{1}{2}, \tfrac{1}{2}\rangle \\ &= (2l + 1)^{-1/2}[(2l)^{1/2}|l, l - 1\rangle|\tfrac{1}{2}, \tfrac{1}{2}\rangle + |l, l\rangle|\tfrac{1}{2}, -\tfrac{1}{2}\rangle]. \end{aligned} \tag{22.8}$$

The state $|\frac{1}{2}, -\frac{1}{2}'\rangle$ has appeared already and is annihilated by j_{2-} next time. Thus, as we already know, $l - \frac{1}{2}$ is the lowest J value. The general term may be written down.

$$\begin{aligned} |l + \tfrac{1}{2}, M\rangle = (2l + 1)^{1/2}[(l + M + \tfrac{1}{2})^{1/2}|l, M - \tfrac{1}{2}\rangle|\tfrac{1}{2}, \tfrac{1}{2}\rangle \\ + (l - M + \tfrac{1}{2})^{1/2}|l, M + \tfrac{1}{2}\rangle|\tfrac{1}{2}, -\tfrac{1}{2}\rangle]. \end{aligned} \tag{22.9}$$

Application of j_- to this reproduces the equation with M replaced by $M - 1$.

The normalized state orthogonal to (22.8) but with the same value of M is

$$|l - \tfrac{1}{2}, l - \tfrac{1}{2}\rangle = (2l + 1)^{-1/2}[(2l)^{1/2}|l, l\rangle|\tfrac{1}{2}, -\tfrac{1}{2}\rangle - |l, l - 1\rangle|\tfrac{1}{2}, \tfrac{1}{2}\rangle]. \tag{22.10}$$

The general term on lowering this is

$$|l - \tfrac{1}{2}, M\rangle = (2l + 1)^{-1/2}[(l + M + \tfrac{1}{2})^{1/2}|l, M + \tfrac{1}{2}\rangle|\tfrac{1}{2}, -\tfrac{1}{2}\rangle - (l - M + \tfrac{1}{2})^{1/2}|l, M - \tfrac{1}{2}\rangle|\tfrac{1}{2}, \tfrac{1}{2}\rangle]. \tag{22.11}$$

These are all the states for this system.

The same can be done for other j_2. Table I contains the coefficients for $j_2 = \frac{1}{2}$ and Table II for $j_2 = 1$.

TABLE I.

VECTOR ADDITION COEFFICIENTS FOR $j_1 = l, j_2 = \frac{1}{2}$

	Coefficient of $|l, M - \frac{1}{2}\rangle\,|\frac{1}{2}, \frac{1}{2}\rangle$	$|l, M + \frac{1}{2}\rangle\,|\frac{1}{2}, -\frac{1}{2}\rangle$
In		
$|l + \frac{1}{2}, M\rangle$	$\left(\frac{l + M + \frac{1}{2}}{2l + 1}\right)^{1/2}$	$\left(\frac{l - M + \frac{1}{2}}{2l + 1}\right)^{1/2}$
$|l - \frac{1}{2}, M\rangle$	$-\left(\frac{l - M + \frac{1}{2}}{2l + 1}\right)^{1/2}$	$\left(\frac{l + M + \frac{1}{2}}{2l + 1}\right)^{1/2}$

TABLE II.

VECTOR ADDITION COEFFICIENTS FOR $j_1 = l, j_2 = 1$

	$|l, M - 1\rangle|1, 1\rangle$	Coefficient of $|l, M\rangle|1, 0\rangle$	$|l, M + 1\rangle|1, -1\rangle$
$|l + 1, M\rangle$	$\left[\frac{(l + M)(l + M + 1)}{(2l + 1)(2l + 2)}\right]^{1/2}$	$\left[\frac{(l - M + 1)(l + M + 1)}{(2l + 1)(l + 1)}\right]^{1/2}$	$\left[\frac{(l - M)(l - M + 1)}{(2l + 1)(2l + 2)}\right]^{1/2}$
$|l, M\rangle$	$\left[\frac{(l + M)(l - M + 1)}{2l(l + 1)}\right]^{1/2}$	$\frac{M}{[l(l + 1)]^{1/2}}$	$\left[\frac{(l - M)(l + M + 1)}{2l(l + 1)}\right]^{1/2}$
$|l - 1, M\rangle$	$\left[\frac{(l - M)(l - M + 1)}{2l(2l + 1)}\right]^{1/2}$	$-\left[\frac{(l - M)(l + M)}{l(2l + 1)}\right]^{1/2}$	$\left[\frac{(l + M)(l + M + 1)}{2l(2l + 1)}\right]^{1/2}$

The vector coupling coefficients, being the expansion coefficients of one state in terms of other states, have an interpretation as probability amplitudes. Thus,

$$|\langle j_1, m_1, j_2, m_2|\, j_1, j_2, J, M\rangle|^2$$

is the probability of finding subsystem 1 in states $|j_1, m_1\rangle$ and subsystem 2 in state $|j_2, m_2\rangle$ when the whole system is known to be in state $|j_1, j_2, J, M\rangle$. There is a perfect correlation between m_1 and m_2 in this case since their sum is specified. Therefore, the above expression is simply the probability of finding subsystem 1 with the value $m_1\hbar$ for j_{1z} when the whole system is in state $|j_1, j_2, J, M\rangle$. This can be given a simple geometrical interpretation when the quantum numbers get large.*

*E. P. Wigner, *op. cit.*

The vector coupling coefficients are conveniently expressed in terms of three-j symbols first defined by Wigner.

$$\langle j_1,m_1, j_2,m_2| j_1, j_2,J,M\rangle = (-)^{j_2-j_1-M}(2J+1)^{1/2}\begin{pmatrix} j_1 & j_2 & J \\ m_1 & m_2 & -M \end{pmatrix}. \tag{22.12}$$

The three-j symbols have the great advantage of high symmetry which makes their tabulation practical. The symmetry properties are best described in connection with tables, and are given in Rotenburg, Bivens, Mitropolis, and Wooten.*

If we know that a state $|J, M\rangle$ arises from two angular momenta j_1 and j_2, then it is possible to find the exact combination of states $|j_1, m_1\rangle$ and $|j_2, m_2\rangle$ which are involved, except, of course, for a common phase factor. When the state $|J, M\rangle$ arises from the combination of three or more angular momenta, this is no longer true. There are more ways than one to combine $|j_1, m_1\rangle$, $|j_2, m_2\rangle$, and $|j_3, m_3\rangle$ to yield a state $|J, M\rangle$. The investigation of this leads to the *recoupling* or *Racah* coefficients.

Consider a system composed of three subsystems with angular momentum variables $\mathbf{j}_1$, $\mathbf{j}_2$, $\mathbf{j}_3$. To describe this system by the quantum numbers J, M of the total angular momentum we might first combine $\mathbf{j}_1$ and $\mathbf{j}_2$ to form a state with $(j_1 j_2)j'$, and then combine this with j_3 to form J. We could equally well combine j_2 and j_3 first, forming $(j_2 j_3)j''$, which we combine with j_1 to form J. In this way we arrive at different states $|J, M\rangle$. It is sufficient to consider only $M = J$, as all other M values can be obtained from this by use of lowering operators. We suppress the index M. The order of combination of the various states is important, for the state $|j_1 + j_2 - 1, j_1 + j_2 - 1\rangle$, to take an example, changes sign if j_1 and j_2 are exchanged, because of the defining equation (22.6).

The state J arrived at by first coupling j_1 and j_2 is denoted by

$$|(j_1 j_2)j' j_3 J\rangle,$$

while the state arrived at by first coupling j_2 and j_3 is denoted by

$$|j_1(j_2 j_3)j'' J\rangle.$$

Then the six-j symbol is defined by

$$\langle (j_1 j_2)j' j_3 J | j_1(j_2 j_3)j'' J\rangle = (-)^{j_1+j_2+j_3+J}[(2j'+1)(2j''+1)]^{1/2}\begin{Bmatrix} j_1 & j_2 & j' \\ j_3 & J & j'' \end{Bmatrix}. \tag{22.13}$$

The six-j symbol has many symmetries which make its tabulation feasible. They are discussed in the previously cited works of Wigner and Rotenburg *et*

* M. Rotenburg, R. Bivens, N. Mitropolis, and J. K. Wooten, Jr., *The 3-j and 6-j Symbols*, Technology Press, Cambridge, Massachusetts, 1959.

al. These symbols are related to the Racah coefficients, differing from them only by a sign at most. They can also be expressed as sums over vector addition coefficients, as is obvious from the manner in which they arise. These relationships are not given here, there being too many of them and their interest being so very specialized.

23. INVARIANCE AND SYMMETRY

Many systems of physical interest have exact or approximate symmetries. The electron in a hydrogen atom moves in a spherically symmetrical field (when spin is neglected). The electrons in a perfect crystal move in a field with periodic structure and hence with certain symmetries. The specifically nuclear forces between protons and protons, between neutrons and neutrons, and between protons and neutrons are the same, leading to symmetries in nuclei. The examples can be multiplied. In this section, we investigate the general relationship between symmetries and the dynamics of systems.

Consider a system described by a complete set of commuting observables α. A typical state is then $|\alpha', t\rangle$. The Schrödinger equation for this state (assuming the operators α not to be explicitly time dependent) is

$$i\hbar \frac{d}{dt}|\alpha', t\rangle = H|\alpha', t\rangle . \tag{23.1}$$

A new set of states may be introduced through the use of a time-dependent or time-independent unitary transformation U. We treat the time-dependent case, the time-independent one following merely by requiring $\dot{U}$ to vanish. The time derivative of the new state is given by

$$\begin{aligned} i\hbar \frac{d}{dt}(U|\alpha', t\rangle) &= i\hbar U \frac{d}{dt}|\alpha', t\rangle + i\hbar \dot{U}|\alpha', t\rangle \\ &= (UHU^{-1} + i\hbar \dot{U}U^{-1})U|\alpha', t\rangle . \end{aligned} \tag{23.2}$$

This is again a Schrödinger equation for the new state with the new Hamiltonian

$$\bar{H} = UHU^{-1} + i\hbar \dot{U}U^{-1} . \tag{23.3}$$

This result is perfectly general. It encompasses such things as the transformation between the Schrödinger and Heisenberg pictures (see Section 7). It is of particular interest when the Hamiltonian is unaltered by the transformation, i.e., when

$$\bar{H} = H . \tag{23.4}$$

When this is so, the system is said to be *invariant* under the transformation U. When U is time independent this leads to the existence of constants of the motion.

If all the observables α used to label the states of a system are invariant under the transformation U, so that

$$U\alpha U^{-1} = \alpha, \qquad [U,\alpha] = 0$$

then the description of the state is said to be *covariant* under the transformation. In this case carrying out the transformation will not alter the *form* of any relation between observables, though of course the numbers involved may change.

In this section certain specific symmetries are studied. They are symmetry under (i) translations, (ii) rotations, (iii) Galilean transformations, (iv) spatial reflections, (v) time reversal, and (vi) gauge transformations.

(i) *Translations.* Consider a system of particles with coordinates $\mathbf{x}_\rho$, momenta $\mathbf{p}_\rho$. The center of mass momentum of the system is

$$\mathbf{P} = \sum_\rho \mathbf{p}_\rho\,. \tag{23.5}$$

Let

$$U = \exp\,[i\mathbf{P}\cdot\mathbf{a}/\hbar]$$

with $\mathbf{a}$ a constant vector. Then

$$\begin{aligned} U\mathbf{x}_\rho U^{-1} &= (\mathbf{x}_\rho U + [U, \mathbf{x}_\rho])U^{-1} \\ &= \mathbf{x}_\rho - i\hbar\frac{\partial U}{\partial \mathbf{p}_\rho}U^{-1} \\ &= \mathbf{x}_\rho + \mathbf{a}\,. \end{aligned} \tag{23.6}$$

This is a translation of the system through $\mathbf{a}$. Also

$$U\mathbf{p}_\rho U^{-1} = \mathbf{p}_\rho\,, \tag{23.7}$$

$$\dot{U} = 0\,. \tag{23.8}$$

If the Hamiltonian of the system can be written as a function of the momenta $\mathbf{p}_\rho$ and the relative coordinates $(\mathbf{x}_\rho - \mathbf{x}_{\rho'})$, then

$$UHU^{-1} = H\,, \tag{23.9}$$

and the system is invariant under translation. In the presence of external fields the Hamiltonian will not depend only on relative coordinates and will not be invariant under translation. Equation (23.9) can be written

$$[U, H] = 0\,. \tag{23.10}$$

According to (7.25), this implies

$$\frac{d}{dt}\langle\, |U|\, \rangle = 0\,. \tag{23.11}$$

Since U is a function of the observable $\mathbf{P}$, this in turn implies the constancy of $\langle\, |\mathbf{P}|\, \rangle$ in any state of a system whose Hamiltonian is translationally invariant.

If the coordinate of any particular particle of the system is used to label the state of the system, the description is not a covariant one, even though the system itself is invariant. It is possible for symmetries to be concealed by inappropriate labelling schemes. To exploit a symmetry, states must be described in a manner which is covariant under the symmetry transformation.

(ii) *Rotations.* Again consider a system of particles described by coordinates $\mathbf{x}_\rho$, momenta $\mathbf{p}_\rho$. Let L_z be the z component of the total orbital angular momentum of the system. Then if

$$\begin{aligned} U &= \exp\,[i\lambda L_z/\hbar] \\ &= \prod_\rho \exp\left[\frac{i\lambda l_{\rho z}}{\hbar}\right], \end{aligned} \tag{23.12}$$

we investigate the effect on the coordinates and momenta. Now

$$x + iy = r \sin\theta\; e^{i\phi}\,.$$

In the coordinate representation

$$l_{\rho z} = -i\hbar\frac{\partial}{\partial\phi_\rho}\,,$$

so that

$$\begin{aligned} \exp\left[\frac{i\lambda l_{\rho z}}{\hbar}\right] &= \exp\left[\lambda\frac{\partial}{\partial\phi_\rho}\right] \\ &= 1 + \lambda\frac{\partial}{\partial\phi_\rho} + \tfrac{1}{2}\lambda^2\frac{\partial^2}{\partial{\phi_\rho}^2} + \cdots\,, \end{aligned} \tag{23.13}$$

which is just a Taylor series with a step of magnitude λ. The effect of U on a function of $r\theta\phi$ is to replace these by r, θ, $\phi + \lambda$. In particular,

$$\begin{aligned} U(x_\rho + iy_\rho)U^{-1} &= Ur_\rho \sin\theta_\rho e^{i\phi_\rho}U^{-1} \\ &= r_\rho \sin\theta_\rho e^{i(\varphi_\rho+\lambda)}\,. \end{aligned}$$

Thus,

$$\begin{aligned} Ux_\rho U^{-1} &= x_\rho\cos\lambda - y_\rho\sin\lambda\,, \\ Uy_\rho U^{-1} &= x_\rho\sin\lambda + y_\rho\cos\lambda\,, \\ Uz_\rho U^{-1} &= z_\rho\,. \end{aligned} \tag{23.14}$$

This is just a rotation *of the system* through angle λ about the z axis. All particles receive the same rotation. The momenta are also rotated. Equivalently, the coordinate system to which the particles are referred is rotated through $-\lambda$ about the z axis.

If the Hamiltonian depends only on scalar products of coordinate and momentum vectors, but not on scalar products with vectors not rotated by U, then U is a constant of the motion. L_z is therefore constant under these circumstances. As the direction of the z axis is arbitrary, all components of $\mathbf{L}$ are constant.

The Hamiltonian may involve external fields. Only if these fields are spherically symmetric are all components of $\mathbf{L}$ conserved. If the external fields possess a common axis of symmetry, then the component of $\mathbf{L}$ along this axis is conserved.

The Hamiltonian may involve spin angular momentum. Spin angular momentum vectors are not reducible to linear coordinates and momenta and are not affected by L_z. Thus, if there is any coupling between spin and orbital angular momenta, the system is not invariant under this transformation. It is invariant under the transformation generated by

$$\exp\,[i\lambda(L_z + S_z)/\hbar]\,, \tag{23.15}$$

where S_z is the total spin angular momentum about the z axis.

(iii) *Galilean Transformations.* A Galilean transformation is one in which all velocity vectors are changed by a constant velocity $\mathbf{u}$. It can be regarded as a transformation to a new coordinate system moving with velocity $-\mathbf{u}$ relative to the original coordinate system. In classical mechanics, invariance under this kind of transformation reflects the fact that the equations of motion contain only the particle acceleration. In the presence of a magnetic field, for instance, there is no Galilean invariance. Galilean transformations are explicitly time dependent.

Let

$$U(\mathbf{u}) = \exp\,[i(\mathbf{P}\cdot\mathbf{u} + \tfrac{1}{2}M\mathbf{u}^2)t/\hbar]\exp\,[-iM\mathbf{u}\cdot\mathbf{X}/\hbar]\,, \tag{23.16}$$

where M is the total mass of the system of particles, and where $\mathbf{X}$ and $\mathbf{P}$ are the center of mass coordinate and momentum. Then, use of the commutation relations between coordinates and momenta leads to

$$\begin{aligned} \mathbf{x}_p' &= U\mathbf{x}_p U^{-1} = \mathbf{x}_p + \mathbf{u}t\,, \\ \mathbf{p}_p' &= U\mathbf{p}_p U^{-1} = \mathbf{p}_p + m_p\mathbf{u}\,, \end{aligned} \tag{23.17}$$

which define a Galilean transformation.

The term $iMu^2t/2\hbar$ in the exponent does not affect the transformations

(23.17), as it is a numerical quantity and commutes with all operators. It is needed to keep the kinetic energy of the center of mass invariant.

$$U \frac{\mathbf{P}^2}{2M} U^{-1} + i\hbar \dot{U} U^{-1} = \frac{\mathbf{P}^2}{2M} \cdot$$

The kinetic energy of relative motion is not changed because the relative motion is unchanged. If the potential depends only on the relative coordinates, it too is unchanged and the Hamiltonian is invariant under the transformation.

U may be the product of two Galilean transformations, U_1 and U_2:

$$U = U_2 U_1 . \tag{23.18}$$

With

$$\bar{H} = U_1 H U_1^{-1} + i\hbar U_1 U_1^{-1} ,$$

then

$$\begin{aligned} \bar{\bar{H}} &= U_2 \bar{H} U_2^{-1} + i\hbar \dot{U}_2 U_2^{-1} \\ &= U_2(U_1 H U_1^{-1} + i\hbar \dot{U}_1 U_1^{-1}) + i\hbar \dot{U}_2 U_2^{-1} \\ &= (U_2 U_1) H (U_2 U_1)^{-1} + i\hbar \left[\frac{d}{dt} (U_2 U_1) \right] (U_2 U_1)^{-1} . \end{aligned} \tag{23.19}$$

Thus even with the additional term present in the transformation of the Hamiltonian, the result of two transformations performed in succession is the product of the separate transformations.

(iv) *Spatial Reflection, Parity*. The three symmetries considered involve operations which can be carried out on physical systems; they can be translated, rotated, and given a common velocity. A physical system cannot be reflected in the origin. Neither can time be made to run backwards. These two symmetries must therefore be discussed in a different way from the first three. We assume that the mirror image of any apparatus can be built and that observables measured by the looking-glass apparatus have the same spectrum of eigenvalues as the observables measured by the original apparatus. The two sets of observables are therefore related by a unitary transformation, denoted by P.

Let the observables measured by the original apparatus be denoted by α, those measured by the reflected apparatus by $\tilde{\alpha}$. Then

$$\alpha = P \alpha P^{\dagger} . \tag{23.20}$$

For observables with classical analogues, we further assume that two reflections are the same as none so that

$$P^2 = 1 . \tag{23.21}$$

When spins are present this is no longer necessarily so. Two reflections might be equivalent to a rotation through 2π which could lead to $P^2 = -1$. We do not consider this possibility here. From (23.21) it is seen that

$$P = P^{-1} = P^{\dagger}, \tag{23.22}$$

so that P is also hermitian. Its eigenvalues are ± 1.

The defining equation for P is

$$P\mathbf{x}P^{\dagger} = -\mathbf{x}, \qquad P\mathbf{x} + \mathbf{x}P = 0. \tag{23.23}$$

This implies a similar relation for momenta because of the commutation relation

$$x_k p_l - p_l x_k = i\hbar\delta_{kl}.$$

Use of (23.23) leads to

$$Px_k p_l P - Pp_l x_k P = -x_k P p_l P + P p_l P x_k = i\hbar\delta_{kl},$$

which can be satisfied only by

$$Pp_l P = Pp_l P^{\dagger} = -p_l. \tag{23.24}$$

In the same way, one can see that

$$[P, \mathbf{l}] = P\mathbf{l} - \mathbf{l}P = 0. \tag{23.25}$$

This property distinguishes the *axial vector* $\mathbf{l}$ from the *polar vectors* $\mathbf{x}$ and $\mathbf{p}$.

Let $|\mathbf{x}'\rangle$ be an eigenstate of the coordinate $\mathbf{x}$. Then

$$\begin{aligned} \mathbf{x}P|\mathbf{x}'\rangle &= -P\mathbf{x}|\mathbf{x}'\rangle \\ &= -\mathbf{x}'P|\mathbf{x}'\rangle, \end{aligned} \tag{23.26}$$

and so

$$P|\mathbf{x}'\rangle = |-\mathbf{x}'\rangle. \tag{23.27}$$

Similarly,

$$P|\mathbf{p}'\rangle = |-\mathbf{p}'\rangle$$

and so on for all observables which are components of polar vectors. The effect of P on a wavefunction can now be found. Consider a state $|\alpha'\rangle$. Then

$$\begin{aligned} P|\alpha'\rangle &= P\int |\mathbf{x}'\rangle\, d^3x'\, \langle \mathbf{x}'|\alpha'\rangle \\ &= \int |-\mathbf{x}'\rangle\, d^3x'\, \langle \mathbf{x}'|\alpha'\rangle \\ &= \int |\mathbf{x}''\rangle\, d^3x''\, \langle -\mathbf{x}''|\alpha'\rangle, \end{aligned}$$

so that with $\psi_\alpha(\mathbf{x}') = \langle \mathbf{x}'|\alpha'\rangle$ we see that

$$P\psi_\alpha(\mathbf{x}) = \psi_\alpha(-\mathbf{x}) \,. \tag{23.28}$$

If the Hamiltonian of a system commutes with P,

$$[H, P] = 0 \,, \tag{23.29}$$

then the eigenvalues of P can be used to label eigenstates of H. These states are called even when P has eigenvalue $+1$ and odd when it has eigenvalue -1. The one-dimensional harmonic oscillator's Hamiltonian commutes with P. Hence the eigenfunctions are either even or odd functions of x. The Hamiltonian of a central potential system commutes with P. Here the evenness or oddness is already specified by the quantum number l. In the presence of spin no simple connection between total angular momentum and parity exists.

An explicit expression for the operator P can be given for systems describable by coordinates and momenta, i.e., systems with classical analogues. Let

$$P_x = \sum_{n=0}^{\infty} \frac{1}{n!}\left(\frac{-2i}{\hbar}\right)^n x^n p_x{}^n \,. \tag{23.30}$$

Acting on wave functions, so that $p_x = -i\hbar\partial/\partial x$, P_x is seen to give a Taylor series with $\Delta x = -2x$, which results in a reflection in the yz plane. Thus,

$$P = P_x P_y P_z \,, \tag{23.31}$$

the order of factors being immaterial. An alternative expression for P is $P_x R_x$, where R_x is a rotation through π about x, this rotation reversing y and z. Clearly, any direction may be chosen as the x direction. This explicit representation does not seem useful.

(v) *Time Reversal.* Consider a classical particle moving in a potential V. The equation of motion is

$$m\frac{d^2\mathbf{x}}{dt^2} = -\nabla V \,,$$

which is invariant under reversal of the sign of t. To every trajectory $\mathbf{x}(t)$ there corresponds another trajectory in which the same values of the coordinates occur, but in reverse order in time. If there are magnetic fields present, the current generating the field must be reversed to obtain the reversed motion. If a moving coordinate system has been introduced, its motion must be reversed.

In Hamiltonian language, time reversal symmetry occurs when H depends in an even way on $\mathbf{p} - (e/c)\mathbf{A}$ and is time independent. The Hamiltonian equations,

$$\dot{\mathbf{x}} = \frac{\partial H}{\partial \mathbf{p}} \,, \qquad \dot{\mathbf{p}} = -\frac{\partial H}{\partial \mathbf{x}} \,,$$

are invariant under the transformation

$$\begin{aligned} \mathbf{x} &\to \tilde{\mathbf{x}} = \mathbf{x}\,, \\ \mathbf{p} &\to \tilde{\mathbf{p}} = -\mathbf{p}\,, \\ \mathbf{A} &\to \tilde{\mathbf{A}} = -\mathbf{A}\,, \\ t &\to -t\,, \end{aligned} \tag{23.32}$$

which defines time reversal.

From a quantum mechanical point of view, t and $\mathbf{A}$ are numerical quantities which are simply to be changed in sign. $\mathbf{x}$ and $\mathbf{p}$ are operators and the time reversal transformation is described by an operator T such that

$$\tilde{\mathbf{x}} = T\mathbf{x}T^{-1} = \mathbf{x}\,, \qquad \tilde{\mathbf{p}} = T\mathbf{p}T^{-1} = -\mathbf{p}\,. \tag{23.33}$$

$\tilde{\mathbf{x}}$, $\tilde{\mathbf{p}}$ are the time reversed coordinate and momentum of the particle. (The generalization to many particles is trivial.) It follows from (21.33) that T cannot be a unitary operator. We have

$$xp_x - p_x x = i\hbar\,,$$

so that

$$\begin{aligned} T(xp_x - p_x x)T^{-1} &= \tilde{x}\tilde{p}_x - \tilde{p}_x\tilde{x} \\ &= -xp_x + p_x x \\ &= -i\hbar\,. \end{aligned} \tag{23.34}$$

But the right side of this equation must be $Ti\hbar T^{-1}$. Thus

$$Ti\hbar T^{-1} = -i\hbar\,, \tag{23.35}$$

which can be satisfied only if T is an *anti-linear* operator.

Let $|\alpha'\rangle$ be a state labelled by the eigenvalue α' of the observable α. Then

$$\begin{aligned} \tilde{\alpha}T|\alpha'\rangle &= T\alpha|\alpha'\rangle \\ &= \alpha' T|\alpha'\rangle \end{aligned} \tag{23.36}$$

since α' is real. If α is unchanged by T, then $T|\alpha'\rangle$ is again an eigenstate of α with eigenvalue α'. If α is reversed in sign by T, then $T|\alpha'\rangle$ is an eigenstate of α with eigenvalue $-\alpha'$. Thus the operation of time reversal reverses the labels of momentum eigenstates but leaves the arguments of coordinate space wave functions unchanged.

Time reversal does not change the norm of any state, but it may change the scalar product of two states. To see this we study the time reversal of the state $|a\rangle + \lambda|b\rangle$ where λ is a number. We require

$$(\,\langle a| + \langle b|\lambda^*)(|a\rangle + \lambda|b\rangle\,) = (\,\langle a|T^\dagger + \langle b|\lambda^* T^\dagger)(T|a\rangle + T\lambda|b\rangle\,)\,. \tag{23.37}$$

Expanding this, the terms involving $\langle a|a\rangle$ and $\langle b|b\rangle$ cancel because these norms are preserved. The cross terms yield

$$\begin{aligned}\langle a|\lambda|b\rangle + \langle b|\lambda^*|a\rangle &= \langle a|T^\dagger T\lambda|b\rangle + \langle b|\lambda^* T^\dagger T|a\rangle \\ &= \langle a|T^\dagger\lambda^* T|b\rangle + \langle b|T^\dagger\lambda T|a\rangle\,,\end{aligned} \tag{23.38}$$

which can be written

$$\lambda\,\langle a|b\rangle + \lambda^*\langle b|a\rangle = \lambda^*\langle a|T^\dagger T|b\rangle + \lambda\,\langle b|T^\dagger T|a\rangle\,. \tag{23.39}$$

The numerical factor comes out of the terms on the right when it is in between the two T's because in this form we are dealing with the scalar product of two state vectors of the same system, the time reversed system, and the ordinary rules are supposed to apply here. First choose $\lambda = 1$, then $\lambda = i$. We obtain

$$\begin{aligned}\langle a|b\rangle + \langle b|a\rangle &= \langle a|T^\dagger T|b\rangle + \langle b|T^\dagger T|a\rangle \\ i\langle a|b\rangle - i\langle b|a\rangle &= -i\langle a|T^\dagger T|b\rangle + i\langle b|T^\dagger T|a\rangle\,,\end{aligned}$$

so that

$$\begin{aligned}\langle a|b\rangle &= \langle b|T^\dagger T|a\rangle \\ &= \langle a|T^\dagger T|b\rangle^*\,.\end{aligned} \tag{23.40}$$

Scalar products are transformed into their complex conjugates by time reversal. Their absolute magnitude is unchanged. Because the wave function of a system is a scalar product, as in (10.10), time reversal changes every wave function into its complex conjugate. With multi-component wave functions such as those of Section 20 there is an additional unitary transformation among those components. For momentum eigenfunctions in coordinate space this replaces $\exp\,[i\mathbf{p}\cdot\mathbf{x}/\hbar]$ by $\exp\,[-i\mathbf{p}\cdot\mathbf{x}/\hbar]$. This is equivalent to the replacements $\langle\mathbf{x}'| \to \langle\mathbf{x}'|$ and $|\mathbf{p}'\rangle \to |-\mathbf{p}'\rangle$.

The condition that a system be invariant under time reversal is

$$THT^{-1} = H\,. \tag{23.41}$$

This requires not only that H be even in $\mathbf{p}$ or in $(\mathbf{p} - (e/c)\mathbf{A})$, but that $\mathbf{A}$ and V be real. In non-relativistic systems this is nothing more than requiring the Hamiltonian to be hermitian. In relativistic systems it imposes new conditions on the permissible interactions.

(vi) *Gauge Invariance.* The Hamiltonian of a charged particle moving in an electromagnetic field involves the vector and scalar potentials of the field explicitly. The physical effects of the electromagnetic field depend only on the fields $\mathbf{E}$ and $\mathbf{B}$ given by

$$\mathbf{B} = \nabla\times\mathbf{A}\,, \qquad \mathbf{E} = -\nabla\phi - \frac{1}{c}\frac{\partial\mathbf{A}}{\partial t}\,. \tag{23.42}$$

If $\mathbf{A}$ and ϕ are replaced by

$$\begin{aligned}\mathbf{A} \to \mathbf{A}' &= \mathbf{A} + \nabla\chi\,, \\ \phi \to \phi' &= \phi - \frac{1}{c}\frac{\partial\chi}{\partial t}\,,\end{aligned} \tag{23.43}$$

where χ is any function of space and time, the field strengths **B** and **E** are unchanged. The transformation (23.43) is called a *gauge transformation* of the *second kind.* All physical quantities must be invariant under this gauge transformation.

It is natural to use the coordinate representation as we are dealing with an external field which may be a complicated function of the coordinates. The Schrödinger equation is affected by the gauge transformation only in that $\mathbf{p} - (e/c)\mathbf{A}$ is replaced by $\mathbf{p} - (e/c)(\mathbf{A} + \nabla\chi)$ and E is replaced by $E + (e/c)\,\partial\chi/\partial t$. Both of these changes are accounted for by a change in phase of the wave function

$$\psi(\mathbf{x}, t) \to \psi'(\mathbf{x}, t) = \psi(\mathbf{x}, t) \exp\,[ie\chi(\mathbf{x}, t)/c\hbar\,]. \tag{23.44}$$

Thus

$$\begin{aligned}\left(\mathbf{p} - \frac{e}{c}\mathbf{A}'\right)\psi' &= \left[-i\hbar\nabla - \frac{e}{c}\mathbf{A} - \frac{e}{c}(\nabla\chi)\right]\psi \exp\left[\frac{ie\chi}{\hbar c}\right] \\ &= \exp\left[\frac{ie\chi}{\hbar c}\right]\left[-i\hbar\nabla - \frac{e}{c}\mathbf{A}\right]\psi \\ (E - e\phi')\psi' &= \left[i\hbar\frac{\partial}{\partial t} - e\phi + \frac{e}{c}\left(\frac{\partial\chi}{\partial t}\right)\right]\psi \exp\,[ie\chi/\hbar c] \\ &= \exp\left[\frac{ie\chi}{\hbar c}\right]\left(i\hbar\frac{\partial}{\partial t} - e\phi\right)\psi\,.\end{aligned}$$

The only change is the common phase factor which makes no difference.

The transformation (23.44) is a *gauge transformation* of the *first kind.* It is left to the reader to verify that the probability current (10.26) is gauge invariant.

PROBLEMS

1. Show that in any central potential the z component of the moment of the probability current is proportional to the z component of the orbital angular momentum, the proportionality factor being independent of the potential.
2. Show that for angular momentum states with $j = 1$, the operator $E_1 = aj_+^2j_-^2$ is, for suitable a, a projection operator onto the state $|j = 1, m = 1\rangle$. That is, show that for states $|1, m\rangle$

$$E_1|1, 1\rangle = |1, 1\rangle, E_1|1, 0\rangle = E_1|1, -1\rangle = 0.$$

   Construct projection operators onto the other two states $|1, 0\rangle$ and $|1, -1\rangle$.
3. Generalize the result of Problem 2 to construct the operator which projects an arbitrary state of angular momentum j onto the state $|j, m\rangle$.
4. The coordinate system is rotated about its x axis through $\pi/2$, about the new y axis through $\pi/2$, then about the new x axis through $-\pi/2$, and about the new

y axis through $-\pi/2$. What further rotation will restore it to its original orientation?

5. Construct as many independent states as possible from three states each with $j = \frac{1}{2}$. How many of these are symmetric? Antisymmetric?

6. Show that the generators $U(\mathbf{u})$ of the Galilean transformations possess the group property, namely that

$$U(\mathbf{u}_2)\, U(\mathbf{u}_1) = U(\mathbf{v}) .$$

Show further that $\mathbf{v} = \mathbf{u}_1 + \mathbf{u}_2$, so that Galilean transformations commute.

V

Approximation methods and applications

24. STATIONARY STATE PERTURBATION THEORY

The exact description of any system occurring in nature is much too complicated to be attempted. A simplified description is given instead, which can then be corrected to a certain extent for features neglected at first. Perturbation theory provides a systematic method for making these corrections. In this section, attention is directed to the energy eigenvalue problem when the system is not subject to influences depending on the time. The effect of time dependent perturbations is considered in Section 26.

The simplified or *unperturbed* system is described by a complete set of commuting observables including the unperturbed Hamiltonian H_0. This set of observables must be large enough to permit the description of whatever perturbations are to be considered. For example the system may be a hydrogen atom; the unperturbed system a charged particle in a Coulomb field. If the effect of spin-orbit coupling is to be investigated, electron spin must be included in the original description even though it does not enter the Hamiltonian H_0. If hyperfine structure is of interest, the nuclear spin must be included in the description of the system even though the unperturbed states are degenerate with respect to it.

The perturbed system is described by the same set of commuting observables as the unperturbed, but its Hamiltonian includes effects neglected in H_0. It is written as

$$H = H_0 + V . \tag{24.1}$$

The object is to construct approximate eigenstates of H assuming that a complete set of eigenstates of H_0 is known. Often one is content with approximate eigenvalues of H.

The method used is to consider an interpolating Hamiltonian

$$H(\lambda) = H_0 + \lambda V . \tag{24.2}$$

Clearly

$$H(0) = H_0 , \qquad H(1) = H .$$

The eigenvalues and eigenstates of $H(\lambda)$ are assumed to be analytic functions of λ in the region $|\lambda| \leq 1$ and therefore expressible as a convergent power series in λ. The rapidity with which this series converges depends on the magnitude of V. The eigenvalues and eigenstates are written

$$\begin{aligned} E(\lambda) &= E_0 + \lambda E_1 + \lambda^2 E_2 + \cdots , \\ |E', \gamma'\rangle &= |E_0', \alpha'\rangle + \lambda|\beta'\rangle + \lambda^2|\beta''\rangle + \cdots . \end{aligned} \tag{24.3}$$

The coefficients in these series can then be found.

A word is needed about the labels used for the states in (24.3). In general, the states of the unperturbed system will be degenerate. H_0 and α are a complete set of observables for this system. The effect of a perturbation is frequently to remove degeneracies. Some of the α's then become functions of the perturbed energy and fewer additional labels are needed. These are denoted by γ. The states $|\beta'\rangle$, $|\beta''\rangle$, etc., are in general not eigenstates of H_0 but are, of course, superpositions of such states.

Consider a perturbation λV which removes the degeneracy between two states $|E_0\alpha'\rangle$ and $|E_0, \alpha''\rangle$. As $\lambda \to 0$, these two states become degenerate, but their limits are two particular unperturbed states, even though any linear combination of degenerate states is again an eigenstate of H_0 with the same eigenvalue E_0. In the presence of degenerate unperturbed states whose degeneracy is removed (or reduced) by a perturbation, it is necessary to allow for the formation of the right linear combinations of degenerate unperturbed states. For this purpose, two states are considered degenerate if the difference of their energy eigenvalues is small compared with the energy shifts produced by the perturbation.

To preserve the normalization of states, it is convenient to write the second of (24.3) in terms of a unitary transformation $U(\lambda)$:

$$\begin{aligned} |E', \gamma'\rangle &= U(\lambda)|E_0', \alpha'\rangle \\ &= \exp\,[iS(\lambda)]U_0|E_0', \alpha'\rangle , \end{aligned} \tag{24.4}$$

with $S(0) = 0$, $S(\lambda)$ hermitian. U_0 is a constant with respect to λ. Its function is to produce the right linear combination of unperturbed states. Then the unitary operator $\exp\,[iS(\lambda)]$ continuously maps these states into the perturbed states. $S(\lambda)$ is expanded as

$$S(\lambda) = \lambda S_1 + \lambda^2 S_2 + \cdots . \tag{24.5}$$

The expansion of $\exp[iS(\lambda)]$ is then

$$\exp[iS(\lambda)] = 1 + i\lambda S_1 + \lambda^2(iS_2 - \tfrac{1}{2}S_1^2) + \lambda^3\left(iS_3 - \tfrac{1}{2}(S_1S_2 + S_2S_1) - \frac{i}{6}S_1^3\right) + \cdots . \tag{24.6}$$

In terms beyond the second, the order of factors is important. The advantage of this relatively complicated expansion is that hermiticity of the S_j guarantees the normalization of all states.

The eigenvalue problem to be solved is

$$H|E', \gamma'\rangle = E'|E', \gamma'\rangle , \tag{24.7}$$

which can be written

$$U_0^{-1} \exp[-iS(\lambda)](H_0 + \lambda V) \exp[iS(\lambda)] U_0|E_0', \alpha'\rangle = E'(\lambda)|E_0', \alpha'\rangle . \tag{24.8}$$

Inserting the various expansions in λ and equating coefficients leads to the following set of equations:

$$U_0^{-1}H_0U_0|E_0', \alpha'\rangle = E_0'|E_0', \alpha'\rangle , \tag{24.9}$$

$$U_0^{-1}\{V - i[S_1, H_0]\} U_0|E_0', \alpha'\rangle = E_1'|E_1', \alpha'\rangle , \tag{24.10}$$

$$U_0^{-1}\{-i[S_2, H_0] - i[S_1, V] - \tfrac{1}{2}[S_1, [S_1, H_0]]\} U_0|E_0', \alpha'\rangle = E_2'|E_0', \alpha'\rangle , \tag{24.11}$$

and so on for higher powers.

Equation (24.9) is equivalent to

$$[U_0, H_0] = 0 . \tag{24.12}$$

Taking matrix elements between unperturbed states leads to

$$\langle E_0'', \alpha''| U_0|E_0', \alpha'\rangle (E_0' - E_0'') = 0 .$$

Thus, U_0 has matrix elements only between unperturbed states whose energies can be considered identical, i.e., between states whose energy values differ by amounts negligible compared with the perturbation. What these matrix elements are is determined only in higher orders, if at all. In the absence of degeneracy U_0 is merely a phase factor which we choose to be unity.

The first order equation (24.10) leads to

$$\langle E_0'', \alpha''| U_0^{-1}VU_0|E_0', \alpha'\rangle + i(E_0'' - E_0')\langle E_0'', \alpha''| U_0^{-1}S_1U_0|E_0', \alpha'\rangle = E_1'\langle E_0'', \alpha''|E_0', \alpha'\rangle . \tag{24.13}$$

First consider the degenerate states, for which $E_0'' - E_0'$ is negligible. The equation becomes a matrix equation in the α's. If the degeneracy is g-fold, this matrix is a $g \times g$ matrix.

$$\langle E_0', \alpha''| U_0^{-1}VU_0|E_0', \alpha'\rangle = E_1'\langle E_0', \alpha''|E_0', \alpha'\rangle = E_1'\delta_{\alpha''\alpha'} . \tag{24.14}$$

This shows that $U_0^{-1}VU_0$ must be diagonal with respect to the degenerate states with eigenvalue E_0'. This, then, is the recipe for finding U_0. It is the unitary transformation which diagonalizes V in the subspaces of degenerate unperturbed states. The eigenvalues of V in these subspaces are the first-order energy corrections.

If the unperturbed state $|E_0', \alpha'\rangle$ is non-degenerate, so that the label α' is redundant, (24.14) becomes one-dimensional. In this case the first-order energy correction is the expectation value of V in the unperturbed state.

Returning to the degenerate case, if the eigenvalues E_1' of V are all distinct, the degeneracy of the states is completely removed and U_0 is determined to within a phase factor for each state. If the eigenvalues of V are not all distinct, some degeneracy remains. It might be removed in higher orders, or it might persist. If it is a degeneracy due to a symmetry such as the degeneracy with respect to the magnetic quantum number m in a central field, it can be removed in any order only by a perturbation which lacks this symmetry. For simplicity we assume either that the degeneracy is completely removed so that U_0 is essentially determined or that it is never removed so that U_0 remains arbitrary in all orders and can be chosen as unity. We therefore drop U_0 from the second order equation. It can be put back in if it is needed in a particular case.

Going back to (24.13), for states in which $E_0'' \neq E_0'$ the right side vanishes. The matrix element of S_1 is (expressed in unperturbed states diagonalizing V so that U_0 is replaced by unity)

$$\langle E_0'', \alpha''|S_1|E_0', \alpha'\rangle = \frac{i\langle E_0'', \alpha''|V|E_0', \alpha'\rangle}{E_0'' - E_0'}. \tag{24.15}$$

S_1 describes the first-order mixing of states by the perturbation. The contribution of unperturbed states to the state considered is small in proportion to the energy separation. Very small denominators are avoided by the use of U_0, the contributions of these states having been considered separately. The denominator on the right is referred to as an *energy* denominator.

Equation (24.15) does not determine the elements of S_1 with $E_0'' = E_0'$. However these elements connect states already mixed by U_0, so they may be set equal to zero.

The first approximation to $|E', \gamma'\rangle$, the perturbed state arising out of $|E_0', \alpha'\rangle$, is

$$|E', \gamma'\rangle = |E_0', \alpha'\rangle - \sum_{E_0'', \alpha''}{}' |E_0'', \alpha''\rangle \frac{\langle E_0'', \alpha''|V|E_0', \alpha'\rangle}{E_0'' - E_0'}. \tag{24.16}$$

The prime on the summation sign means that the terms with $E_0'' = E_0'$ are to be omitted in accordance with the discussion above. Contributions from states remote in energy are small.

The discussion of the second order proceeds like that of the first. In (24.11) put $U_0 = 1$, and multiply by $\langle E_0'', \alpha''|$:

$$i(E_0'' - E_0')\langle E_0'', \alpha''|S_2|E_0', \alpha'\rangle - i\langle E_0'', \alpha''|\,\{[S_1, V] + \frac{i}{2}[S_1, [S_1, H_0]]\}\,|E_0', \alpha'\rangle$$

$$= E_2'\langle E_0'', \alpha''|E_0', \alpha'\rangle. \tag{24.17}$$

Consider states for which $E_0'' - E_0' = 0$. Then we can solve for E_2' to get

$$\begin{aligned} E_2' &= -\sum_{E_0''', \alpha'''}{}' \frac{\langle E_0', \alpha'|V|E_0''', \alpha'''\rangle\langle E_0''', \alpha'''|V|E_0', \alpha'\rangle}{E_0''' - E_0'} \\ &= -\sum_{E_0''', \alpha'''}{}' \frac{|\langle E_0''', \alpha'''|V|E_0', \alpha'\rangle|^2}{E_0''' - E_0'}, \end{aligned} \tag{24.18}$$

where use has been made of (24.15). The second-order correction to a ground state energy is always negative.

The matrix elements of S_2 may be found. Of more interest is the entire second-order correction,

$$\langle E_0'', \alpha''|iS_2 - \tfrac{1}{2}S_1^2|E_0', \alpha'\rangle = \sum_{E_0''', \alpha'''}{}' \frac{\langle E_0'', \alpha''|V|E_0''', \alpha'''\rangle\langle E_0''', \alpha'''|V|E_0', \alpha'\rangle}{(E_0''' - E_0'')(E_0'' - E_0')}. \tag{24.19}$$

Here it is assumed that the diagonal elements of S_2 vanish, just as was assumed for S_1.

To illustrate the method just described, we consider a simple example which is also exactly soluble. Let

$$H_0 = \tfrac{1}{2}(p_1^2 + p_2^2) + \tfrac{1}{2}(x_1^2 + x_2^2). \tag{24.20}$$

This is the Hamiltonian of a two-dimensional oscillator with equal frequencies. Take

$$V = ax_1, x_2, \qquad |a| < |. \tag{24.21}$$

The complete Hamiltonian $H = H_0 + V$ can be brought into the form

$$H = \tfrac{1}{2}(P_1^2 + P_2^2) + \tfrac{1}{2}(1 + a)X_1^2 + \tfrac{1}{2}(1 - a)X_2^2 \tag{24.22}$$

by the coordinate transformation

$$\begin{aligned} X_1 &= \frac{1}{\sqrt{2}}(x_1 - x_2), \qquad X_2 = \frac{1}{\sqrt{2}}(x_1 + x_2), \\ P_1 &= \frac{1}{\sqrt{2}}(p_1 - p_2), \qquad P_2 = \frac{1}{\sqrt{2}}(p_1 + p_2), \end{aligned} \tag{24.23}$$

which amounts to a rotation through $\pi/4$. In this form, the eigenvalues are seen to be

$$E = (N_1 + \tfrac{1}{2})\hbar(1 - a)^{1/2} + (N_2 + \tfrac{1}{2})\hbar(1 + a)^{1/2} \approx (N_1 + N_2 + 1)\hbar + \tfrac{1}{2}(N_2 - N_1)\hbar a\,, \qquad |a| \ll 1\,. \tag{24.24}$$

We investigate the first excited states $N_1 = 1$, $N_2 = 0$, and $N_1 = 0$, $N_2 = 1$, by perturbation theory.

The unperturbed states we consider are the degenerate pair

$$|1\ 0\rangle = |1\rangle\,|0\rangle\,, \qquad |0\ 1\rangle = |0\rangle\,|1\rangle\,,$$

where the first ket refers to the unperturbed oscillator of coordinate x_1, the second ket to the other. V has matrix elements between states in which both quantum numbers change, according to (8.21)

$$\langle 1\ 0|V|0\ 1\rangle = \langle 0\ 1|V|1\ 0\rangle = a\langle 1|x_1|0\rangle\,\langle 0|x_2|1\rangle = \tfrac{1}{2}a\hbar\,. \tag{24.25}$$

These are the only matrix elements of V between these degenerate states. There are, of course, finite matrix elements, such as $\langle 0\ 1|V|1\ 2\rangle$, connecting nondegenerate states. These enter the expression for S_1, but not for U_0.

The first problem is to find U_0 in the two-dimensional subspace of the first excited states. Let

$$U_0|1\ 0\rangle = A|1\ 0\rangle + B|0\ 1\rangle\,, \qquad U_0|0\ 1\rangle = -B^*|1\ 0\rangle + A^*|0\ 1\rangle\,,$$

with $|A|^2 + |B|^2 = 1$. The eigenvalue equation is

$$(V - E_1)U_0|1\ 0\rangle = 0\,.$$

Written out in matrix fashion using the matrix elements of V just calculated, it becomes

$$\begin{pmatrix} -E_1 & a\hbar/2 \\ a\hbar/2 & -E_1 \end{pmatrix}\begin{pmatrix} A \\ B \end{pmatrix} = 0\,.$$

The determinant must vanish, so

$$E_1 \begin{cases} = E_1' = -\hbar a/2\,, \\ = E_1'' = +\hbar a/2\,. \end{cases} \tag{24.26}$$

Choosing the negative eigenvalue, we find

$$A + B = 0\,.$$

An acceptable solution is thus

$$A = -B = 1/\sqrt{2}\,.$$

The right linear combination of unperturbed states is therefore

$$U_0|1\,0\rangle = \frac{1}{\sqrt{2}}(\,|1\,0\rangle - |0\,1\rangle)\,, \tag{24.27}$$

and this combination develops continuously into the perturbed state with energy $E_0 + E_1' = 2\hbar - a\hbar/2$. A linear combination orthogonal to this, namely,

$$U_0|0\,1\rangle = \frac{1}{\sqrt{2}}(\,|1\,0\rangle + |0\,1\rangle) \tag{24.28}$$

develops continuously into the perturbed state with first order corrected eigenvalue $E_0 + E_1'' = 2\hbar + a\hbar/2$.

Had we picked the other eigenvalue in (24.26), the only change would have been that $U_0|1\,0\rangle$ would be the right linear combination for the state with the higher energy, and $U|0\,1\rangle$ that for the state with the lower energy. This is simply a relabelling and contains the same results as before.

The corrected eigenvalues derived in this way agree with the exact eigenvalues in the limit of small a, that is of weak perturbation, as is seen by looking at (24.24) and (24.26).

For further discussion of this problem, the two states (24.27) and (24.28) should be used as the unperturbed states. Similar calculations can be done for other sets of degenerate levels. Note, however, that (24.16) can be evaluated for first excited state levels without diagonalizing V for other degenerate sets of levels because the sum in (24.16) will contain no zero or near zero denominators coming from other degeneracies.

We have seen that two energy levels are to be considered as non-degenerate if the energy difference of the unperturbed levels is large compared with the shift in level produced by the perturbation of interest. This perturbation may be of variable strength, and as its strength is increased the original levels may be shifted by amounts comparable to their original separation. Indeed the levels as given by non-degenerate, first-order perturbation theory may cross, as shown in Figure 24–1. At $\lambda = \lambda_0$, the levels have, in first order, become degenerate. We examine the neighborhood of $\lambda = \lambda_0$ in second order.

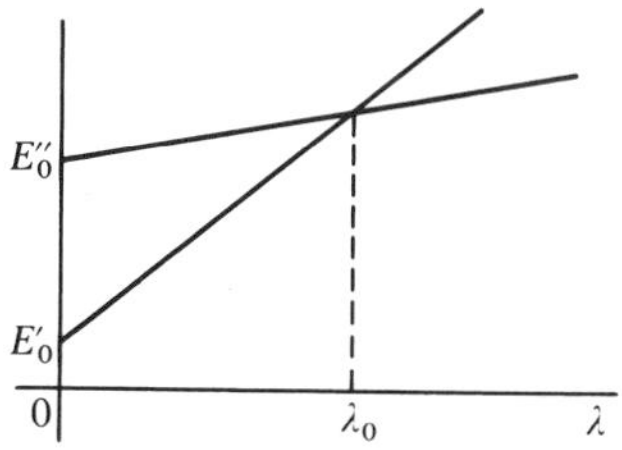

Fig. 24-1

For $\lambda \ll \lambda_0$, the original states $|E_0'\rangle$ and $|E_0''\rangle$, being non-degenerate, are the appropriate ones to use. For $\lambda \gg \lambda_0$, the states $|E_0'\rangle$ and $|E_0''\rangle$ must be considered degenerate and the right linear combinations must be chosen in order to obtain the perturbed eigenvalues. Thus, as λ goes through the value λ_0 the character of the states changes rapidly unless the perturbation has no matrix elements between these two states. This is seen in (24.15). At $\lambda \approx \lambda_0$, the denominator is of the order of magnitude of E_1', namely,

$$E_0'' - E_0' \approx E_1' - E_1'' \approx \langle E_0', \alpha'|V|E_0', \alpha'\rangle ,$$

so that, taking the off-diagonal matrix elements of V to be of the same order as the diagonal ones,

$$|\langle E_0'', \alpha''|S_1|E_0', \alpha'\rangle| \approx 1 . \tag{24.29}$$

The mixing is not small.

This argument also shows that the second-order energy correction is not small compared with the first. In the expression for E_2' take the term in the sum with $E_0''' = E_0''$, which has the smallest denominator and is therefore largest.

$$E_2' \approx -\frac{|\langle E_0'', \alpha''|V|E_0', \alpha'\rangle|^2}{E_0'' - E_0'} \tag{24.30}$$
$$< 0 .$$

Similarly,

$$E_2'' \approx -\frac{|\langle E_0'', \alpha''|V|E_0', \alpha'\rangle|^2}{E_0' - E_0''} \tag{24.31}$$
$$> 0 .$$

The upper level is shifted up in second order, the lower down, by amounts not small compared with the first-order shift which brings the levels together. The levels do not cross but act as shown in Fig. 24–2.

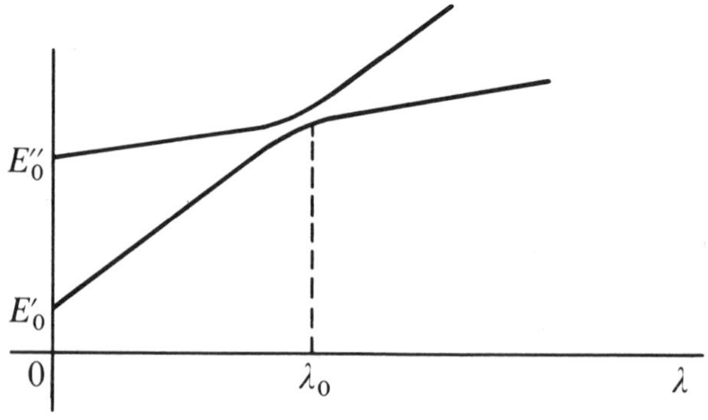

Fig. 24-2

25. THE PHASE INTEGRAL APPROXIMATION

The perturbation theory developed in the last section is applicable only when a reasonable zeroth-order Hamiltonian is known. The phase integral approximation does not depend on the existence of exact solutions of a simplified model, but has other limitations which will be discussed. The method is closely related to the classical method of action and angle variables and like the classical method is essentially restricted to one-dimensional systems or to systems which can be separated into one-dimensional systems.

We consider a particle described by the coordinate x moving in the potential $V(x)$. The time-independent Schrödinger equation, the eigenvalue equation for the energy, is

$$\frac{d^2\psi}{dx^2} + \frac{2m}{\hbar^2}(E - V(x))\psi = 0 . \tag{25.1}$$

In a region where $V(x)$ is constant this has the solutions

$$\psi = Ae^{ikx} + Be^{-ikx} , \tag{25.2}$$

where

$$k = +\left[\frac{2m(E - V)}{\hbar^2}\right]^{1/2} . \tag{25.3}$$

This solution represents a wave of amplitude A travelling to the right (because of the suppressed time factor $e^{-i\omega t}$) and one of amplitude B travelling to the left. These solutions are independent of each other.

If $V(x)$ is slowly varying, the two solutions in (25.2) remain almost independent. The two solutions are related through reflection of the waves. A wave travelling to the right through an inhomogeneous medium will undergo reflection giving rise to a wave travelling to the left. If the medium is very nearly homogeneous, meaning that the change in local wavelength per wavelength is small, then reflection becomes small and it is a valid approximation to neglect it entirely. The criterion for this neglect is that

$$\left|\frac{\Delta\lambda\!\!\!^{-}}{\lambda\!\!\!^{-}}\right| = \left|\frac{\Delta k}{k}\right| = \tfrac{1}{2}\left|\frac{\Delta V}{E - V}\right| \ll 1 . \tag{25.4}$$

When this criterion is satisfied, a good approximation to a solution of the wave equation is

$$\psi(x) = A(x) \exp\left[i\int^x k(x')\, dx'\right] , \tag{25.5}$$

with a slowly varying function $A(x)$ as amplitude. The lower limit of integration is immaterial, affecting only the overall phase. This solution consists of a wave travelling to the right without reflection.

The amplitude $A(x)$ must be chosen so as to conserve the probability current associated with this wave. In evaluating the current the dependence of A on x is neglected so that

$$j = \frac{\hbar k}{m} |A|^2 = \frac{p}{m} |A|^2 . \tag{25.6}$$

Thus we may choose A to be given by

$$A = Ck^{-1/2} = C\left[\frac{2m(E - V(x))}{\hbar^2}\right]^{-1/4} . \tag{25.7}$$

A similar solution with waves travelling to the left can be constructed.

The criterion (25.4) cannot apply near a classical turning point where $E - V(x) = 0$. Here the momentum vanishes and the de Broglie wavelength becomes infinite. Expressions of the form (25.5) are, at best, asymptotic approximations to the exact wave function, becoming better far from the turning point provided $V(x)$ is well behaved. When there is a second turning point present, it must be far (in terms of de Broglie wavelengths) from the first for the approximation to be good.

It is necessary to connect the two approximate wave functions on the two sides of a turning point so as to insure they are approximations to the same exact wave function. This can be done by simplifying the potential near the turning point so that the Schrödinger equation is soluble. The exact and approximate wave functions for this simplified problem are then matched. We follow another method due in its details to Furry.* Assuming the potential $V(x)$ to be an analytic function of x in a region around the turning point, the solution desired is also an analytic function of x in this region and is therefore single valued. This permits an analytic continuation along a path in the complex plane which avoids the turning point and along which the asymptotic form (25.5) is everywhere valid.

Let the turning point be at x_0, where $E - V(x)$ has a simple zero as shown in Figure 25–1.

* W. H. Furry Phys. Rev. **71** 360, (1947).

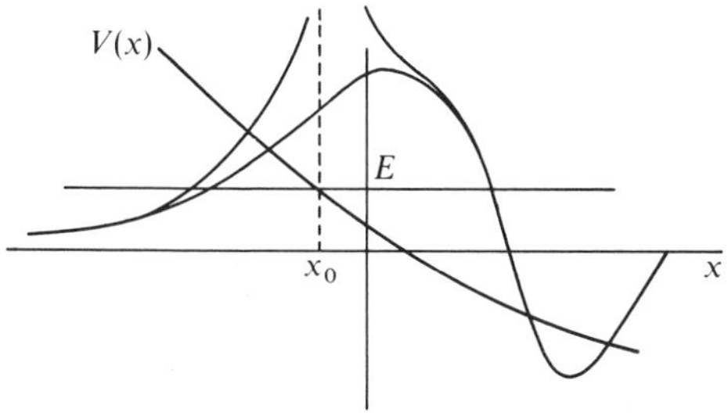

Fig. 25-1

Near x_0 the amplitude behaves like

$$(25.8)\qquad \begin{aligned} A(x) &\propto p^{-1/2} \\ &\propto (E - V(x)^{-1/4} \\ &\propto (x - x_0)^{-1/4} . \end{aligned}$$

The phase w behaves like

$$(25.9)\qquad \begin{aligned} w &= \int_{x_0}^{x} k(x')\, dx' \\ &\propto \int_{x_0}^{x} \tfrac{3}{2}(x' - x_0)^{1/2}\, dx' \\ &= (x - x_0)^{3/2} \end{aligned}$$

near x_0. w is real on the real x-axis to the right of x_0, because $V(x)$ is real, at least until another turning point is reached. It is also real on two other loci starting out from x_0 in directions making angles $2\pi/3$ and $4\pi/3$ with the positive real axis as shown in Figure 25–2.

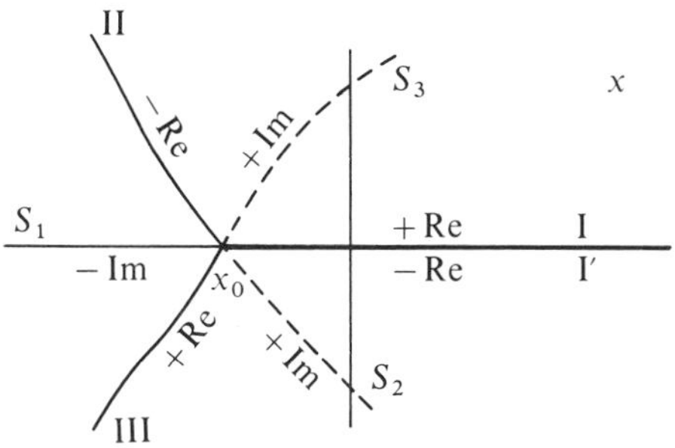

Fig. 25-2

These loci are called I, II, and III, respectively. Between them lie loci, called Stokes lines S_1, S_2, S_3, along which w is imaginary. Starting with w real and positive on I and going counterclockwise about the turning point, w is positive imaginary on S_3, negative real on II, negative imaginary on S_1, positive real on III, positive imaginary on S_2, and negative real on I. In function theoretic terms, x_0 is a branch point of w and the real axis to the right of x_0 is a branch cut.

On I the general solution of the Schrödinger equation is approximated by

$$A_{\rm I}e^{iw} + B_{\rm I}e^{-iw}\,, \tag{25.10}$$

and similarly along II and III. On S_3 the term $A_{\rm I}e^{iw}$ becomes exponentially small and is dominated by the term $B_{\rm I}e^{-iw}$ unless $B_{\rm I} = 0$. The solution along S_3 may also be written in terms of that along II. By the same token the $A_{\rm II}$ term is dominated by the $B_{\rm II}$ term unless $B_{\rm II} = 0$. If the approximation along II is to match the approximation along I at S_3, the coefficients must be related by

$$B_{\rm II} = B_{\rm I}\,, \qquad A_{\rm II} = A_{\rm I} + \alpha B_{\rm I}\,. \tag{25.11}$$

This states that the coefficients of the growing exponential must be equal, but that those of the shrinking exponential need be equal only if the other terms are absent. This conditional equality of the coefficients of the small exponential is called the *Stokes phenomenon.*

In the same way the solutions along II and III are matched across S_1. The result is

$$A_{\rm III} = A_{\rm II}\,, \qquad B_{\rm III} = B_{\rm II} + \beta A_{\rm II}\,. \tag{25.12}$$

Finally, solutions along III and I′ are matched. I′ denotes the locus I as arrived at from III, that is, the lower edge of the branch cut. On I′ w is negative real. We obtain

$$B_{\rm I'} = B_{\rm III}\,, \qquad A_{\rm I'} = A_{\rm III} + \gamma B_{\rm III}\,. \tag{25.13}$$

The wave function is analytic, and so we must be able to relate $A_{\rm I}$ and $B_{\rm I}$ directly to $A_{\rm I'}$ and $B_{\rm I'}$. The tour around x_0 changes w to $-w$, but alsoc hanges the phase of the amplitude by $(-\frac{1}{4} \times 2\pi)$ according to (25.8). The A's and B's have not been considered as functions of x_0 and have not suffered any phase changes. Therefore, the solution on I′, written as a function of w on the upper edge of the cut is

$$-iA_{\rm I'}e^{-iw} - iB_{\rm I'}e^{iw}$$

This is the same as the solution (25.10) along I when

$$A_{\rm I'} = iB_{\rm I}\,, \qquad B_{\rm I'} = iA_{\rm I}\,. \tag{25.14}$$

This is consistent with the previous equations only if

$$\alpha = \beta = \gamma = i \,. \tag{25.15}$$

The result is that a solution along I of the form

$$A_{\mathrm{I}} e^{iw} + B_{\mathrm{I}} e^{-iw} \tag{25.16}$$

is paired with a solution along S_1 of the form

$$e^{-i\pi/4}[(A_{\mathrm{I}} + iB_{\mathrm{I}})e^{|w|} + B_{\mathrm{I}} e^{-|w|}] \,. \tag{25.17}$$

In this second expression, however, it must be noticed that if the first term is present, the second term is usually meaningless as it was assumed to be negligibly small when solutions were matched. It is customary, therefore, to state that (25.16) is paired with

$$e^{-i\pi/4}(A_{\mathrm{I}} + iB_{\mathrm{I}})e^{|w|} \tag{25.18}$$

unless this vanishes, in which case it is paired with

$$e^{-i\pi/4} B_{\mathrm{I}} e^{-|w|} \,, \qquad A_{\mathrm{I}} + iB_{\mathrm{I}} = 0 \,. \tag{25.19}$$

The connection formulae are often stated as follows:
A purely decaying exponential in the classically forbidden region gives rise to an oscillating function in the allowed region according to

$$|p^{1/2}| e^{-|w|} \longrightarrow 2|p^{1/2}| \cos\left(w - \tfrac{1}{4}\pi\right) . \tag{25.20}$$

An oscillating function in the allowed region gives rise to an increasing exponential in the forbidden region according to

$$|p^{1/2}| \cos\left(|w| - \tfrac{1}{4}\pi + \theta\right) \longrightarrow \sin\theta |p^{1/2}| e^{|w|} \,, \qquad |\sin\theta| > 0 \,. \tag{25.21}$$

These are easily obtained. By choosing $A_{\mathrm{I}} = -iB_{\mathrm{I}} = e^{i\pi/4}$, we arrived at (25.20). Equation (25.21) is obtained by choosing $A_{\mathrm{I}} = e^{-i(\pi/4-\theta)}$, $B_{\mathrm{I}} = e^{+i(\pi/4-\theta)}$.

The energy levels in a potential well with two distant turning points may be found. Let the turning points be x_0, x_1 as shown in Figure 25–3. In the region $x < x_0$ there must occur only the decaying exponential. By (25.20), therefore, for $x > x_0$

$$\psi(x) = C_0 \cos\left[\int_{x_0}^{x} |k(x')|\, dx' - \frac{\pi}{4}\right] . \tag{25.22}$$

In the region $x > x_1$ there must occur only the decaying exponential. Therefore, for $x < x_1$,

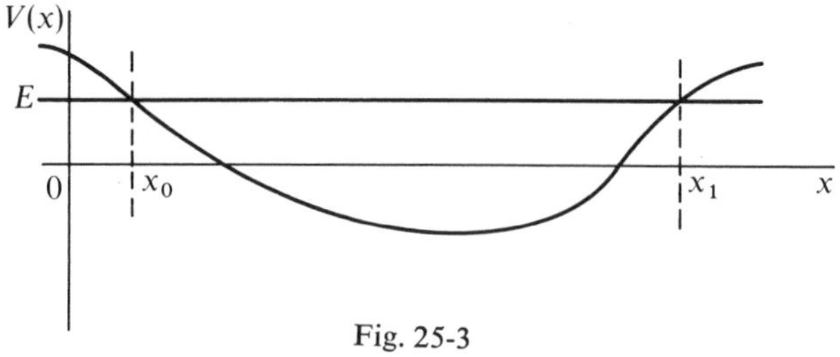

Fig. 25-3

(25.23)
$$\psi(x) = C_1 \cos\left[\left|\int_{x_1}^{x} k(x')\,dx'\right| - \frac{\pi}{4}\right]$$
$$= C_1 \cos\left[\int_{x_1}^{x} |k(x')|\,dx' + \frac{\pi}{4}\right].$$

These two functions must be the same. Therefore, writing (25.22) as

$$\psi(x) = C_0 \cos\left[\left(\int_{x_0}^{x_1} + \int_{x_1}^{x}\right) |k(x')|\,dx' - \frac{\pi}{4}\right],$$

we see that

$$\int_{x_0}^{x_1} |k(x')|\,dx' - \frac{\pi}{2} = n\pi \qquad \begin{array}{ll} C_0 = C_1, & n \text{ even} \\ C_0 = -C_1, & n \text{ odd} \end{array}$$

or, multiplying by $\hbar$,

(25.24)
$$\int_{x_0}^{x_1} |p(x')|\,dx' = \int_{x_0}^{x_1} |[2m(E - V(x')]^{1/2}|\,dx'$$
$$= (n + \tfrac{1}{2})\pi\hbar\,.$$

The integral on the left is just half of the classical action integral defined by

(25.25)
$$J = \oint p(x)\,dx\,.$$

Thus, we have the quantization rule for bound states:

(25.26)
$$J = (n + \tfrac{1}{2})2\pi\hbar\,,$$

which is, aside from the $\frac{1}{2}$, the old semiclassical rule. The energy of a bound state in the phase integral approximation does not depend at all on the potential in the classically forbidden region as long as that region is indeed forbidden. The method can be applied to a symmetrical two-minimum problem such as that illustrated in Figure 25–4. Because of symmetry under reflection,

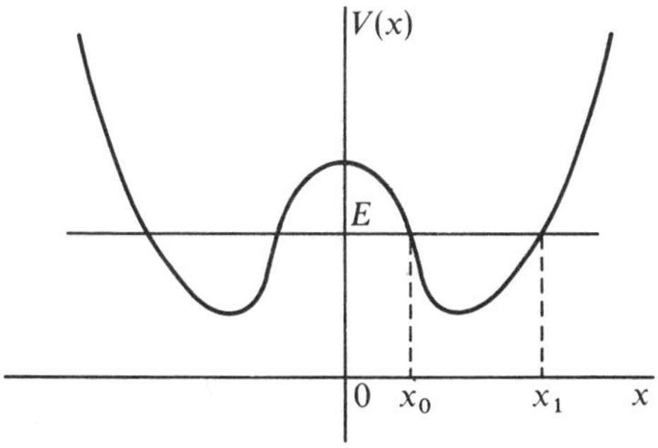

Fig. 25-4

the solutions must be even or odd functions of x. In the middle region the two exponentials must have equal or opposite coefficients, the exponents being expressed as integrals starting from the origin, not the turning points. This gives a definite value to the coefficients at one of the inner turning points, x_0, say. This yields the coefficients in the right allowed region via (25.17) and (25.16). Here one must use (25.17) rather than (25.18) because the two exponentials are related by a symmetry requirement. The connection at x_1 presents no new problem. The details are left as exercises at the end of this chapter.

The phase integral approximation is also used to find the transmission through potential barriers. The method is based on (25.16) and (25.18). To the right of the barrier in Figure 25–5 the solution contains only a wave to the

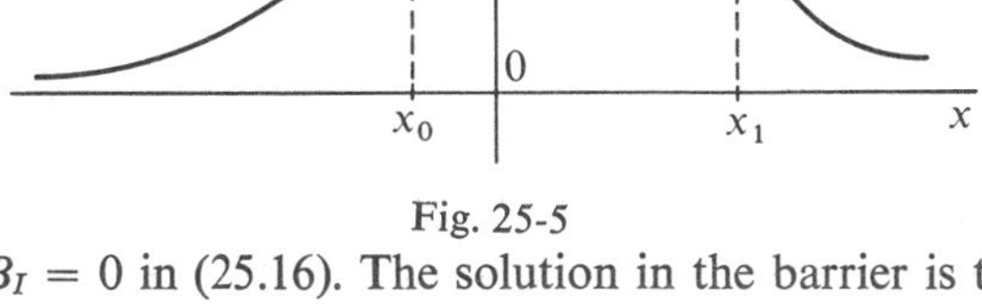

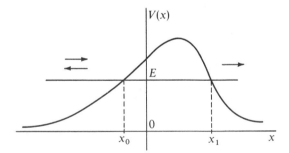

Fig. 25-5

right so that $B_I = 0$ in (25.16). The solution in the barrier is then, choosing $A_I = e^{i\pi/4}$,

$$\psi(x) = \exp\left[\left|\int_{x_1}^{x} k(x')\,dx'\right|\right]$$

$$= \exp\left[\int_{x_0}^{x_1} |k(x')|\,dx' - \int_{x_0}^{x} |k(x')|\,dx'\right].$$

As seen from turning point x_0, this is a decaying exponential with coefficient

$$C = \exp\left[\int_{x_0}^{x_1} |k(x')|\, dx'\right],$$

which is paired with an oscillating solution

$$2C \cos\left[\int_{x_0}^{x} |k(x')|\, dx' + \frac{\pi}{4}\right], \qquad x < x_0 .$$

If $V(x)$ approaches the same value on the two sides of the barrier, the transmission coefficient is just the square of the ratio of the amplitudes of the waves travelling to the right.

$$T = \exp\left[-2\int_{x_0}^{x_1} |k(x')|\, dx'\right]. \tag{25.27}$$

Otherwise there is a velocity ratio also. This calculation is unsatisfactory as there is no current in the barrier, the wave function there being real, and no loss in the incident beam, the reflected beam being just as intense as the incident one. Nevertheless, for very small penetrabilities it is a valuable approximation.

The phase integral approximation is often called the WKB approximation, after Wentzel, Kramers, and Brillouin.

26. TIME-DEPENDENT PERTURBATION THEORY

So far in our development of quantum mechanics we have been concerned with individual states of a system labelled by the eigenvalues of certain observables. When the observables are complicated, these eigenstates and eigenvalues have been calculated according to one or another approximation method. We now want to consider perturbations as causing transitions between states of an unperturbed system. This problem requires careful formulation as a variety of circumstances can be of interest.

In order to prepare a system in a definite state, or range of states, of an unperturbed Hamiltonian, the perturbation must be absent. It must then effectively be switched on. Later it must again effectively be switched off in order to allow us to determine which unperturbed states occur in the resulting state of the system. The manner of turning the perturbation on and off makes a difference. If this is done very slowly, adiabatically, the energy of the system is not affected by the process. If it is done rapidly energy can be exchanged between the system and the apparatus providing the perturbation.

The turning on and turning off are often not actually carried out, it not being necessary. Consider a scattering experiment. This may be described as follows: A wave packet of particles is prepared which has a large enough spatial extension so that it does not spread in time to any important extent, and which has a fairly well-defined momentum. The wave function associated with this packet has the value zero, or nearly zero, in the region where the scatterer, described by V, is located. The packet then proceeds to the scatterer, interacts with it, and becomes an outgoing packet. This final packet will, in general, not have a well-defined momentum, but will eventually have almost zero value at the scatterer. The wave packet at the beginning and at the end is not greatly influenced by the scatterer and may be discussed in terms of free particle wave functions. In this way, the perturbation is effectively turned on and off.

The perturbation may be time dependent aside from the switching. Thus the wave packet of the above discussion might pass through a region containing an oscillating magnetic field. We consider this time dependence later. For the present, the perturbation V is considered to be constant in time except for being turned on and then off.

It is convenient to work in the interaction picture of Section 7. Here the equation of motion for an observable is

(26.1) $$i\hbar \frac{d\alpha}{dt} = [\alpha, H_0] ,$$

where H_0 is the unperturbed Hamiltonian. The state vectors change in time according to

(26.2) $$i\hbar \frac{d}{dt} |t\rangle = V(t) |t\rangle .$$

Let the perturbation be described in the Schrödinger picture by $V_S(t)$, where

(26.3) $$V_S(t) = g(t)V_0 .$$

$g(t)$ is a numerical function commuting with all observables. Then the quantity $V(t)$ appearing in (26.2) is given by

(26.4) $$V(t) = g(t)e^{iH_0t/\hbar}V_0e^{-iH_0t/\hbar} .$$

The differential equation (26.2) for the state can be converted into an integral equation.

(26.5) $$|t\rangle = |t_0\rangle + \frac{1}{i\hbar}\int_{t_0}^{t} dt'\, V(t')\, |t'\rangle .$$

This also contains the initial condition that at $t = t_0$ the state is $|t_0\rangle$. If V is small, this equation can be solved by iteration. The right side of (26.5) is substituted into the integral on the right of (26.5), and the process is repeated at each appearance of $|t\rangle$ on the right. We define $|t, 1\rangle$ by

$$|t, 1\rangle = \frac{1}{i\hbar}\int_{t_0}^{t} dt'\, V(t)\,|t_0\rangle \tag{26.6}$$

and $|t, n\rangle$ by

$$|t, n\rangle = \frac{1}{i\hbar}\int_{t_0}^{t} dt'\, V(t')\,|t', n-1\rangle\,. \tag{26.7}$$

Then a solution of the integral equation is

$$|t\rangle = \sum_{n=0}^{\infty} |t, n\rangle\,, \tag{26.8}$$

with $|t, 0\rangle = |t_0\rangle$. We see that

(26.9)

$$|t, n\rangle = \left(\frac{1}{i\hbar}\right)^n \int_{t_0}^{t} dt' \int_{t_0}^{t'} dt'' \cdots \int_{t_0}^{t^{(n-1)}} dt^{(n)}\, V(t')V(t'')\cdots V(t^{(n)})\,|t_0\rangle\,,$$

so that the solution (26.8) is a power series expansion in the strength of the perturbation.

In order to evaluate this we insert between adjacent factors V in the integral the unit operator

$$\sum_j |E_j, \alpha_j'\rangle\,\langle E_j, \alpha_j'|$$

constructed from eigenstates of H_0. This enables us to replace the H_0 in the exponentials of (26.4) by the energy eigenvalues E_j. This yields, assuming $|t_0\rangle$ to be an eigenket of H_0 with energy E_i,

$$|t, n\rangle = \left(\frac{1}{i\hbar}\right)^n \int_{t_0}^{t} dt' \int_{t_0}^{t'} dt'' \cdots \int_{t_0}^{t^{(n-1)}} dt^{(n)}\, g(t')g(t'')\cdots g(t^{(n)})$$

$$\times \sum_{j,k,\ldots l} \exp\left[\frac{i}{\hbar}\{(H_0 - E_j)t' + (E_j - E_k)t'' + \cdots + (E_l - E_i)t^{(n)}\}\right] \tag{26.10}$$

$$\times V_0|E_j, \alpha_j'\rangle\,\langle E_j, \alpha_j'|V_0|E_k, \alpha_k'\rangle \cdots \langle E_l, \alpha_l'|V_0|E_i, \alpha_i'\rangle\,.$$

The integrations over $t'' \cdots t^{(n)}$ can now be carried out. We take t_0 to be in the remote past, $t_0 = -T/2$. The effect of the functions $g(t)$ is primarily to cause the oscillating integrands to be damped as t gets large and negative, so that the contribution to the integral at the lower limit is vanishingly small. This is accomplished by the choice

(26.11) $$g(t) = e^{\epsilon t/\hbar}$$

in the limit as $T \to +\infty$. We keep the lower limit as $-T/2$ but neglect the quantity $e^{-\epsilon T}$ relative to unity. Instead of doing the general case now, we consider the first and second orders separately.

In first order there is no integration other than that over t':

(26.12) $$|t, 1\rangle = \frac{1}{i\hbar}\int_{-T/2}^{t} dt'\, e^{\epsilon t'/\hbar} \exp\left[\frac{i}{\hbar}(H_0 - E_i)t'\right] V_0|E_i, \alpha_i\rangle .$$

We look for the amplitude with which the state $|E_f, \alpha_f'\rangle$ is present in the state $|t, 1\rangle$ at time $t = +T/2$. It is

(26.13) $$\langle E_f, \alpha_f'|T/2, 1\rangle = \frac{1}{i\hbar}\int_{-T/2}^{T/2} dt' \exp\left[\frac{i}{\hbar}(E_f - E_i - i\epsilon)t'\right] \times \langle E_f, \alpha_f'|V_0|E_i, \alpha_i'\rangle .$$

The integrand being regular, the limit $\epsilon \to 0$ can be taken before doing the integration, which is equivalent to putting $g(t') = 1$. Thus,

(26.14) $$\langle E_f, \alpha_f'|T/2, 1\rangle = \frac{1}{i\hbar}\int_{-T/2}^{T/2} dt' \exp\left[\frac{i}{\hbar}(E_f - E_i)t'\right] \langle E_f, \alpha_f'|V_0|E_i, \alpha_i'\rangle .$$

This is the first-order *transition amplitude* from the initial to the final state when the perturbation acts for a time T.

The probability of finding the state $|E_f, \alpha_f'\rangle$ after time T is the absolute square of this amplitude. It can be written as

$$W_{fi}^{(1)} = |\langle E_f, \alpha_f'|V_0|E_i, \alpha_i'\rangle|^2 \frac{1}{\hbar}\int_{-T/2}^{T/2} dt' \exp\left[\frac{i}{\hbar}(E_f - E_i)t'\right] \times \frac{1}{\hbar}\int_{-T/2}^{T/2} dt'' \exp\left[\frac{i}{\hbar}(E_f - E_i)t''\right].$$

As $T \to \infty$, the last integral becomes $2\pi\hbar\delta(E_f - E_i)$. The other integral then becomes just T and thus,

(26.15) $$W_{fi}^{(1)} = \frac{1}{\hbar^2}|\langle E_f, \alpha_f'|V_0|E_i, \alpha_i'\rangle|^2 2\pi\hbar\, \delta(E_f - E_i)T .$$

This result has physical meaning only when integration is done over the argument of the δ-function. Either E_f or E_i must be an element of a continuum. The usual situation is that E_f is in a continuum. Then the physically meaningful probability is not that of making a transition to a particular state, but to any state lying in a finite range of states. This probability is non-vanishing only when the initial energy falls in this range.

The expression for $W_{fi}^{(1)}$ given by (26.15) grows without limit as $T \to \infty$. The limit is to be taken only formally. No experiment lasts an infinite time, and the result desired is the transition probability per unit time, denoted by $w_{fi}^{(1)}$.

$$w_{fi}^{(1)} = \frac{1}{T}\int dN_f\, W_{fi} \tag{26.16}$$

where $\int dN_f$ is the number of final states which are accepted.

When the final states to be summed over are those of free particles, as occurs in scattering problems, we need an expression for the number of states of a particle in a momentum range d^3p. When box normalization is used, the states are discrete and can be counted. The momentum components can have the values

$$p_i = \frac{2\pi\hbar}{L}\, n_i$$

with integer n_i. In n-space there is one state at each point with integer coordinates, or one state per unit volume. In p-space there are therefore $L^3/(2\pi\hbar)^3$ states per unit volume, or

$$\frac{d^3p}{(2\pi\hbar)^3}\, L^3 \tag{26.17}$$

states in the momentum range d^3p. On going over to delta-function normalization, the wave function of the free particle acquires an amplitude unity rather than $L^{-3/2}$. The final state of this particle appears squared in (26.15), so the factor L^3 changes the normalization from box to delta function, and we are left with the number of states being given by

$$dN = \frac{d^3p}{(2\pi\hbar)^3}\,. \tag{26.18}$$

This shows that the rule for putting this factor $(2\pi\hbar)$ under each momentum differential has physical meaning. For other more complicated systems dN is found in similar ways.

In general we define a *density of final states* ρ_f by

$$dN_f = \rho_f\, \frac{dE_f}{2\pi\hbar}\,. \tag{26.19}$$

This enables us to write the important formula*

*In most texts this is written

$$w_{fi}^{(1)} = \frac{2\pi}{\hbar}\,|\langle E_f, \alpha_f'|V_0|E_i, \alpha_i'\rangle|^2 \bar{\rho}_{f\,E_f=E_I}$$

in which the density of states $\bar{\rho}_f$ differs from ours by $\rho_f = 2\pi\hbar\bar{\rho}_f$. We have written it as we have because, for free particles, the density of final states ρ_f is given by

$$\frac{d^3p}{(2\pi\hbar)^3} \times 2\pi\hbar\, \delta\!\left(\frac{p^2}{2m} - E\right)$$

which accords with the general rule for factors of $2\pi\hbar$.

$$w_{fi}^{(1)} = \frac{1}{\hbar^2} \,|\, \langle E_f, \alpha_f' | V_0 | E_i, \alpha_i' \rangle \,|^2 \rho_f(E_Q)_{E_f = E_I} \,. \tag{26.20}$$

Fermi dubbed this the "Golden Rule."

If neither the initial nor the final state is a member of a continuum, one cannot define a transition probability per unit time. In this situation the time-dependent perturbation theory is equivalent to the time-independent theory, the shift in an energy eigenvalue appearing as a change in the time dependence of the state. If the perturbation is slowly switched on and then slowly switched off, the only transitions which can occur are those between initially degenerate states, and if there are none, or if proper linear combinations of such states have been introduced so that they are not coupled by the perturbation, then no transitions occur and the system returns to its initial state. This is known as the *adiabatic theorem*. In the old semi-classical quantum mechanics one of the requirements for a quantity to be quantized was that it be an adiabatic invariant.

Now we look at the second order.

$$|t, 2\rangle = \left(\frac{1}{i\hbar}\right)^2 \int_{-T/2}^{t} dt' \int_{-T/2}^{t'} dt'' \sum_j \exp\left[\frac{i}{\hbar}\{(H_0 - E_j - i\epsilon)t' + (E_j - E_i - i\epsilon)t''\}\right] V_0 | E_j, \alpha_j' \rangle \langle E_j, \alpha_j' | V_0 | E_i, \alpha_i' \rangle \,. \tag{26.21}$$

The new features are the integration over t'' and the summation over the intermediate states j. The integration over t'' can be done.

$$i\hbar \int_{-T/2}^{t'} dt'' \exp\left[\frac{i}{\hbar}(E_j - E_i - i\epsilon)t''\right] = -\frac{\exp\,[i(E_j - E_i - i\epsilon)t'/\hbar]}{E_j - E_i - i\epsilon} \,,$$

where the lower limit contribution has been neglected because of the small exponential factor. The time factor involving E_j now cancels out of (26.21). Therefore, the sum over j becomes simply

$$\sum_j -\frac{V_0 | E_j, \alpha_j' \rangle \langle E_j, \alpha_j' | V_0 | E_i, \alpha_i' \rangle}{E_j - E_i - i\epsilon} = V_0^{(2)} | E_i, \alpha_i' \rangle \,. \tag{26.22}$$

This defines the second order perturbation operator $V_0^{(2)}$. We can now write

$$|t, 2\rangle = \frac{1}{i\hbar} \int_{-T/2}^{t} dt' \, g^2(t') \exp\left[\frac{i}{\hbar}(H_0 - E_i)t'\right] V_0^{(2)} | E_i, \alpha_i' \rangle \,, \tag{26.23}$$

which is the same as (26.12) except that $V_0^{(2)}$ replaces V_0, and $g^2(t')$ replaces

$g(t')$. The latter is trivial as in evaluating (26.12) we put $g(t') = 1$. We therefore get to second order

(26.24) $\langle E_f, \alpha_f'|T/2, 2\rangle =$

$$\frac{1}{i\hbar}\int_{-T/2}^{T/2} dt' \exp\left[\frac{i}{\hbar}(E_f - E_i)t'\right]\langle E_f, \alpha_f'|V_0^{(2)}|E_i, \alpha_i'\rangle .$$

If the first order vanishes, the transition probability per unit time is given to second order by (26.20) with V_0 replaced by $V_0^{(2)}$. If the first order does not vanish, the first and second order amplitudes must be added before squaring, as interference terms occur. Thus, correct to second order we have

$$w_{fi}^{(2)} = \frac{1}{\hbar^2}\left|\langle E_f, \alpha_f'|V_0 + V_0^{(2)}|E_i, \alpha_i'\rangle\right|^2 \rho_f . \tag{26.25}$$

The only correction term of significance is the cross, or interference, term. The term in $|V_0^{(2)}|^2$ involves the perturbation strength to the fourth power. Another such term comes from interference between V_0 and $V_0^{(3)}$. Thus, the term of fourth order is meaningless unless the third order is also calculated. In a shortened notation, the cross term is

$$\langle f|V_0|i\rangle\langle f|V_0^{(2)}|i\rangle^* + \langle f|V_0|i\rangle^*\langle f|V_0^{(2)}|i\rangle = 2\,\mathrm{Re}\,\langle f|V_0|i\rangle^*\langle f|V_0^{(2)}|i\rangle .$$

The final expression is now

$$w_{fi}^{(2)} = \frac{1}{\hbar^2}\{\,|\langle f|V_0|i\rangle|^2 + 2Re\langle f|V_0|i\rangle^*\langle f|V_0^{(2)}|i\rangle\,\}\rho_f , \qquad w_{fi}^{(1)} \neq 0 , \tag{26.26}$$

or

$$w_{fi}^{(2)} = \frac{1}{\hbar^2}|\langle f|V_0^{(2)}|i\rangle|^2\rho_f , \qquad w_{fi}^{(1)} = 0 . \tag{26.27}$$

The importance of the switching function $g(t)$ can now be seen by examining the expression for $V_0^{(2)}$.

$$V_0^{(2)} = -\sum_j \frac{V_0|E_j, \alpha_j'\rangle\langle E_j, \alpha_j'|V_0}{E_j - E_i - i\epsilon} . \tag{26.28}$$

We are concerned about systems in which the states form a continuum, so that in the summation over intermediate states zero denominators could occur. The term $i\epsilon$ prevents this. The summation is here really an integration, and the integrand has a pole. The effect of $i\epsilon$ is to displace this pole from the real axis of E_j. Its contribution is then well defined in the sense of the theory of functions of a complex variable. Without the $i\epsilon$ the effect of this pole would be ambiguous.

The extension to higher order is straightforward. The nth order perturbation operator $V_0^{(n)}$ is obtained by integrating over $t'' \cdots t^{(n)}$ in (26.10), and then noting the cancellation of all intermediate energies in the exponential involving t'. The result is

(26.29)

$$V_0^{(n)}|E_i, \alpha_i'\rangle = (-)^{n-1} \sum_{j,k,\ldots,l} \frac{V_0|E_j\alpha_j'\rangle \langle E_j\alpha_j'|V_0|E_k, \alpha_k'\rangle \cdots \langle E_l, \alpha_l'|V_0|E_i, \alpha_i'\rangle}{(E_j - E_i - i\epsilon)(E_k - E_i - i\epsilon) \cdots (E_l - E_i - i\epsilon)} .$$

The actual evaluation of the integrals in (26.29) is usually very difficult.

In using (26.29) in calculating transition probabilities, it is important to avoid the spurious accuracy of keeping high-order terms and simultaneously neglecting interference terms of the same order of magnitude, as was pointed out in the second-order calculation giving (26.26) and (26.27).

If the perturbation is explicitly time dependent in addition to the switching function $g(t)$, the results are modified. Let the new time dependence be expressed as a Fourier integral so that

$$V_S(t) = g(t) \int_{-\infty}^{\infty} V_0(\omega) e^{-i\omega t} \frac{d\omega}{2\pi} . \tag{26.30}$$

Because $V_S(t)$ is necessarily real,

$$V_0(\omega) = V_0^*(-\omega) . \tag{26.31}$$

The term

$$V_+(\omega,t) = V_0(\omega) e^{-i\omega t} , \qquad \omega > 0 , \tag{26.32}$$

is called a positive frequency part of $V_S(t)$. To every positive frequency part corresponds a negative frequency part of equal magnitude

$$\begin{aligned} V_-(\omega, t) &= V_0(-\omega) e^{i\omega t} \\ &= V_0^*(\omega) e^{i\omega t} . \end{aligned} \tag{26.33}$$

We now consider the effect of a single Fourier component of V, say a positive frequency component, in producing transitions. The only change which occurs in (26.14) is the inclusion of an extra exponential factor. This equation becomes

$$\begin{aligned} \langle E_f, \alpha_f'|T/2, 1\rangle = \frac{1}{i\hbar} \int_{-T/2}^{T/2} dt' \exp\left[\frac{i}{\hbar}(E_f - E_i - \hbar\omega)t'\right] \\ \times \langle E_f, \alpha_f'|V_0(\omega)|E_i, \alpha_i'\rangle . \end{aligned} \tag{26.34}$$

On carrying out the integration over t' we now obtain the δ-function

$$2\pi\hbar\delta(E_f - E_i - \hbar\omega)\,.$$

This shows that in first order the transition amplitude vanishes unless the final energy is greater than the initial energy by one quantum. The perturbation V_+ describes the *absorption* of energy by the system. In a similar way V_- describes the *emission* of energy by the system.

Proceeding just as before we obtain

$$W_{fi}^{(1)} = \frac{1}{\hbar^2}\,|\langle f|V_0(\omega)|i\rangle|^2 2\pi\hbar\,\delta(E_f - E_i - \hbar\omega)T \tag{26.35}$$

as the total transition probability. Again, we divide by T to get a transition probability per unit time, and again we have a δ-function which must be integrated out. There are now three possibilities. The initial energy, or the final energy, or the quantum energy may be an element of a continuum. (Combinations are also possible.) We have seen that a continuum of final states leads to a factor ρ_f, the density of final states. We now discuss what happens when the initial and final states of the system are discrete, but the perturbation is continuous in ω, as when an atom makes a transition between two bound states.

$V_0(\omega)$ describes the coupling of the system to the perturbing field. It is therefore of the form of a field amplitude times a displacement of the system. Therefore, $|V_0(\omega)|^2$ is proportional to the square of a field amplitude, which, in general, is in turn proportional to the energy density of the field. (A specific illustration of these remarks occurs in Section 27 where the absorption of light by atoms is described.) The factor that replaces ρ_f in making the integration over ω is therefore the spectral distribution of the perturbation, suitably normalized. Thus, if we write

$$V_0(\omega) = F(\omega)\,d\,, \tag{26.36}$$

where $F(\omega)$ is the field amplitude, and d is the displacement of the system, we may write

$$\begin{aligned} w_{fi}^{(1)} &= \frac{1}{\hbar^2}\,|\langle f|d|i\rangle|^2 \int\frac{d\omega}{2\pi}\,2\pi\hbar\,\delta(E_f - E_i - \hbar\omega)\,|F(\omega)|^2 \\ &= \frac{1}{\hbar^2}\,|\langle f|d|i\rangle|^2 \left|F\left(\frac{E_f - E_i}{\hbar}\right)\right|^2. \end{aligned} \tag{26.37}$$

The procedure just given is justified only when the various Fourier components of the perturbation can be treated as independent. If the perturbation consists of a pulse whose duration is not very long compared with the characteristic time $\hbar/(E_f - E_i)$, this condition is clearly not satisfied. In such a case the transition amplitude must be integrated over ω before being squared.

If the times involved are long, the cross terms average to zero, and (26.37) results.

By considering negative frequency parts ($\omega < 0$), we can find the probability for emission. Only *stimulated* emission can be found in this way. An atom, for example, can radiate spontaneously in the absence of any perturbation. This is discussed in Section 27. The probability per unit time is the same for stimulated emission and stimulated absorption.

Higher-order processes can occur. They correspond to the emission and absorption of additional quanta of energy. They contain higher powers of $|V_0|^2$ than does the first order, and therefore depend on the energy density of the perturbing field in a nonlinear way. Such effects as two quantum jumps have been calculated and observed. We do not discuss them here.

Equation (26.9) can be given a graphical interpretation. In taking the scalar product with the state $|f\rangle$ it becomes

$$\langle f|t, n\rangle = \left(\frac{1}{i\hbar}\right)^n \int_{t_0}^{t} dt' \int_{t_0}^{t'} dt'' \cdots \int_{t_0}^{t^{(n-1)}} dt^{(n)} \times \langle f|V(t')V(t'') \cdots V(t^{(n)})|i\rangle . \tag{26.38}$$

The nth order contribution to $\langle f|t\rangle$ can be viewed as arising from n successive interactions at times $t^{(n)}, t^{(n-1)}, \ldots, t'$. The system is prepared in the eigenstate $|i\rangle$ of the unperturbed Hamiltonian at time t_0. It develops in time according to the unperturbed equations of motion until time $t^{(n)}$ when the perturbation acts to change the state. From time $t^{(n)}$ to time $t^{(n-1)}$ the system again develops according to the unperturbed Hamiltonian when the perturbation again acts to change the state. This goes on until the perturbation has acted n times.

On a graph with t drawn vertically, the perturbation series is represented by a series of paths. Each line segment represents a development described by H_0, each corner an effect of the perturbation V. Because each time $t^{(l)} \leqslant t^{(l-1)}$, the lines have no downward component. The "scatterings" are ordered in time.

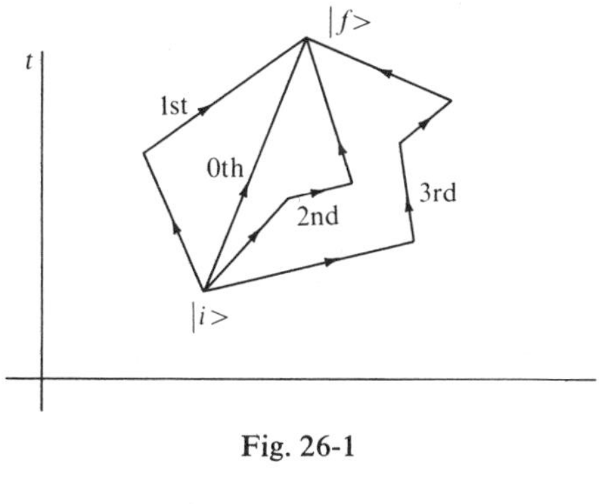

Fig. 26-1

The expression (26.38) can be written in a more symmetrical form by introducing a time-ordering operator P. The operator P has the effect of ordering all quantum mechanical operators following it according to the time at which they act. Thus,

$$
\begin{aligned}
P[V(t')V(t'')] &= V(t')V(t'')\,, \qquad t' > t''\,, \\
&= V(t'')V(t')\,, \qquad t' < t''\,.
\end{aligned} \tag{26.39}
$$

Using P, we may write

$$
\begin{aligned}
\langle f\,|t, n\rangle = \frac{1}{n!}\left(\frac{1}{i\hbar}\right)^n \int_{t_0}^{t} dt' \int_{t_0}^{t} dt'' \cdots \int_{t_0}^{t} dt^{(n)} \\
\times \langle f\,|P[V(t')V(t'')\cdots V(t^{(n)})]\,|i\,\rangle\,.
\end{aligned} \tag{26.40}
$$

The factor $\frac{1}{n!}$ is needed because (26.40) is symmetric in the n variables t', . . . , $t^{(n)}$, but only one ordering of these variables appears in (26.38). This form is particularly useful in quantum field theory.

27. ABSORPTION AND EMISSION OF LIGHT

The processes of absorption and emission of light by atoms and molecules are complicated ones whose complete description requires the application of quantum mechanics to the electromagnetic field. Fortunately, a great deal of information can be obtained treating the field classically except at one point. It will be necessary to use the Planck law for the distribution of frequencies in black body radiation, a non-classical result which follows from the existence of quanta of electromagnetic energy.

The idea is the following. Time-dependent perturbation theory can be used to describe the absorption of light by an atom. There is no "spontaneous" absorption because of energy conservation. The inverse of this process is stimulated emission of light by an atom. However, an atom can emit light even when it is in the dark, so there is spontaneous emission. In a thoroughgoing quantum description, the electromagnetic field is subject to uncertainty relations so that even in the "dark" the electric field does not vanish but has quantum fluctuations. These fluctuations provide the perturbation which stimulates the spontaneous emission. Instead of going through the details of such a calculation we can, following Einstein, develop a relation between spontaneous and stimulated emission which is necessary for thermal equilibrium in a cavity at a definite temperature. This enables us to evaluate the probability for spontaneous emission of light by an atom in an excited state.

According to the Planck law, the energy density of electromagnetic radiation in a cavity at temperature T due to light of frequencies between ω and $\omega + d\omega$ is

$$u(\omega, T)\, d\omega = \frac{\hbar\omega^3\, d\omega}{\pi^2 c^3}\left(\exp\frac{\hbar\omega}{kT} - 1\right)^{-1} . \tag{27.1}$$

This equilibrium situation requires that each atom in the cavity emit and absorb quanta of frequency ω with equal probability, according to the principle of detailed balance. Consider two states of an atom with energies E_{I} and $E_{\mathrm{II}} = E_{\mathrm{I}} + \hbar\omega$. According to (26.20) the transition probability $\omega_{\mathrm{II,I}}$ from state I to state II is, in first order, proportional to the square of the strength of the perturbation. As we see later, this strength is proportional to the electric field **E**, and so the transition probability is proportional to the density of electromagnetic energy at the atom. Therefore, we write

$$\omega_{\mathrm{II,I}} = Bu . \tag{27.2}$$

For downward transitions, however, we must add in the spontaneous transition probability. Note the assumption that probabilities, not probability amplitudes, are to be added. This is a consequence of a complete quantum theory. Hence

$$\omega_{\mathrm{I,II}} = Bu + A . \tag{27.3}$$

The transition probabilities (27.2) and (27.3) assume that the atom is in the appropriate initial state. In thermal equilibrium, the relative probabilities of two states of a system being found are related by the Boltzmann factor

$$\frac{N_{\mathrm{I}}}{N_{\mathrm{II}}} = \exp\left[-\frac{E_{\mathrm{I}} - E_{\mathrm{II}}}{kT}\right]. \tag{27.4}$$

Thus, the equality of probability of upward and downward transitions requires

$$\begin{aligned} N_{\mathrm{I}}\omega_{\mathrm{II,I}} - N_{\mathrm{II}}\omega_{\mathrm{I,II}} &= N\left\{Bu\exp\left[-\frac{E_{\mathrm{I}}}{kT}\right] - (Bu + A)\exp\left[-\frac{E_{\mathrm{II}}}{kT}\right]\right\} \\ &= 0 . \end{aligned} \tag{27.5}$$

This may be solved for u:

$$\begin{aligned} u(\omega, T) &= \frac{A}{B}\left[\exp\frac{E_{\mathrm{II}} - E_{\mathrm{I}}}{kT} - 1\right]^{-1} \\ &= \frac{A}{B}\left(\exp\frac{\hbar\omega}{kT} - 1\right)^{-1} . \end{aligned} \tag{27.6}$$

Comparing this with the Planck law we see that

$$A = \frac{\hbar\omega^3}{\pi^2 c^3} B . \tag{27.7}$$

This result is independent of temperature, of the number of atoms, etc. It depends only on the frequency and on universal constants. It can, therefore, be assumed to apply in the absence of thermal equilibrium. The weakness of this derivation lies in the assumption of Planck's law. A rigorous derivation of this law requires a quantum treatment of the field.

We now calculate B using time-dependent perturbation theory. We consider a plane polarized light wave with electric vector given by

$$\mathbf{E} = \mathbf{E}_0 \cos (\mathbf{k} \cdot \mathbf{r} - \omega t) , \tag{27.8}$$

where

$$k^2 c^2 = \omega^2 . \tag{27.9}$$

Associated with $\mathbf{E}$ is a magnetic field $\mathbf{B}$ of equal magnitude. The coupling of an electron to the magnetic field is through the factor ev/c, and for slowly moving electrons it may be neglected. We further consider only light waves for which the wavelength $\lambdabar = c/\omega$ is large compared with the atomic radius, so that $\mathbf{E}$ may be considered constant over the entire volume of the atom. For optical transitions these conditions are well satisfied. Thus we write

$$V_0(\omega) = -\mathbf{E}_0 \cdot \mathbf{d} \cos \omega t = -\tfrac{1}{2}\mathbf{E}_0 \cdot \mathbf{d}(e^{i\omega t} + e^{-i\omega t}) , \tag{27.10}$$

where $\mathbf{d}$ is the electric dipole moment of the atom. Often only one electron is involved in a transition. Then

$$\mathbf{d} = e\mathbf{r} , \tag{27.11}$$

where $\mathbf{r}$ is the coordinate vector of the electron involved.

This form of $V_0(\omega)$ is just that considered in (26.36). The results of that section may be immediately applied. The amplitude $F(\omega)$ is to be identified with the coefficient of $e^{-i\omega t}$ in the expression for the electric field strength, namely $-\frac{1}{2}E_r$. The displacement d is to be identified with the component d_r of the atomic dipole moment. As the incident light is collimated and plane polarized, there is only one component of $\mathbf{E}$ present, and, therefore, only one component of $\mathbf{d}$ is involved in the transition. According to (26.37),

$$\omega_{fi} = \frac{1}{\hbar^2} | \langle f | d_r | i \rangle |^2 \left| \frac{E_r}{2} \right|^2 \tag{27.12}$$

To evaluate the Einstein coefficient B, $|F|^2 = |-\frac{1}{2}E_r|^2$ must be expressed in terms of the energy density of an unpolarized, isotropic radiation field with the same value of $|E_r|^2$ on the average.

The energy density in an unpolarized, isotropic radiation field in the frequency range $d\omega/2\pi$ is, on the average,

$$\frac{1}{2}\frac{1}{8\pi}[\mathbf{E}^2(\omega) + \mathbf{B}^2(\omega)] ,$$

where $\mathbf{E}^2(\omega)$, $\mathbf{B}^2(\omega)$ are peak values. The magnetic and the electric contributions are equal, so using the assumed isotropy and recalling that the energy density U defined by the Planck law (27.1) is per frequency interval $d\omega$, not $d\omega/2\pi$, we have

$$U = \frac{1}{32\pi^2}(2\mathbf{E}^2) = \frac{3}{16\pi^2}E_r^2, \tag{27.13}$$

where E_r is any one component of $\mathbf{E}$. Thus

$$E_r^2 = \frac{16\pi^2}{3}U.$$

In an isotropic radiation bath, all components of $\mathbf{E}$ are effective, and so all components of $\mathbf{d}$ must be considered. Thus, with

$$\omega_{fi} = B_{fi}U$$

by definition, we finally obtain

$$B_{fi} = \frac{4\pi^2}{3\hbar^2}|\langle f|\mathbf{d}|i\rangle|^2. \tag{27.14}$$

The rate of absorption or of stimulated emission is given by (27.14). The rate of spontaneous emission is then obtained from (27.7) and (27.14). A_{fi} is the probability per unit time that the atom will make a transition from state $|i\rangle$ to state $|f\rangle$ emitting a quantum of frequency in the range $d\omega$ about the value $\omega = (E_i - E_f)/\hbar$. It is given by

$$A_{fi} = \frac{4\omega^3}{3\hbar c^3}|\langle f|\mathbf{d}|i\rangle|^2. \tag{27.15}$$

There are many important consequences of this result. In particular, *selection rules* and *sum rules* can be derived from (27.14) and (27.15).

Selection rules are usually consequences of symmetries. The important selection rules of spectroscopy follow from conservation of angular momentum and parity in electromagnetic interactions. In the process of light emission and absorption, the angular momentum which is conserved includes that of the light, and the parity is that of the atom plus whatever light quanta are present. For the electric dipole transitions considered here, both the angular momentum and the parity of the atom change.

The Hamiltonian H_0 of the atom without the light wave is invariant under rotation. The interaction V between the atom and a light wave is not invariant under rotation unless the electric field of the light wave is rotated also. The same is true for reflection in the origin. Rotating or reflecting the electric field **E** is, in our semiclassical treatment, equivalent to rotating or reflecting the quantized radiation field.

The interaction term V is independent of electron spin, and therefore commutes with $\mathbf{S}^2$, the square of the total spin. It also commutes with each component of **S**, but as these components do not commute with H_0 in the presence of spin-orbit coupling, this is of little interest. The act of emitting or absorbing a light quantum does not change the spin of the atom. We arrive at the first electric dipole selection rule.

$$\Delta S = 0 \,. \tag{27.16}$$

From now on we ignore the presence of spin.

Under reflection the electric dipole moment of the atom, **d**, changes sign. Therefore, the state $d_a|i\rangle$ has parity opposite to that of $|i\rangle$.

$$\begin{aligned} P\, d_a|i\rangle &= P\, d_a P^{-1} P|i\rangle \\ &= -\, d_a P|i\rangle \,. \end{aligned} \tag{27.17}$$

This yields a second selection rule. In an electric dipole transition, the parity of the atomic state must change. This is called *Laporte's rule*. The parity is given by the parity of the total orbital angular momentum L. Therefore, this rule can be stated as

$$\Delta L = \text{odd integer} \,. \tag{27.18}$$

Under rotation the electric dipole moment transforms like the vector it is. We may write

$$R\, d_a R^{-1} = \sum_b D_{ab}{}^{(1)}(R)\, d_b \,. \tag{27.19}$$

The $D_{ab}{}^{(1)}$ is a 3×3 matrix and therefore is appropriately labelled by the index $j = 1$. $D_{ab}{}^{(1)}$ is equivalent to the matrix $D_{mm'}{}^{(j)}$ of (19.30) with $j = 1$. Under this same rotation the state $|i\rangle = |L_i, M_i, \gamma_i\rangle$ becomes

$$R|L_i, M_i, \gamma_i\rangle = \sum_{M_i'} D_{M_iM_i'}{}^{(L_i)}|L_i, M_i', \gamma_i\rangle \tag{27.20}$$

according to (19.30). Thus, the effect of a rotation on the state $d_a|i\rangle$ is the same as the effect of this rotation on the product of two states, one with angular momentum unity, the other with angular momentum L_i. The resultant angular momentum of this combination can be $L_i + 1$, L_i, or $L_i - 1$. If $L_i = 0$, however, the only possible resultant is unity. The matrix element $\langle f|\, d_a|i\rangle$ will therefore vanish unless

$$\begin{aligned} L_f &= L_i + 1, \quad L_i, \quad \text{or } L_i - 1; \qquad L_i \neq 0 \,, \\ &= 1 \qquad\qquad\qquad\qquad\qquad ; \qquad L_i = 0 \,. \end{aligned} \tag{27.21}$$

The selection rule (27.21) can be combined with the selection rule (27.18) to yield the general electric dipole selection rule

$$\Delta L = \pm 1 \,. \tag{27.22}$$

A generalization of this rule, when the interaction can cause spin changes, but when the interaction is still given by the scalar product of a vector (such as **d**) describing the atom with a vector (such as **E**) describing the field, is

$$\begin{aligned} \Delta J &= \pm 1, 0\,, \\ J = 0 \text{ to } J &= 0 \text{ forbidden}\,. \end{aligned} \tag{27.23}$$

This must be supplemented by a parity selection rule. If the vector describing the atom is a polar vector, the parity must change. If it is an axial vector (pseudovector), the parity must not change. The latter occurs in magnetic dipole transitions.

To investigate the polarization of the light emitted or absorbed during a particular atomic transition we write the electric field **E** in the form

$$\mathbf{E} = [A_1\mathbf{e}_x + A_2\mathbf{e}_y + A_3\mathbf{e}_z]e^{-i\omega t} + \text{complex conjugate}\,. \tag{27.24}$$

Here A_1, A_2, and A_3 are complex numbers which determine the amplitude and phase of the possible components of **E**. The interaction with the atom then takes the form

$$-\mathbf{E}\cdot\mathbf{d} = -\mathbf{A}\cdot\mathbf{d}e^{-i\omega t} - \mathbf{A}^*\cdot\mathbf{d}e^{i\omega t}\,, \tag{27.25}$$

where **A** is the vector with complex components A_1, A_2, A_3. The factor **d** is real.

For a transition with $E_f = E_i + \hbar\omega$ (absorption), only the first term contributes as we saw in (26.34). If, in addition, $M_f = M_i + 1$, the matrix elements of d_z and of $(d_x - id_y) = d_-$ vanish. This happens because $d_z|L_iM_i\rangle$ is a state with M-value M_i and $(d_x - id_y)|L_iM_i\rangle$ is a state with M-value $M_i - 1$, since d_z transforms under rotation like $\Omega_{1,0}$ and $(d_x - id_y)$ like $\Omega_{1,-1}$. Thus, only the combination $d_+ = -(d_x + id_y)$ has a finite matrix element. Under these conditions, then,

$$\begin{aligned} -\langle f|\mathbf{E}\cdot\mathbf{d}|i\rangle &= -\mathbf{A}\cdot\langle f|\,\mathbf{d}|i\rangle \\ &= \tfrac{1}{2}A_-\langle f|\,d_+|i\rangle\,. \end{aligned}$$

We can now consider several cases. Let the absorbed light be travelling in the $+z$ direction so that $A_3 = 0$. If $A_2 = -iA_1$, $A_- = 0$ and the matrix element vanishes. However $A_2 = -iA_1$ gives left circularly polarized light, for taking A_1 real, then

$$\begin{aligned} \mathbf{E} &= A_1(\mathbf{e}_x - i\mathbf{e}_y)e^{-i\omega t} + A_1(\mathbf{e}_x + i\mathbf{e}_y)e^{i\omega t} \\ &= 2A_1(\mathbf{e}_x \cos\omega t - \mathbf{e}_y \sin\omega t)\,. \end{aligned} \tag{27.26}$$

Therefore, the absorption comes entirely from the right circularly polarized component of the light wave. For emission ($E_f = E_i - \hbar\omega$) and $M_f = M_i + 1$, the result is reversed because the relevant time factor is exp $[i\omega t]$. Thus in this transition only left circularly polarized light can be emitted in the $+z$ direction.

With $E_f = E_i + \hbar\omega$ (absorption) and $M_f = M_i + 1$ as before, let the light be travelling the $+x$ direction. Then $A_1 = 0$. The coefficient of A_3 in the matrix element vanishes, so light plane polarized in the z direction is not absorbed. The coefficient of A_2 is finite, so that light plane polarized in the y direction will be absorbed. It can also be emitted if the transition is downward in energy.

If transitions with $M_f = M_i - 1$ are considered, similar arguments lead to similar conclusions.

If the light is not travelling along z or along x but along a direction in the xz plane, elliptically polarized light will be emitted or absorbed. The ellipse degenerates to a line when the propagation is along x, and becomes a circle for propagation along z.

For transitions in which $M_f = M_i$, $E_f = E_i + \hbar\omega$,

$$\langle f|\mathbf{E} \cdot \mathbf{d}|i\rangle = A_3\langle f|\, d_z|i\rangle\,.$$

The light affected must have a z component, and only the z component is involved. Thus, only light polarized in a plane containing the z axis is absorbed. The absorption vanishes when the light is travelling in the z direction.

It will be noted that all the transitions considered here are consistent with assigning an angular momentum component $+\hbar$ along the propagation direction to a right circularly polarized photon. A left circularly polarized photon similarly can be considered to have a component of angular momentum $-\hbar$ in the direction of motion. A photon thus has properties of a particle with $S = 1$. The third polarization state with $M_S = 0$ is, however, lacking.

The matrix elements of the electric dipole moment are restricted by a sum rule. We here derive this rule only for an atom with one "optically active" electron. It can easily be extended to more general atoms. When only one electron participates in the optical transitions we may write

$$\mathbf{d} = e\mathbf{r}\,. \tag{27.27}$$

In the absence of a magnetic field the momentum and velocity are related by

$$\mathbf{p} = m\dot{\mathbf{r}} = \frac{m}{i\hbar}[\mathbf{r}, H]\,. \tag{27.28}$$

The commutation relations between coordinates and momenta imply that

$$\mathbf{r} \cdot \mathbf{p} - \mathbf{p} \cdot \mathbf{r} = 3i\hbar\,. \tag{27.29}$$

Using (27.28) and taking a diagonal matrix element of (27.29) leads to

$$\langle i\,|\mathbf{r}^2H - 2\mathbf{r}H\mathbf{r} + H\mathbf{r}^2|\,i\,\rangle = -\frac{3\hbar^2}{m}\,. \tag{27.30}$$

This may be simplified on introducing a complete set of states $|\,f\,\rangle$, eigenstates of H with eigenvalues E_f.

$$\sum_f \{\,\langle i\,|\mathbf{r}|\,f\,\rangle\,\langle f\,|\mathbf{r}H|\,i\,\rangle - 2\langle i\,|\mathbf{r}|\,f\,\rangle\,\langle f\,|H\mathbf{r}|\,i\,\rangle + \langle i\,|H\mathbf{r}|\,f\,\rangle\,\langle f\,|\mathbf{r}|\,i\,\rangle\,\} = -2\sum_f (E_f - E_i)\,|\,\langle f\,|\mathbf{r}|\,i\,\rangle\,|^2\,.$$

Finally, therefore, we see that the sum of the absolute squares of the matrix elements connecting an arbitrary initial state with any final state is restricted by

$$\sum_f (E_f - E_i)\,|\,\langle i\,|\mathbf{d}|\,f\,\rangle\,|^2 = \frac{3e^2\hbar}{2m}\,. \tag{27.31}$$

This result is called a *dipole sum rule*. It is most interesting when $|\,i\,\rangle$ is the ground state, as all terms on the left are then positive.

28. IDENTICAL PARTICLES

To say that two particles are identical means that any observable associated with the two particles depends on the variables describing the two particles in the same way. By definition, any observable is symmetric in the variables of two (or more) identical particles. Let $X(\xi_1, \xi_2)$ be an observable depending on variables ξ_1 associated with particle 1 and on variables ξ_2 associated with particle 2. Then, if particles 1 and 2 are identical,

$$X(\xi_1, \xi_2) = X(\xi_2, \xi_1)\,. \tag{28.1}$$

If $|\alpha_1', \alpha_2''\rangle$ is an eigenket of X, then so is $|\alpha_2', \alpha_1''\rangle$, and these two eigenkets have the same eigenvalue.

The operation of exchanging the particle indices 1 and 2 is a unitary operation. It is denoted by P_{12}.

$$P_{12}|\alpha_1', \alpha_2''\rangle = |\alpha_2', \alpha_1''\rangle\,. \tag{28.2}$$

Because $X(\xi_1, \xi_2)$ is necessarily symmetric in ξ_1 and ξ_2,

(28.3)
$$[X, P_{12}] = 0 .$$

Further,

(28.4)
$$P_{12}^2 = 1 ,$$

so that P_{12} is also hermitian, as $P_{12}^\dagger = P_{12}^{-1} = P_{12}$. P_{12} is an observable of the system containing the two identical particles 1 and 2. Its eigenvalues are, from (28.4), ± 1. Thus, since P_{12} commutes with all observables constructed out of the individual particle variables, its eigenvalues can be used as an additional label of a state. States of systems containing two identical particles can be chosen to be either symmetric or antisymmetric on interchange of the particle labels. A state's symmetry or antisymmetry is permanent because P_{12} commutes with the Hamiltonian and is a constant of the motion.

If three identical particles are present, there are more complicated permutations of particle indices possible. The square of these new operations need not be unity and the choice is not one between symmetry and antisymmetry alone. For reasons that do not follow from the principles of non-relativistic quantum mechanics, these more complicated symmetries do not occur in nature. All naturally occurring states are either symmetric or antisymmetric on interchange of the indices labelling identical particles. It appears in a relativistic theory that all states involving identical particles are symmetric in particles of integer spin and antisymmetric in particles of half integer spin. Particles of the former type are called *bosons*, of the latter type *fermions*. Deuterons, alpha particles, and pions are bosons, while protons, neutrons, and electrons are fermions.

The exchange operator P_{12} exchanges all the labels associated with the particles 1 and 2. In the coordinate representation it exchanges coordinates, and spins if the particles have spin. It is sometimes useful to introduce other exchange operators which exchange only certain of the single particle labels, such as the spins alone. Under such partial exchange, fermion states can be symmetric and boson states antisymmetric.

Fermions obey the *exclusion principle* of Pauli. Any state of a system containing two fermions is antisymmetric under exchange of the single particle labels specifying the state. The state vanishes, therefore, if the two sets of labels are the same. *Two-fermion states cannot exist with identical sets of single particle labels.* No such restriction applies to bosons. Any number of bosons can be labelled in the same way in a physical state. Electrons are fermions and therefore obey the exclusion principle. This principle accounts for the periodic table of the elements, as successive electrons must be added in unoccupied single particle states. They cannot accumulate in the single particle ground state. Helium atoms are bosons when regarded as single objects. This accounts for many of the unique properties of liquid helium at very low temperatures. (The atoms of helium-3 are fermions, as they contain an odd number of fermion constituents, and liquid helium-3 does not show such properties as superfluidity shown by helium-4.)

We consider several examples of systems containing two identical particles:

(i) *Two electrons in a central field* (*helium atom*). We neglect the interaction of the electrons with each other and consider only their states in the nuclear field. A set of single particle labels is n, l, m_l, m_s, being, respectively, the principal quantum number, the angular momentum quantum number, the z component of orbital angular momentum quantum number, and the z component of spin quantum number. A complete set of states for the system consists of

(28.5) $$|n_1, l_1, m_{l1}, m_{s1}\rangle\, |n_2, l_2, m_{l2}, m_{s2}\rangle\,.$$

Of these, only those which are antisymmetric in the two sets of labels are of physical interest, as for electrons $P_{12} = -1$.

Because the spin has only two states it is easy to consider symmetrical and antisymmetrical spin combinations. It was seen in Section 22 that the two spins can be added to give a total spin $S = 1$ or 0. The former states, of which there are $2S + 1 = 3$, are symmetric in the two spins, the latter being antisymmetric. These states, $|S, m_s\rangle$, are given by

(28.6) $$\begin{aligned} |1, 1\rangle &= |\tfrac{1}{2}\rangle\, |\tfrac{1}{2}\rangle\,, \\ |1, 0\rangle &= \frac{1}{\sqrt{2}}\left(\,|\tfrac{1}{2}\rangle\, |-\tfrac{1}{2}\rangle + |-\tfrac{1}{2}\rangle\, |\tfrac{1}{2}\rangle\,\right), \\ |1, -1\rangle &= |-\tfrac{1}{2}\rangle\, |-\tfrac{1}{2}\rangle\,, \end{aligned}$$

and

(28.7) $$|0, 0\rangle = \frac{1}{\sqrt{2}}\left(\,|\tfrac{1}{2}\rangle\, |-\tfrac{1}{2}\rangle - |-\tfrac{1}{2}\rangle\, |\tfrac{1}{2}\rangle\,\right).$$

The states (28.6) are the *triplet states* and are symmetric. The state (28.7) is the *singlet state* and is antisymmetric.

If the states of the two electron system are classified into singlet and triplet states, we see that the singlet spin state must be combined with symmetric orbital states, and that the triplet spin states must be combined with antisymmetric orbital states.

(ii) *Electron–electron scattering*. This example is the same as (i) except that the external field is absent, so we consider the Coulomb repulsion of the two electrons. The orbital angular momentum is now that of the two electrons about their center of mass, which we take to be at rest. Exchange of the two particles involves the change in sign of the relative coordinate $\mathbf{x}_1 - \mathbf{x}_2$, which is the only relevant coordinate in the center of mass system. Therefore, symmetric orbital wave functions involve even l values, antisymmetric ones odd l values.

The scattering of two electrons in a triplet state can take place only in orbital states of odd l. If the electron motion is initially along the z axis, $m_l = 0$ and the angular part of the wave function involves only $P_l(\cos\theta)$ with odd l. Now,

(28.8)
$$\begin{aligned} P_l(\cos\theta) &= -P_l(-\cos\theta) \\ &= -P_l(\cos(\pi-\theta)), \qquad l \text{ odd} \end{aligned}$$

so that

(28.9)
$$P_l(\cos\pi/2) = 0, \qquad l \text{ odd}.$$

There is no scattering at $\pi/2$ in the center of mass system when the electrons are in a triplet state. In a singlet state only even l values enter and the scattering through $\pi/2$ does not vanish.

(iii) *α-particle–α-particle scattering.* The α-particle has no spin and is, therefore, a boson. The exchange of two α-particles can be looked on as the exchange of four nucleons and therefore results in a factor $(-)^4 = +1$. The relative orbital motion must be in states of even l as only these are symmetric under interchange of the particles. There can be scattering through $\pi/2$ in the center of mass system.

When more than two identical particles are present in a system there are more exchange operators. Any observable is symmetric in the single particle variables and is, therefore, invariant under any permutation of these variables. The operations of permutation of three or more things do not commute in general, so that not all exchange operators can be simultaneously diagonal. We are, however, never interested in complete sets of states labelled by all possible eigenvalues of exchange operators. The states of physical interest are either symmetric or antisymmetric under interchange of two identical particles and linear combinations of symmetric and antisymmetric states do not occur. Exchange operators are, therefore, not observables as the term is used in quantum mechanics. In any physical state, the expectation value of the commutator of any pair of two particle exchange operators vanishes, for acting on a physical state such an operator has the effect of multiplying by ± 1. It is, therefore, consistent with the uncertainty principle to consider only symmetric and antisymmetric states. There exist unphysical states of different symmetries which cannot be expanded in terms of physical states.

Forming symmetrical states is not a difficult problem. A symmetrical state can be formed from any set of one particle states by summing over all assignments of particles to states, there being in general $N!$ such assignments when N identical particles are present. Let the single particle states be labelled by $\alpha^{(\nu)}$, the particles by μ. Then

$$
\begin{aligned}
|\text{sym}\rangle &= |1, \alpha^{(\nu)}\rangle\, |2, \alpha^{(\nu')}\rangle \cdots |N, \alpha^{(\nu''')}\rangle \\
&\quad + |2, \alpha^{(\nu)}\rangle\, |1, \alpha^{(\nu')}\rangle \cdots |N, \alpha^{(\nu''')}\rangle \\
&\quad + \cdots \\
&= \sum_P |1, \alpha^{(\nu)}\rangle\, |2, \alpha^{(\nu')}\rangle\, |3, \alpha^{(\nu'')}\rangle \cdots |N, \alpha^{(\nu''')}\rangle\,.
\end{aligned} \tag{28.10}
$$

Forming antisymmetrical states is formally no harder. One has merely to insert a $\pm$ sign in (28.10), $+$ for every permutation involving the exchange of an even number of pairs of identical particles, -1 for every permutation involving an odd number of exchanges. This can be done by writing the state as a determinant whose elements are single particle states. The rows are labelled by the single particle observables characterizing the single particle states, and the columns by the particles' identifying index. Thus,

$$
|\text{antisym}\rangle = \begin{vmatrix}
|1, \alpha^{(1)}\rangle & |2, \alpha^{(1)}\rangle \cdots & |N, \alpha^{(1)}\rangle \\
|1, \alpha^{(2)}\rangle & |2, \alpha^{(2)}\rangle & |N, \alpha^{(2)}\rangle \\
|1, \alpha^{(3)}\rangle & \vdots & \vdots \\
\vdots & & \\
|1, \alpha^{(N)}\rangle & |2, \alpha^{(N)}\rangle \cdots & |N, \alpha^{(N)}\rangle
\end{vmatrix} \tag{28.11}
$$

This is called a *Slater determinant.* It clearly vanishes unless there are as many distinct single particle states as there are particles, which is the essence of the exclusion principle.

Most fermions of interest have spin $\frac{1}{2}\hbar$. It is impossible to construct an antisymmetrical state out of three such spins, though with two it is possible. A system containing three identical fermions is therefore more difficult to describe than one containing two. The failure of the spin state to be antisymmetric by itself means that no completely symmetrical orbital states are possible.

There are only two distinct ways to combine three spins. They can be combined into a quartet state ($S = \frac{3}{2}$, $2S + 1 = 4$) or into a doublet ($S = \frac{1}{2}$, $2S + 1 = 2$). The former is completely symmetrical and must be combined with a completely antisymmetric orbital state. The latter is neither symmetrical nor antisymmetrical and must be combined with an orbital state of complementary symmetry. We do not go further into this matter here. Group theory, in particular the theory of the symmetric group, is needed to give a compact and usable treatment of these problems.

It is to a large extent arbitrary whether two particles are considered to be identical or not. Consider a system containing two particles with equal masses and charges, each with spin $\frac{1}{2}\hbar$, but one with $s_z = +\frac{1}{2}\hbar$, the other with $s_z =$

$-\frac{1}{2}\hbar$. The Hamiltonian of the system is taken to be independent of the spin. Are the two particles identical or not? One can choose to say that they are identical, but that as they always occupy single particle states with different spin labels, the Pauli exclusion principle puts no restriction on other quantum numbers. One can also choose to regard them as distinct particles, distinguished from each other by the value of s_z. The value of s_z can be regarded as either a label associated with the state occupied by the particle, or as a label associated with the particle, like mass and charge. Only in the former case is s_z an observable of the system represented by a hermitian operator.

In the case of electrons and the label s_z, there is no doubt which is the more useful description. The question arises, whether there are other particles in nature which are regarded as distinct, but which could profitably be regarded as identical particles occupying states carrying a distinguishing label. The answer is in the affirmative. We give a sketch of the ideas involved in such situations.

Let us first return to two electrons occupying states labelled by the eigenvalue of s_z. These states are not independent of each other, for if the coordinate axes are rotated so that the new z axis is not parallel to the original z axis, the original state $|s_z = +\frac{1}{2}\hbar\rangle$ is transformed into a linear combination of $|s_z = +\frac{1}{2}\hbar\rangle$ and $|s_z = -\frac{1}{2}\hbar\rangle$ according to (21.13). If the dynamics of the system does not depend on s_z, this rotation has no dynamical effect and any states mixed by such a rotation must be degenerate. This is so if the Hamiltonian is invariant under the rotation group. We recall from Section 21 that s_z is the generator of an infinitesimal rotation about the z axis, so that our degenerate states are labelled by having one of the generators of rotations, s_z, in diagonal form. Only one can be in diagonal form since the generators of rotations about different axes do not commute.

Experimentally, the properties of the proton and the neutron are very similar, except for the electric charge. The nuclear interactions of proton and neutron, proton and proton, and neutron and neutron, in the same states of spin and orbital angular momentum, appear to be the same. Their masses are also very nearly equal. Can they be regarded as different states of a particle, the *nucleon*, N, labelled by the eigenvalues of a generator of some symmetry group? The symmetry group cannot be the group of rotations as this does nothing to the electric charge. If the proton and neutron states alone are to be transformed into each other by transformations of the group, there must exist a 2×2 unitary matrix which describes this transformation. The obvious choice of a symmetry group is then just that used to transform the spin states of a particle of spin $\frac{1}{2}$, except that its physical interpretation is not taken to consist of rotations in coordinate space but of transformations in a new, two-dimensional space. This group is the unitary unimodular group in two dimensions, denoted by SU(2), described at the beginning of Section 21.

The observable whose eigenvalues distinguish the two states of the nucleon, proton and neutron, is called the 3-component of *isotopic spin*, I_3. This name derives from its similarity with the z component of ordinary spin. The proton state has the eigenvalue $+\frac{1}{2}$, the neutron state the eigenvalue $-\frac{1}{2}$. The usefulness of this description comes from the observed invariance of the Hamiltonian describing strong (nuclear) interactions under rotations in isotopic spin space.

To illustrate the use of isotopic spin, we classify the states of the two nucleon system according to the quantum numbers I, I_3, S, P, which are, respectively, the total isotopic spin quantum number (which corresponds to S, the total ordinary spin), the 3-component of isotopic spin, the total spin, and the parity of the state. The rules for combining isotopic spins are the same as those for combining ordinary spins, both coming from the properties of the group SU(2). Thus we have the following.

I	I_3	S	P	System
1	+1	1	−	p + p
1	0	1	−	p + n
1	−1	1	−	n + n
1	+1	0	+	p + p
1	0	0	+	p + n *A*
1	−1	0	+	n + n
0	0	1	+	p + n *B*
0	0	0	−	p + n

The two states labelled *A* and *B* are the singlet and triplet states of the deuteron, only the latter of which is bound. All these states are antisymmetric on exchange of the two particles, the states $I = 1$ being symmetric under exchange of isotopic spins, those with $I = 0$ being antisymmetric.

There is a connection between the electric charge Q, measured in proton charges e, and the eigenvalue of I_3.

$$Q = \tfrac{1}{2}B + I_3 , \tag{28.12}$$

where B is the number of nucleons in the system. Q is thus dependent on a particular component of the isotopic spin I and is not invariant under rotations in isotopic spin space. The electromagnetic interaction has less symmetry than the strong interaction, a fact which is supposed to explain the mass difference between the neutron and proton, these two particles having different electromagnetic self-energies, i.e., masses. One speaks of a *broken symmetry* in such cases. If the interaction which breaks the symmetry is not too strong, the existence of the symmetry is evident and the classification of states by use of the symmetry is useful. In the case of the Zeeman effect in atoms, the magnetic field breaks the rotational symmetry of the atom in field free space, but the quantum numbers j and m associated with the rotational symmetry are still useful in the weak field case.

From the theory of angular momentum we know that the group of transformations SU(2) has irreducible representations of any integer number of dimensions. The one-dimensional representation corresponds to an isotopic singlet or *isoscalar*, which is invariant under all transformations of the group. The two-dimensional representation is the defining representation of the group. The three-dimensional irreducible representation transforms three states among themselves, these constituting an isotopic triplet or *isovector* with $I = 1$. The two-dimensional representation is realized in nature by the nucleon. Any particle which is to be considered as a realization of the other irreducible representations must be a strongly interacting particle, since only these interactions are known to be invariant under isospin transformations.

While we cannot go into the experimental grounds for the assignments made here, we can state that there exists an isoscalar, the Λ-particle, a second isotopic doublet, the Ξ-particle, and an isotopic triplet or isovector, the Σ-particle. The experimental evidence for these assignments is overwhelming, but belongs in the field of high energy physics.

The assumption of isotopic spin symmetry of strong interactions allows us to replace eight distinct particles by four particles which can occupy various isotopic spin states. These four particles are distinct from each other. One can now ask whether there is a symmetry group which will allow us to consider these four particles, N, Λ, Ξ and Σ, as states of a still more basic particle. This larger symmetry group must contain SU(2) to describe the isotopic spin symmetry, and must possess an eight-dimensional irreducible representation to describe the transformations of the eight states among themselves. There exists more than one possible group, but the most interesting one is SU(3), the group of unitary, unimodular transformations in three dimensions. If the strong interactions are assumed to be invariant under this group of transformations, then the eight baryons listed above all become different states of one particle, the baryon. The mass differences are then to be accounted for by a breaking of this symmetry by some not-very-strong interaction.

The subject of *higher symmetry* (higher than isotopic spin) is too large to be gone into further here. It has been mentioned mainly to illustrate the important point that whether particles are identical or not is to a large extent an arbitrary matter, and to show the natural way that the group concept is related to the existence of identical particles.

29. THE THOMAS–FERMI MODEL

To give a complete description of an atom in its ground state one must give a properly antisymmetrized wave function which satisfies the Schrödinger equation for the atom in question. Even for helium, this is impossible. The self-consistent field methods described briefly in Section 30 give approximate wave functions. For some purposes it is sufficient to know approximately how the electrons are distributed around the nucleus, which amounts to giving an approximation to the square of the wave function. This is done by the Thomas–Fermi model of the atom.

In Section 9 the problem of a particle in a box was discussed. If the box is a cube with edges of length L, the components of **p** parallel to the edges of the box may take on the values

$$p_i = \frac{2\pi\hbar}{L} n_i \,, \tag{29.1}$$

n_i being an integer. If the particles have spin $\frac{1}{2}$, two single particle states correspond to each momentum. The number of states with momentum in the range d^3p is then

$$dN = \frac{2d^3p}{(2\pi\hbar)^3} L^3 \,. \tag{29.2}$$

If all the states with kinetic energy less than E_K are occupied and all those with kinetic energy greater than E_K are empty, the total number of particles present in the volume L^3 is

$$\begin{aligned} N &= \int_0^{(2mE_K)^{1/2}} 4\pi p^2 \, dp \frac{2L^3}{(2\pi\hbar)^3} \\ &= \frac{(2mE_K)^{3/2}}{3\pi^2\hbar^3} L^3 \,. \end{aligned} \tag{29.3}$$

If the entire box is at a potential energy V, the highest energy state which is filled has an energy $E_F = E_K + V$. Expressed as a function of E_F,

$$N = \frac{[2m(E_F - V)]^{3/2}}{3\pi^2\hbar^3} L^3 \,. \tag{29.4}$$

The Thomas–Fermi model of an atom can be described as an assemblage of boxes around the nucleus. The potential of each box is regarded as constant over the volume of the box, being some mean value of the potential due to the nuclear charge Ze and the electrons in the other boxes. The energy E_F is taken to be the same for all boxes so that there is no tendency for electrons to migrate to boxes of lower energy. The potential V is simply $-e\phi$, where ϕ, the electrostatic potential, satisfies Poisson's equation

$$\nabla^2\phi = -4\pi\rho \,. \tag{29.5}$$

The charge density outside the nucleus is $-eNL^{-3}$, N being the particle number given in (29.4)

$$\rho = -e\frac{[2m(E_F + e\phi)]^{3/2}}{3\pi^2\hbar^3}. \tag{29.6}$$

The electrons being discussed are in bound states, so that as $r \to \infty$, ρ must tend to zero. Also, ϕ must tend to zero at least as fast as $1/r$ when $r \to \infty$. Therefore, E_F must vanish. Poisson's equation becomes

$$\nabla^2\phi = \frac{4e^{5/2}(2m)^{3/2}}{3\pi\hbar^3}\phi^{3/2}. \tag{29.7}$$

The desired solution is to behave like Ze/r for small r, and is to vanish faster than $1/r$ for large r, since a neutral atom does not give rise to a Coulomb field. Assuming spherical symmetry, we write

$$\phi(r) = \frac{Ze}{r}f(r) \tag{29.8}$$

and obtain

$$\frac{Ze}{r}\frac{d^2f}{dr^2} = \frac{4e^{5/2}(2m)^{3/2}}{3\pi\hbar^3}\left(\frac{Ze}{r}\right)^{3/2}f^{3/2}. \tag{29.9}$$

On introducing the variable x, through $r = \beta x$, and choosing

$$\beta = \tfrac{1}{2}\left(\frac{3\pi}{4}\right)^{2/3}\frac{\hbar^2}{me^2}Z^{-1/3}, \tag{29.10}$$

equation (29.9) becomes a universal equation independent of Z. Calling $f(r) = f(\beta x) = \chi(x)$, the differential equation for χ is

$$\chi'' = x^{-1/2}\chi^{3/2}. \tag{29.11}$$

The boundary conditions to be satisfied by $\chi(x)$ are

$$\chi(0) = 1, \qquad \chi(\infty) = 0. \tag{29.12}$$

Tables of the solution of (29.11) satisfying these boundary conditions exist.*

If the atom is not neutral but is ionized, one would like a solution $\chi(x)$ which approaches the value z/Z as $x \to \infty$, where z is the net charge of the ion. No such solution of (29.11) exists, as is seen by inspection. Thus, the Thomas–Fermi model does not describe ions in a simple way. The reason is that the number of electrons enters the model only through the boundary condition $\chi(\infty) = 0$. That this makes the atom neutral follows from Gauss' theorem, which may be written as

$$\begin{aligned} q(r) &= -r^2\frac{\partial}{\partial r}\left(\frac{Zef(r)}{r}\right) \\ &= Ze[f(r) - rf'(r)] \\ &= Ze[\chi(x) - x\chi'(x)], \end{aligned} \tag{29.13}$$

*P. Gombas, *Encyclopedia of Physics*, Vol. XXXVI. Springer Verlag, Berlin, 1956.

with $q(r)$ the total charge within a sphere of radius r about the nucleus. If $\chi(\infty) = 0$ it follows that $x\chi'(x)$ also tends to zero for large x and so $q(\infty) = 0$. The best one can do to describe an ion on this model is to consider the Thomas–Fermi equation as meaningful only for a finite range of x, from $x = 0$ to $x = x_0$, where $\chi(x_0) = 0$. Beyond this point, which is a branch point of $\chi^{3/2}$, the model says nothing. The total charge of the ion is

$$ze = -Zex_0\chi'(x_0). \tag{29.14}$$

The boundary of the ion is at $x_0 = 0$. The argument used above to conclude that $E_F = 0$ for neutral atoms no longer applies, and E_F can be adjusted so that the charge density vanishes at x_0. At the boundary, the potential ϕ should be ze/r_0, $(r_0 = \beta x_0)$, so that the equation

$$0 = -e\frac{[2m(E_F + Ze^2/r_0)]^{3/2}}{3\pi\hbar^3} \tag{29.15}$$

leads to

$$E_F = -Ze^2/r_0(z)\,. \tag{29.16}$$

No analogous treatment of a negative ion seems possible because there is no natural cutoff, the charge density never vanishing.

30. VARIATIONAL METHODS

In classical mechanics, the equations of motion of a non-dissipative system can be derived from a variational principle such as Hamilton's principle or the principle of least action. These do not, in general, furnish good starting points for approximation methods. In quantum mechanics, the equations of motion can also be derived from a variational principle, and in this case a useful computational scheme can be based on it. The classical principles are, in most cases of interest, statements of the stationary character of an integral rather than of extremal properties, despite the name "least action." In the case of quantum mechanical ground states, one deals with a minimum value for an integral. For ground states, then, the principle can be used rather directly.

In the coordinate representation the variational principle states that the expectation value of the Hamiltonian H is to be stationary under independent variations of ψ and ψ^* as long as the normalization is maintained. That is,

$$\delta\int\psi^*H\psi\,d(x) = 0 \tag{30.1}$$

for arbitrary $\delta\psi$ and $\delta\psi^*$ for which

(30.2) $$\delta \int \psi^* \psi \, d(x) = 0 \, .$$

This constraint on the variation is most easily accounted for by using a Lagrange multiplier, E, so that the variational principle becomes

(30.3) $$\delta \int \psi^*(H - E)\psi \, d(x) = 0 \, .$$

If H is given as a differential operator, it operates to the right on ψ in (30.3). The coefficient of an arbitrary $\delta\psi^*$ must vanish, which gives the Schrödinger equation for ψ,

(30.4) $$(H - E)\psi = 0 \, .$$

If ψ is varied, terms coming from $H \, \delta\psi$ which involve derivatives of $\delta\psi$ must be integrated by parts until $\delta\psi$ appears only undifferentiated. This causes ψ^* to be differentiated, and in this way the Schrödinger equation for ψ^* is obtained. Because H is hermitian, this equation is the complex conjugate of that for ψ.

The computational usefulness of the variational principle comes from the fact that the Hamiltonian H for physically interesting systems has a lowest eigenvalue. Its expectation value in any state is, therefore, not less than this lowest eigenvalue E_0. If $|\,\rangle$ is any state, not necessarily normalized to unity, it can be expanded in the eigenstates of H:

$$|\,\rangle = \sum_i |E_i, \alpha_i\rangle \langle E_i, \alpha_i|\,\rangle \, .$$

Then,

$$\begin{aligned} \langle\,|H|\,\rangle &= \sum_i \langle\,|H|E_i, \alpha_i\rangle \langle E_i, \alpha_i|\,\rangle \\ &= \sum_i E_i \langle\,|E_i, \alpha_i\rangle \langle E_i, \alpha_i|\,\rangle \\ &\geqslant E_0 \sum_i \langle\,|E_i, \alpha_i\rangle \langle E_i, \alpha_i|\,\rangle \qquad (30.5) \\ &= E_0 \langle\,|\,\rangle \, . \end{aligned}$$

Thus, we get the result that

(30.6) $$E_0 \leq \frac{\langle\,|H|\,\rangle}{\langle\,|\,\rangle} \, ,$$

which holds for any state $|\,\rangle$. If the *trial state* $|\,\rangle$ now is made to depend on some parameters a_j, which we indicate by writing $|a\rangle$, the right side of (30.6) can be minimized with respect to these parameters, thus improving the upper limit on E_0 obtained. By a good choice of the form of $|a\rangle$ and inclusion of enough parameters, very good values for E_0 can be found. The formula is

$$E_0 \leq \text{Min}_a \frac{\langle a|H|a\rangle}{\langle a|a\rangle} . \tag{30.7}$$

This method works only for the ground state, as only there can the inequality (30.5) be established. If one could guarantee that the trial state were orthogonal to the ground state, the method could be used for the first excited state. To do this would require a knowledge of the exact ground state, however, and not just a good approximation to it, so that, in fact, the method is useful only for ground states.

The simplest system to which the variational method has been applied to any effect is the helium atom. Here there is no good starting point for a perturbation calculation, but one has a fairly good form for the wave function in the hydrogen wave function. The scale parameter $a_0' = \hbar^2/mZ_{eff}e^2$ can be used as a variational parameter. Thus, we use a trial wave function

$$\psi = \exp\left[(r_1 + r_2)/a_0'\right] , \tag{30.8}$$

to find the expectation value of the Hamiltonian

$$H = -\frac{\hbar^2}{2m}(\nabla_1^2 + \nabla_2^2) - \frac{Ze^2}{r_1} - \frac{Ze^2}{r_2} + \frac{e^2}{r_{12}} , \tag{30.9}$$

where Z is the actual value of the nuclear charge in contrast to Z_{eff} which appears in a_0'. The integrals are easily carried out and the minimum is found to occur for

$$Z_{eff} = 27/16 , \qquad Z = 2\,(\text{helium}) . \tag{30.10}$$

The value of Z_{eff} is less than 2, reflecting the screening of the nucleus by one electron as seen by the other. The trial function (30.8) does not include any correlations between the electrons. A more elaborate trial function would include such correlations. A summary of the results of variational calculations for helium and two electron ions is given by Bethe and Salpeter.*

Another variational approach is the self-consistent field method of Hartree. As applied to helium, say, it proceeds as follows: Assume a wave function for electron 1, $\psi_1(x_1)$. This leads to a "charge distribution" $e\psi_1^*(x_1)\psi_1(x_1)$ in which electron 2 moves. The problem of the motion of electron 2 in the presence of the nuclear charge and the charge distribution of electron 1 is solved variationally as above. The wave function so found is now used to give a "charge distribution" for the motion of electron 1, and a new wave function for it is found. If the new wave function is close enough to the original assumption,

* H. A. Bethe and E. E. Salpeter, *Quantum Mechanics of One- and Two-Electron Atoms*, Academic Press, New York, 1957.

the solution is self-consistent. If it is not close enough, the process can be continued. This method neglects electron correlations to some extent, and neglects the antisymmetry required of the states of two electrons (including spin). The Hartree–Fock method involves the use of trial functions of the proper symmetry. It is somewhat more complicated and leads to elaborate computations. These methods will not be discussed further.

31. MAGNETIC FIELDS AND SPIN

In Section 20 it was pointed out that angular momentum operators exist which have no classical analogues, operators with half-integer eigenvalues. It is our task in this section to show how the existence of these spin angular momentum operators enables us to describe many features of the energy spectrum of atoms. The first effect of a spin $\frac{1}{2}$ associated with electrons is the doubling of the number of states as counted in the semiclassical picture. Each classical orbit now corresponds to two states with different spins. This we described in Section 28 in connection with the exclusion principle. Here we confine our attention to one electron systems.

The effect of a magnetic field on an atom with a spinless electron is easily found. The Hamiltonian is

$$\begin{aligned} H &= \frac{[\mathbf{p} + (e/c)\mathbf{A}]^2}{2m} + V(r) \\ &= H_0 + \frac{e}{2mc}(\mathbf{p}\cdot\mathbf{A} + \mathbf{A}\cdot\mathbf{p}) + \frac{e^2}{2mc^2}\mathbf{A}^2 . \end{aligned} \tag{31.1}$$

H_0 is the Hamiltonian in the absence of the magnetic field, and the other two terms represent the effect of the field. Here, for the first time, the sign of e matters. We choose $e > 0$ so that the charge on an electron is $-e$. The second of these terms is very small for all attainable fields, having as its coefficient the classical electron radius $r_0 = e^2/mc^2 = 2.80 \times 10^{-13}$ cm. Lengths characteristic of atoms are of the order of magnitude $a = \hbar^2/me^2 \approx 5 \times 10^{-9}$ cm. We therefore neglect this term completely.

The vector potential of a uniform magnetic field $\mathbf{B}$ may be written as

$$\mathbf{A} = \tfrac{1}{2}\mathbf{B} \times \mathbf{r} . \tag{31.2}$$

For this potential

$$\nabla \cdot \mathbf{A} = 0 ,$$

so that

$$\mathbf{p}\cdot\mathbf{A}+\mathbf{A}\cdot\mathbf{p} = 2\mathbf{A}\cdot\mathbf{p} = (\mathbf{B}\times\mathbf{r})\cdot\mathbf{p} = \mathbf{B}\cdot(\mathbf{r}\times\mathbf{p}) = \mathbf{B}\cdot\mathbf{l}\,. \tag{31.3}$$

The Hamiltonian (31.1) is therefore given by

$$H = H_0 + \frac{e}{2mc}\,\mathbf{l}\cdot\mathbf{B}\,. \tag{31.4}$$

The additional term is the energy of a magnetic dipole of moment $\boldsymbol{\mu} = -e\mathbf{l}/2mc$ in a uniform field **B**. This magnetic moment is related to the angular momentum, charge, and mass just as in classical mechanics.

Only one component of **l** enters the energy correction term, the component in the direction of **B**. One component of **l** is chosen to be diagonal in the usual description of central field systems. The additional term is thus automatically diagonal if the z axis is chosen to lie in the direction of **B** and the labels of Section 12 are used. The $2l+1$ levels previously degenerate are split into $2l+1$ equally spaced levels with a separation between adjacent levels of

$$\Delta E = \frac{e\hbar}{2mc}\,B\,. \tag{31.5}$$

This splitting is called the *normal Zeeman effect*. It is usually observed only when **B** is large, as otherwise spin effects mask it. The magnetic moment associated with unit orbital angular momentum, the Bohr magneton, is

$$\mu_0 = \frac{e\hbar}{2mc} = 0.57883\times10^{-8}eV/G\,. \tag{31.6}$$

The normal Zeeman effect for $l = 1$ is also a result of classical mechanics.*

Since energy levels as observed in nature do not follow the normal Zeeman pattern, it is necessary to modify the Hamiltonian. The modification that most accurately reproduces the results of observation is to admit electron spin as an observable of the system and to associate a magnetic moment with this spin.

The spin angular momentum has three components,

$$s_x,\ s_y,\ s_z\,.$$

They follow the usual angular momentum commutation rules which are neatly summed up in

$$\mathbf{s}\times\mathbf{s} = i\hbar\mathbf{s}\,. \tag{31.7}$$

The eigenvalues of any component of **s** are to be $\pm\frac{1}{2}\hbar$, so that the eigenvalue of $\mathbf{s}^2$ is $\frac{1}{2}(\frac{1}{2}+1)\hbar^2 = \frac{3}{4}\hbar^2$. We choose s_z to be diagonal and use its eigenvalues to label the states of an electron if s_z commutes with the Hamiltonian.

* H. A. Lorentz, *Theory of Electrons*, Dover Publications, Inc., New York, 1952.

It is convenient to write

$$\mathbf{s} = \tfrac{1}{2}\hbar\boldsymbol{\sigma}\,, \tag{31.8}$$

where $\boldsymbol{\sigma}$ is the *Pauli spin vector*. Its components obey the rules

$$\begin{aligned} \sigma_k^2 &= 1\,, \\ \sigma_1\sigma_2 &= -\sigma_2\sigma_1 = i\sigma_3 \qquad \text{(cyclic)}\,. \end{aligned} \tag{31.9}$$

The operators σ_k can be represented by 2×2 matrices

$$\sigma_1 = \begin{pmatrix} 0 & 1 \\ 1 & 0 \end{pmatrix}, \quad \sigma_2 = \begin{pmatrix} 0 & -i \\ i & 0 \end{pmatrix}, \quad \sigma_3 = \begin{pmatrix} 1 & 0 \\ 0 & -1 \end{pmatrix}. \tag{31.10}$$

When this form is used, the wave function of the electron must be regarded as a two-component function:

$$\psi = \begin{pmatrix} \psi_1 \\ \psi_2 \end{pmatrix}. \tag{31.11}$$

ψ_1 corresponds to the value $+1$ for σ_3, ψ_2 to the value -1.

The Hamiltonian describing the spinning electron in the central field and the magnetic field is now taken to be

$$H = H_0 + \frac{e}{2mc}\,\mathbf{l}\cdot\mathbf{B} + g\,\frac{e}{2mc}\,\mathbf{s}\cdot\mathbf{B}\,. \tag{31.12}$$

The additional spin term is the energy of a magnetic moment $g\,\dfrac{-e}{2mc}\,\mathbf{s}$ in the field **B**. The factor g is to be determined to fit observation. If the spin were a classical angular momentum, g should be unity and not much new would result. The value of g which works very well is two. This value also results from the Dirac theory of the electron. There are quantum electrodynamic corrections to g, but they are very small. We take $g = 2$.

Writing the Hamiltonian as

$$H = H_0 + \frac{e}{2mc}\,\mathbf{l}\cdot\mathbf{B} + \frac{e}{mc}\,\mathbf{s}\cdot\mathbf{B}\,, \tag{31.13}$$

we see that this also can be diagonalized by choosing the z axis along **B** and using the usual labels but now including s_z or σ_3. We again get a normal Zeeman effect, but each Zeeman level is split in two by the spin term. This is, indeed, observed at strong fields, but for weak fields it does not describe the situation. What is lacking for weak fields is the effect of the internally generated magnetic field of the atom. The electron is moving through an electric field and therefore sees a magnetic field. This field is weak and its effects are negligible in the presence of a strong external field.

The magnetic field seen by the electron can be written, to first order in v/c, as

$$\mathbf{B} = -\frac{\mathbf{v}}{c} \times \mathbf{E} = \frac{\mathbf{v}}{(-e)c} \times \nabla V$$

where V is the central potential. Because the potential is central,

$$\nabla V = \mathbf{r}\left(\frac{1}{r}\frac{dV}{dr}\right).$$

Then,

$$\begin{aligned} \mathbf{B} &= -(m\mathbf{v} \times \mathbf{r})\frac{1}{mec}\frac{1}{r}\frac{dV}{dr} \\ &= \frac{1}{mec}\frac{1}{r}\frac{dV}{dr}\mathbf{l}. \end{aligned} \tag{31.14}$$

The scalar product of this with the magnetic moment due to the spin is the desired interaction energy except for a factor of one half, the Thomas factor. This factor is a result of relativistic kinematics and follows automatically from the Dirac theory. We accept it and write the energy as

$$\begin{aligned} &-\frac{1}{2}\left(\frac{-e}{mc}\mathbf{s}\right)\cdot\left(\frac{1}{mec}\frac{1}{r}\frac{dV}{dr}\mathbf{l}\right) \\ &\qquad = \frac{1}{4m^2c^2}\frac{1}{r}\frac{dV}{dr}\boldsymbol{\sigma}\cdot\mathbf{l}. \end{aligned} \tag{31.15}$$

This term represents *spin-orbit coupling*. When it is present, atomic states cannot be labelled by the value of a component of orbital angular momentum or of spin, for neither of these commutes with the spin-orbit term.

The total angular momentum, $\mathbf{j}$, of the atom is conserved in the absence of an external field. We have

$$\mathbf{j} = \mathbf{l} + \mathbf{s}. \tag{31.16}$$

This leads to

$$\mathbf{j}^2 = \mathbf{l}^2 + \mathbf{s}^2 + 2\mathbf{l}\cdot\mathbf{s}$$

in which $\mathbf{l}\cdot\mathbf{s}$ commutes with each of the other terms. A state of the atom can be labelled by l and j, the quantum numbers associated with $\mathbf{l}^2$ and $\mathbf{j}^2$. The eigenvalue of $\mathbf{s}^2$ is always the same and is therefore not a useful label. From above,

$$\begin{aligned} \mathbf{l}\cdot\mathbf{s} &= \frac{\mathbf{j}^2 - \mathbf{l}^2 - \mathbf{s}^2}{2} \\ &= \tfrac{1}{2}[j(j+1) - l(l+1) - s(s+1)]\hbar^2. \end{aligned} \tag{31.17}$$

If $l \neq 0$, there are two possible values of j according to the rules for adding angular momenta,

(31.18) $$j = l + \tfrac{1}{2}, \quad l - \tfrac{1}{2}, \quad l \neq 0.$$

If $l = 0$, of course $j = \frac{1}{2}$. Then (31.17) gives

(31.19) $$\begin{aligned} \mathbf{l} \cdot \mathbf{s} &= \tfrac{1}{2} l\hbar^2, & j &= l + \tfrac{1}{2}, \\ \mathbf{l} \cdot \mathbf{s} &= -\tfrac{1}{2}(l+1)\hbar^2, & j &= l - \tfrac{1}{2}. \end{aligned}$$

If the atom being considered is hydrogen-like with a pure Coulomb field as a first approximation, the spin-orbit coupling removes the accidental Coulomb degeneracy completely. States with $l = 0$ are unaffected. All other states become doublets with a splitting between components proportional to $(2l + 1)$. Historically it was this doublet structure that led to the introduction of electron spin. If the field is not a pure Coulomb one, the degeneracy is not present but the doublet structure appears in each spinless level other than levels with $l = 0$.

Atomic states for one electron atoms are labelled by n, l, j. In the spectroscopic notation one electron states are labelled by the letters

$$\begin{array}{ccccccc} & s & p & d & f & g & h \ldots \\ l = & 0 & 1 & 2 & 3 & 4 & 5 \ldots \end{array}$$

(the l equivalents are written below). The n-value is prefixed and the j value is written as a subscript. Thus, a state with $n = 3$, $l = 2$, $j = \frac{3}{2}$ is labelled a $3d_{3/2}$ state. When more electrons are present the total orbital angular momentum is denoted by L, the total spin by S, and the grand total by J. A state is labelled

$${}^{2s+1}(L \text{ symbol})_J ,$$

where the L symbol is $S, P, D, F, G, \ldots$ as in the one-electron case except for the capital letters and the spin superscript. This notation assumes that L and S are good quantum numbers, which is not necessarily the case.

Now assume the presence of an external magnetic field. The Hamiltonian is

(31.20) $$H = H_0 + \frac{1}{2m^2c^2} \frac{1}{r} \frac{dV}{dr} \mathbf{s} \cdot \mathbf{l} + \frac{e}{2mc} (\mathbf{l} + 2\mathbf{s}) \cdot \mathbf{B} .$$

For sufficiently small $\mathbf{B}$ the levels can be considered non-degenerate in j, being split by the spin-orbit coupling. The effect of $\mathbf{B}$ is then to shift these levels by an amount equal to the expectation value of the last term.

We have, choosing $\mathbf{B}$ in the z-direction, to evaluate the average of

$$l_z + 2s_z = j_z + s_z$$

in a state in which j is conserved. It is intuitively clear, and it can be shown explicitly, that the average of s_z is proportional to j_z.

(31.21) $$\langle s_z \rangle = (g_L - 1) j_z$$

g_L is the *Landé g-factor*. This says that only the component of **s** parallel to **j** is relevant, the other components averaging out as the non-constant vector **s** precesses about the constant **j**. Thus,

$$\langle s_z \rangle = \frac{\mathbf{s}\cdot\mathbf{j}}{\mathbf{j}^2} j_z .$$

$\mathbf{s}\cdot\mathbf{j}$ is easily evaluated from

$$\mathbf{l} = \mathbf{j} - \mathbf{s} .$$

Squaring this leads to

$$\frac{\mathbf{s}\cdot\mathbf{j}}{\mathbf{j}^2} = \frac{j(j+1) + s(s+1) - l(l+1)}{2j(j+1)} . \tag{31.22}$$

Thus,

$$\begin{aligned}\langle l_z + 2s_z \rangle &= j_z + \langle s_z \rangle \\ &= g_L j_z\end{aligned}$$

with

$$g_L = 1 + \frac{j(j+1) + \frac{3}{4} - l(l+1)}{2j(j+1)} . \tag{31.23}$$

The effect of a weak external magnetic field is thus to split each component of a doublet into $2j + 1$ subcomponents which are equally spaced. The spacing depends on the quantum numbers of the unsplit component through g_L.

$$\Delta E = \frac{e\hbar}{2mc} g_L B .$$

This effect is called the *anomolous Zeeman effect*. The best known example is the splitting of the levels of sodium which give rise to the D lines in the spectrum of that element.

The anomalous Zeeman effect observed in a weak magnetic field gradually changes to a normal Zeeman effect in a strong magnetic field. This transition is called the *Paschen–Back effect*. It can be thought of as a gradual decoupling of the spin and orbital angular momenta as the separate couplings to the external field grow.

32. DIATOMIC MOLECULES

The description of the stationary states of an atom presents, as we have seen in Sections 29 and 30, formidable problems. Here the electrons move in a central field which can be regarded as fixed in space because of the large nuclear mass and which is independent of the electronic state of the atom. Even here, calculations are possible only for the ground state in most cases. A diatomic molecule presents a much more complicated problem. The field of two nuclei is not spherically symmetrical; the nuclei are not fixed in space, their relative motion being governed by the electronic state of the molecule. Molecular states cannot, therefore, be calculated as accurately as atomic states. The problem can be broken down in somewhat tractable parts, however, because of the large ratio of the nuclear to the electronic mass.

Consider a diatomic molecule with zero total linear momentum. The momentum associated with the electrons must be equal in magnitude to that associated with the nuclei. The kinetic energy of the electrons will be roughly M/m times the kinetic energy of the nuclei, M being the nuclear mass and m the electronic mass. This suggests that in the total Hamiltonian of the system, the kinetic energy of the relative nuclear motion be neglected at first, the problem of the electronic motion being solved when the nuclei are held fixed at a separation R.

The total Hamiltonian is

$$\begin{aligned} H &= H_N + H_e \\ H_N &= K_N + \frac{Z_a Z_b e^2}{R} \\ H_e &= \sum_i \left\{ K_i - \frac{Z_a e^2}{r_{ai}} - \frac{Z_b e^2}{r_{bi}} \right\} + \sum_{i<j} \frac{e^2}{r_{ij}} . \end{aligned} \tag{32.1}$$

H_N involves only the nuclei. H_e involves the electrons and also the nuclear coordinates since

$$\mathbf{r}_{ai} - \mathbf{r}_{bi} = \mathbf{R} . \tag{32.2}$$

The approximation to be made is to solve first the problem

$$H_e|n\rangle = E_n(R)\,|n\rangle , \tag{32.3}$$

where the nuclear separation R appears as a parameter. The eigenvalue $E_n(R)$ is then regarded as an effective potential for the nuclear motion, and the total energy of the molecule is the eigenvalue $E_{n\gamma}$ obtained from the equation

$$(H_N + E_N(R))\,|\gamma\rangle = E_{n\gamma}|\gamma\rangle . \tag{32.4}$$

γ is a complete set of labels for the nuclear motion. This approximation, known as the Born–Oppenheimer approximation, can be described semiclassically by saying that the nuclear motion is so slow, because of the large nuclear mass, that the electronic state can adapt itself continuously to the changing internuclear distance without making transitions between electronic levels. It is, therefore, an adiabatic approximation. The quantum mechanical criterion for its validity is that the energy spacing of the states of nuclear motion should be very small compared with the spacing between electronic levels.

Carrying out the first part of the Born–Oppenheimer approximation leads rapidly into complicated numerical calculations. The only feasible methods involve the use of the variational principle and so are restricted to electronic ground states. A comprehensive account of the methods which can be used is given by Slater.* Here we give a brief outline of the two principle methods.

The first method approximates the wave function by a product of *atomic orbitals*. An atomic orbital for one electron is a function of the form of an atomic wave function, but perhaps containing parameters not present in the original function. For example, in the molecule H_2, an atomic orbital for one electron would be $\exp[-r/a]$. This has the form of a ground state wave function for the hydrogen atom, but a is not necessarily the Bohr radius of hydrogen. The wave function for the two electrons in H_2 can then be approximated by

$$\exp[-(r_{a1} + r_{b2})/a]$$

where r_{a1} is the separation of electron 1 from proton a, and r_{b2} is the separation of electron 2 from proton b. This function may be generalized by including spin factors and by antisymmetrization. It is used in a variational calculation to determine the lowest value for H_e for any given nuclear separation.

The second method is called the molecular orbital method. It is the molecular analogue of the Hartree–Fock method described in Section 30. The molecular orbitals are functions possessing any symmetry which is imposed by the known molecular structure. These are then used in a self-consistent field calculation. Often the molecular orbitals are constructed of linear combinations of atomic orbitals which have the molecular symmetry (LCAO method), but this is not necessary. For a diatomic molecule there is axial symmetry. The wave function can be chosen to have a definite value of the component of angular momentum along the internuclear axis, being thus an eigenfunction of the operator generating rotations about this axis. For more complicated molecules, such as benzene, the consequences of the symmetry of the molecule are much less obvious.

There is only one orbital angular momentum quantum number for the electronic state relative to the fixed nuclei, that corresponding to the component along the internuclear axis. Because no direction along this axis is

* J. C. Slater, *Quantum Theory of Molecules and Solids*, McGraw-Hill, New York, 1963, Vol. I.

preferred, the component can be chosen to have a non-negative value which is written $\Lambda\hbar$. Λ has values 0, 1, 2, ... Λ is similar to the quantum number L of the total orbital angular momentum in an atom. States with $\Lambda = 1, 2, 3$ are denoted Σ, Π, Δ states, this being the Greek equivalent of S, P, D. All states except that with $\Lambda = 0$ are doubly degenerate at this stage of the approximation. If the two nuclei are alike, which means of equal charge as here the nuclear mass is irrelevant, the operation of reflection in the plane bisecting the molecule is a symmetry operation which has eigenvalues ± 1. Electronic states with the eigenvalue $+1$ are labelled with the subscript g (for the German gerade), and those with -1 by u (ungerade). This quantum number exists for molecules such as H_2 and HD, but not for molecules like NO.

If $E_n(R)$ is known, the states of nuclear motion can be found. This is a three-dimensional problem, so the nuclear motion can involve orbital angular momentum of the nuclei. This can be treated simply only when $\Lambda = 0$, as only then is the nuclear angular momentum separately a constant of the motion. According to the Born–Oppenheimer approximation, Λ is conserved even when nuclear motion is allowed for, as this is to be so slow that no transitions are caused. When the internuclear axis rotates, a conserved Λ does not correspond to a conserved electronic angular momentum vector. What is conserved is the sum of the electronic and nuclear orbital angular momenta, denoted by $\mathbf{K}$, at least in the absence of spin-orbit coupling. We neglect spin-orbit coupling throughout this discussion. $\mathbf{K}^2$ has eigenvalues $K(K+1)\hbar^2$, and the component of $\mathbf{K}$ along an arbitrary z axis has as eigenvalues integer multiples of $\hbar$.

When the molecular state is not one with $\Lambda = K = 0$, the energy depends on the sense of the electronic angular momentum about the internuclear axis, and the degeneracy of the states with $\Lambda \neq 0$ is removed. This is called Λ-doubling.

We now consider the radial motion of the nuclei. For there to be bound states of the nuclei, the eigenvalues $E_n(R)$ must have a minimum for some value of R, say R_n, at least for some electronic states. R_n then gives the molecular size. A minimum occurs when the electronic wave function is large between the nuclei, as in this case the attraction of the negative charge distribution between the nuclei can overcome the nuclear repulsion, since the opposite charges are closer than the like charges, until the nuclei get so close that there is no room for the electrons in between. In H_2, the electron wave function can be large in the middle only in the even state. When $\Lambda = 0$, this must be a singlet state to satisfy the exclusion principle. The ground state of H_2 is a singlet state, the triplet state with $\Lambda = 0$ not being bound.

There are three separate kinds of energy levels which occur in molecules. First are the electronic levels. Their spacings are of the same order of magnitude as the spacings of atomic levels, and transitions between them give radiation in the visible or near it. Next are the vibrational levels. These are closer together if the Born–Oppenheimer approximation is to be valid, and transitions between them lie in the infra-red. Third are the rotational levels, levels which differ only in the eigenvalues of $\mathbf{K}^2$. The spacings of these levels are close because of the large molecular moment of inertia, $\frac{1}{2}MR_n^2$, which occurs in the denominator of the kinetic energy of rotation. Observed transitions involve these levels in all combinations, the close lying rotational levels giving the spectra the character of band spectra. A complete description of these spectra is given by Herzberg.*

It can happen that the effective nuclear potential curves $E_n(R)$ cross at some value of R, as is shown in Figure 32–1. At this point the two electronic states, labelled 1 and 2 in the figure, become degenerate. This requires a modi-

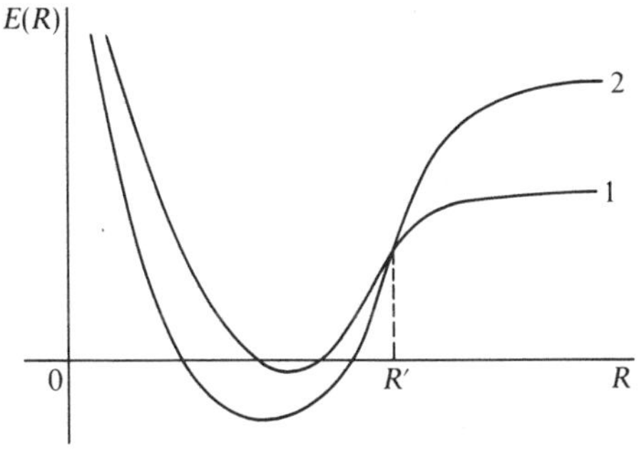

Fig. 32-1

fication of the Born–Oppenheimer approximation. The modification is not hard to make if one can treat the neglected parts of the Hamiltonian as a perturbation connecting these two degenerate states. One introduces the matrix U_0 of Section 24 to diagonalize the perturbation between these two states. The effect is, if oscillation in electronic state 2 becomes highly enough excited to make the vibrational wave function appreciable at R', the vibrational state does not remain pure but is mixed with the vibrational states of about the same energy in electronic state 1. If the nuclear motion is described semi-classically, the nuclear position and velocity are not changed by the mixing, but afterwards the nuclei may move in a different potential. This lack of change in the nuclear motion while the electronic state is changing is called the Franck–Condon principle.

An extreme example of these vibrational–electronic transitions is the phenomenon of predissociation. This occurs when the vibrational state in the electronic potential, $E_2(R)$ of Figure 32–1, is greater than the energy of the highest bound state in the potential $E_1(R)$. In such a situation the molecule

* G. Herzberg, *Molecular Spectra and Molecular Structure*, D. Van Nostrand, New York, 1950, Vol. I.

dissociates "spontaneously," the impetus for the dissociation not having directly caused a transition to an unbound state, but merely having excited a bound vibrational level in the electronic state 2. If the electronic levels have such different symmetries that the perturbation has matrix element zero between them, then, of course, none of this happens.

33. A PARTICLE IN A PERIODIC POTENTIAL

An electron in a crystalline solid can be considered in a certain approximation to be moving in a fixed potential which has the periodicity of the crystal lattice. This is an approximation, because any one electron interacts with the other electrons present so that fundamentally the problem is a many-body problem. So many important features appear in the *single particle approximation*, which we describe here, that this approximation is useful.

A lattice in three dimensions is an array of points whose radius vectors from one of the points as origin are of the form

$$\mathbf{r}_j = \mathbf{a}_1\nu_{1j} + \mathbf{a}_2\nu_{2j} + \mathbf{a}_3\nu_{3j} \tag{33.1}$$

with integer ν_{ij}. The vectors $\mathbf{a}_i$ are assumed to be linearly independent so that the structure is three-dimensional. The vectors $\mathbf{a}_i$ are the *lattice vectors.* A crystal is made by placing atoms or groups of atoms at each lattice point. We choose the vectors $\mathbf{a}_i$ so that they describe the smallest displacements in three different directions which will carry the crystal into itself.

The parallelepiped with $\mathbf{a}_1$, $\mathbf{a}_2$, $\mathbf{a}_3$, as concurrent edges is called a *primitive cell* of the lattice. It is to be distinguished from a *unit cell* which is any parallelepiped out of which the lattice can be constructed by repetition in three directions. The unit cell most often of interest is the smallest one exhibiting the full symmetry of the crystal. It may be a primitive cell.

Whenever one has to deal with sets of non-orthogonal vectors, as the lattice vectors $\mathbf{a}_i$ may be, it is convenient to introduce a second set of vectors which defines a new lattice, the reciprocal lattice. We denote these by $\mathbf{b}_i$ and define them by

$$\mathbf{b}_1 = \frac{\mathbf{a}_2 \times \mathbf{a}_3}{\mathbf{a}_1 \cdot (\mathbf{a}_2 \times \mathbf{a}_3)} \qquad \text{(cyclic)}\,. \tag{33.2}$$

These have the property that

$$\mathbf{a}_i \cdot \mathbf{b}_j = \delta_{ij}\,. \tag{33.3}$$

Thus, if the radius vector $\mathbf{r}$ of a space point is expanded in the form

$$\mathbf{r} = \mathbf{a}_1\xi_1 + \mathbf{a}_2\xi_2 + \mathbf{a}_3\xi_3 \tag{33.4}$$

the components ξ_i are given by

$$\xi_i = \mathbf{b}_i \cdot \mathbf{r}\,. \tag{33.5}$$

Similarly, if a vector **k** is expanded as

$$\mathbf{k} = \mathbf{b}_1\kappa_1 + \mathbf{b}_2\kappa_2 + \mathbf{b}_3\kappa_3\,, \tag{33.6}$$

then

$$\kappa_i = \mathbf{a}_i \cdot \mathbf{k}\,. \tag{33.7}$$

Lastly, the scalar product of **k** and **r** is given by

$$\mathbf{k} \cdot \mathbf{r} = \sum_{i=1}^{3} \kappa_i \xi_i\,. \tag{33.8}$$

If the lattice vectors are likened to kets, the reciprocal lattice vectors are like bras.

We turn now to our physical problem, which is to study the system consisting of a single particle moving in the potential $V(\mathbf{r})$ when $V(\mathbf{r})$ is periodic, so that

$$V(\mathbf{r}) = V\left(\mathbf{r} + \sum_j \mathbf{a}_j \nu_j\right). \tag{33.9}$$

The kinetic energy is independent of the coordinates, so the Hamiltonian H is also periodic with the lattice periods. Let U be the linear operator which is defined by

$$Uf(\mathbf{r}) = f(\mathbf{r} + \Sigma \mathbf{a}_j \nu_j)\,. \tag{33.10}$$

Because the order of making translations does not affect the result, the U's representing any translations commute. Further, if

$$U_1 f(\mathbf{r}) = f(\mathbf{r} + \mathbf{a}_1)\,, \tag{33.11}$$

then

$$U_1^2 f(\mathbf{r}) = f(\mathbf{r} + 2\mathbf{a}_1)\,,$$

etc., so that it is sufficient to consider translations described by U_1, given by (33.11), and by U_2 and U_3, which differ from U_1, only by the replacement of $\mathbf{a}_1$ by $\mathbf{a}_2$ and $\mathbf{a}_3$, respectively. These are denoted by U_j.

The U_j commute with each other and with the Hamiltonian H. A state of the particle can thus be labelled by the eigenvalues of the Hamiltonian and of the U_j.

For an infinite lattice the operators U_j are unitary. This follows from the fact that

$$\int_{-\infty}^{\infty} f^*(\mathbf{r} + \mathbf{a}_j)g(\mathbf{r} + \mathbf{a}_j)\, d^3r = \int_{-\infty}^{\infty} f^*(\mathbf{r})g(\mathbf{r})\, d^3r \tag{33.12}$$

for any functions f and g. If the integral were over a finite domain this would not be true. A unitary operator can be expressed in terms of a hermitian operator in several ways, for example, by

$$U = \exp[i\Gamma], \tag{33.13}$$

or by

$$U = \frac{1 + i\Gamma'}{1 - i\Gamma'},$$

where Γ and Γ' are hermitian. Diagonalizing U is equivalent to diagonalizing Γ or Γ', and $[U, H] = 0$ is equivalent to $[\Gamma, H] = 0$. Thus, the fact that U is unitary rather than hermitian does not preclude our using the eigenvalues of U as labels of states. It will turn out that Γ is really the relevant operator.

The eigenvalue problem to be solved is

$$H|\alpha'\rangle = E|\alpha'\rangle \tag{33.14}$$

together with

$$U_j|\alpha'\rangle = \exp[i\gamma_j]|\alpha'\rangle. \tag{33.15}$$

Let us expand the wave function $\langle x'|\alpha'\rangle$ in a Fourier integral.

$$\langle x'|\alpha'\rangle = \int \frac{d^3\kappa}{(2\pi)^3} w(\kappa) \exp[i\boldsymbol{\kappa} \cdot \mathbf{r}]. \tag{33.16}$$

Here wavenumbers are used instead of momenta, so the usual $2\pi\hbar$ becomes simply 2π. Then,

$$\begin{aligned}\langle x'|U_j|\alpha'\rangle &= \int \frac{d^3\kappa}{(2\pi)^3} w(\boldsymbol{\kappa}) \exp[i\boldsymbol{\kappa} \cdot (\mathbf{r} + \mathbf{a}_j)] \\ &= \exp[i\gamma_j] \int \frac{d^3\kappa}{(2\pi)^3} w(\boldsymbol{\kappa}) \exp[i\boldsymbol{\kappa} \cdot \mathbf{r}],\end{aligned} \tag{33.17}$$

so that

$$\int \frac{d^3\kappa}{(2\pi)^3} w(\boldsymbol{\kappa}) \exp[i\boldsymbol{\kappa} \cdot \mathbf{r}]\{\exp[i\boldsymbol{\kappa} \cdot \mathbf{a}_j] - \exp[i\gamma_j]\} = 0. \tag{33.18}$$

Because the functions $\exp[i\boldsymbol{\kappa} \cdot \mathbf{r}]$ are linearly independent, the integral can vanish only if

$$w(\boldsymbol{\kappa})\{\exp[i\boldsymbol{\kappa} \cdot \mathbf{a}_j] - \exp[i\gamma_j]\} = 0. \tag{33.19}$$

The solution of this is

(33.20) $$w(\boldsymbol{\kappa}) = W(\boldsymbol{\kappa})(2\pi)^3 \prod_{j=1}^{3} \delta(\boldsymbol{\kappa} \cdot \mathbf{a}_j - \gamma_j - 2\pi n_j)\,,$$

where the n_j are integers. Recalling that $\boldsymbol{\kappa} \cdot \mathbf{a}_j$ is the jth component of $\boldsymbol{\kappa}$ in the system of reciprocal lattice vectors, the argument of the δ-function becomes $\kappa_j - \gamma_j - 2\pi n_j$. Inserting (33.20) into (33.15) we see that

(33.21)
$$\begin{aligned}\langle x'|\alpha'\rangle &= \int \frac{d^3\kappa}{(2\pi)^3}\, W(\boldsymbol{\kappa})(2\pi)^3 \prod_j \delta(\kappa_j - \gamma_j - 2\pi n_j) \exp[i\boldsymbol{\kappa} \cdot \mathbf{r}] \\ &= \sum_{n_1,n_2,n_3=-\infty}^{\infty} W_{n_1n_2n_3} \exp[i\Sigma(\gamma_j + 2\pi n_j)\xi_j] \\ &= \sum_{n_1,n_2,n_3} W_{n_1n_2n_3} \exp[i(\mathbf{k} + 2\pi n_j\mathbf{b}_j) \cdot \mathbf{r}] \\ &= \exp[i\mathbf{k} \cdot \mathbf{r}]\chi(\mathbf{r})\,.\end{aligned}$$

Here the expression (33.8) for the scalar product has been used in the first and second steps. $\mathbf{k}$ is the vector with components γ_j in the reciprocal lattice vectors, and thus, in effect, labels the behavior of the state under translation. $\chi(\mathbf{r})$ is a periodic function with the periods of the lattice. Wave functions of the form of the last line of (33.20) are called Bloch wave functions. In the limit of vanishing potential, $\chi(\mathbf{r})$ approaches a constant.

The energy eigenvalues can be investigated easily only when the potential is weak so that perturbation theory may be used, and also in certain special models. We use perturbation theory here. In the absence of a magnetic field the Hamiltonian is real. Thus, if

(33.22) $$\langle x'|\alpha'\rangle = \exp[i\mathbf{k} \cdot \mathbf{r}]\chi(\mathbf{r})$$

is a solution of the Schrödinger equation, then so is

(33.23) $$\langle \alpha'|x'\rangle = \exp[-i\mathbf{k} \cdot \mathbf{r}]\chi^*(\mathbf{r})$$

for the same energy. All states are thus at least doubly degenerate, and the degeneracy may be higher. The states of the unperturbed system, a free particle, are infinitely degenerate because all directions are open to $\mathbf{k}$, the energy depending on $\mathbf{k}^2$ only.

The zero of the energy scale may be chosen so that the average value of $V(\mathbf{r})$ vanishes. Then $V(\mathbf{r})$ may be expanded in a Fourier series

(33.24) $$V(\mathbf{r}) = \sum_{m_1,m_2,m_3} V_{m_1m_2m_3} \exp[i2\pi(m_1\mathbf{b}_1 + m_2\mathbf{b}_2 + m_3\mathbf{b}_3) \cdot \mathbf{r}]$$

with no constant term. This has matrix elements only between states with wave vectors differing by 2π times some reciprocal lattice vector. Thus, the only states of nearly equal energy coupled by $V(\mathbf{r})$ are those for which

$$\mathbf{k}_1 - \mathbf{k}_2 = 2\pi\mathbf{b}' , \tag{33.25}$$

where $\mathbf{b}'$ is some reciprocal lattice vector and

$$E(\mathbf{k}_1) \approx E(\mathbf{k}_2) , \qquad \text{i.e.,} \quad \mathbf{k}_1^2 \approx \mathbf{k}_2^2 . \tag{33.26}$$

These two conditions can be satisfied when

$$\mathbf{k}_1 = \pi\mathbf{b}' - \boldsymbol{\varepsilon} , \qquad \mathbf{k}_2 = -\pi\mathbf{b}' - \boldsymbol{\varepsilon} , \tag{33.27}$$

$\boldsymbol{\varepsilon}$ being small. The first-order energy correction vanishes because the diagonal elements of V are just the average value of V, which vanishes. The second-order correction is given by

$$\begin{aligned} \Delta E(\mathbf{k}_1) &= -\frac{|\langle \mathbf{k}_1|V|\mathbf{k}_2\rangle|^2}{E(\mathbf{k}_2) - E(\mathbf{k}_1)} \\ &= -\frac{|\langle \mathbf{k}_1|V|\mathbf{k}_2\rangle|^2}{2(\hbar^2/m)\mathbf{b}' \cdot \boldsymbol{\varepsilon}} \\ &= -\Delta E(\mathbf{k}_2) . \end{aligned} \tag{33.28}$$

The energy of the lower state is lowered and the energy of the upper state is raised, since for the lower state $\mathbf{b}' \cdot \boldsymbol{\varepsilon}$ is positive, while for the upper state it is negative. We cannot go to the limit $\boldsymbol{\varepsilon} \to 0$ because we have not picked the right linear combinations of unperturbed states to make the numerator vanish in this limit. The effect gets small for large $\boldsymbol{\varepsilon}$.

This effect may be visualized graphically. Let us plot the energy as a function of $|\boldsymbol{\varepsilon}|$ when $\boldsymbol{\varepsilon}$ is along the direction of $\mathbf{b}'$ in the reciprocal lattice. The unperturbed energies are shown as solid curves in Figure 33–1, the perturbed energies as dotted curves. Because the lower energy is always depressed and the higher energy is always raised, the two curves can never meet and there is

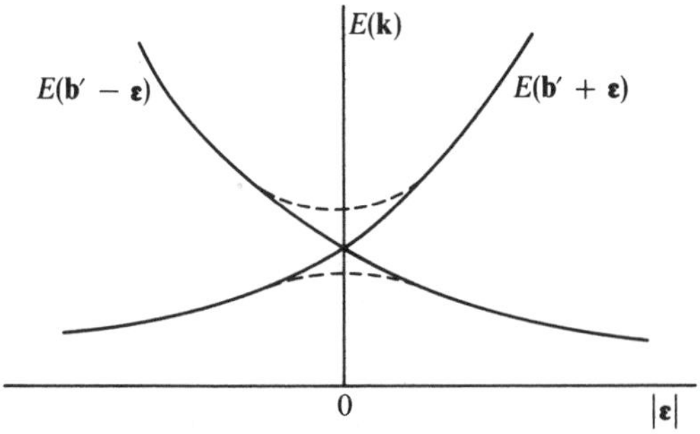

Fig. 33-1

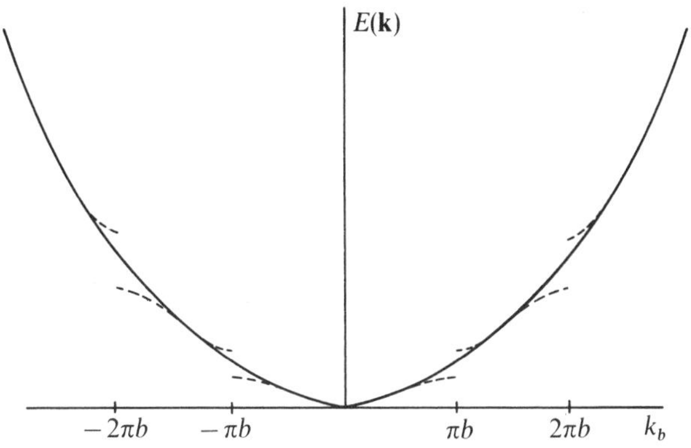

Fig. 33-2

an energy gap. No stationary states exist with energy eigenvalues within this gap. We now plot E as a function of the magnitude of **k** along the direction fixed by **b**′. This is shown in Figure 33–2. The two curves of Figure 33–1 appear on opposite sides of Figure 33–2. At each of the values $n\pi\mathbf{b}$ of $\mathbf{k}_b$ there is a discontinuity in the energy. These values of $\mathbf{k}_b$ are just those which lead to Bragg reflection of the electron wave by the planes of the lattice, since b, the magnitude of the vector **b**′, is the reciprocal of the perpendicular distance between members of a family of lattice planes.

It is possible to add 2π times any reciprocal lattice vector to **k** without affecting the Bloch form of the wave function, though the periodic part χ is of course changed in the process, and, in particular, the simplicity of the free particle wave functions is hidden when this is done in the perturbation theory approach. This is frequently convenient, however, and leads to a *reduced* diagram of the dependence of E on k_b, as shown in Figure 33–3. The lowest branch of the curve in this figure is the same as the lowest part of Figure 33–2. The next branch is obtained by adding or subtracting $2\pi b$ from the k values of the next-to-lowest branch in Figure 33–2, etc.

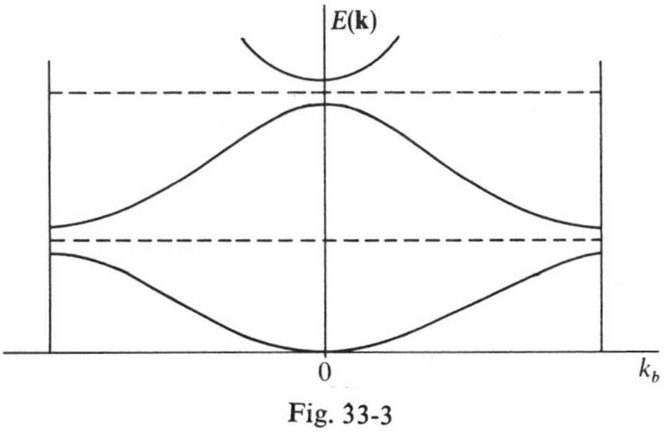

Fig. 33-3

In the three-dimensional space of the wave vector **k** the equation

$$\mathbf{k} \cdot \mathbf{b} = \pi \,, \tag{33.29}$$

which determines the existence of a Bragg reflection, defines a plane. These planes divide the k-space up into *Brillouin zones*. The first Brillouin zone is the region about the origin in k-space bounded by the nearest such planes. The shape of the zone depends on the crystal structure. By subtracting a suitable multiple of a reciprocal lattice vector, the wave vector **k** of any state may be brought into the first Brillouin zone.

When many electrons are present, as in a solid, the periodic potential being so chosen as to approximate the effect on a given electron of all the other electrons as well as of the nuclei, the lowest state of the system will have the energy levels filled in order of ascending energy until all the electrons are accounted for, and all the higher levels remain empty. The energy of the topmost filled level is called the Fermi energy, E_f. The surface defined by

$$E(\mathbf{k}) = E_f \tag{33.30}$$

is the *Fermi surface*. Its experimental determination is an important subject of solid state physics. Because the energy here depends on the direction as well as the magnitude of k, the Fermi surface may have a very complicated structure.

The existence of *bands* of energy levels in a crystalline solid can be arrived at in another way. Above, the potential has been treated as weak and the electrons whose energies are being found are almost free. The energy gaps are narrow. For the electrons which are in low-lying atomic energy levels the presence of the other atoms of the solid has a relatively weak effect. Let us consider N atoms in a symmetrical array. If the interatomic distances are large, the atoms are independent and there are $2N$ electrons in each of $2N$ states, say S-states, all being degenerate. As the atoms are brought closer these degenerate levels are split into N different energies (neglecting spin effects). For large N this set of $2N$ levels is indistinguishable from a band, and would be called an S-band. This approximation is of interest when the electrons are to some extent bound to individual atoms, so that the angular momentum value of the states is not completely lost. This is called the *tight-binding* approximation. It is closely related to the Heitler–London approximation in molecular structure theory.

If an electron is near the bottom of an unoccupied energy band, its energy is a quadratic function of the components of the momentum or wave vector of the electron. If the electron were free this function would be just $p^2/2m$, but in the crystal the energy can depend on the direction of the momentum as well as on its magnitude. It is convenient to write the energy as

(33.31) $$E(\mathbf{p}) = \frac{1}{2}\sum_{ij} \mu_{ij}p_ip_j ,$$

where the p_i are the components of $\mathbf{p}$ as given by (33.6). μ_{ij} is called the *reciprocal mass tensor*, and is symmetric. When E depends only on $\mathbf{p}^2$, this reduces to

(33.32) $$\mu_{ij} = \frac{1}{m^*}\,\delta_{ij} ,$$

and then

(33.33) $$E(\mathbf{p}) = \mathbf{p}^2/2m^* .$$

m^* is called the *effective* mass of the electron.

By a suitable choice of coordinate axes, the energy $E(p)$, given by (33.31), can be reduced to a sum of squares so that the reciprocal mass tensor is diagonal. In a cubic crystal, since there are three equivalent directions the eigenvalues of the reciprocal mass tensor must be equal and there is a single effective mass, m^*. If, however, there is a minimum in $E(\mathbf{p})$ for some non-vanishing $\mathbf{p}_0$, even in a cubic crystal two distinct eigenvalues can appear, as the energy need not depend in the same way on components of $\mathbf{p}$ parallel and perpendicular to $\mathbf{p}_0$. This situation actually occurs in some semiconductors.

34. LATTICE VIBRATIONS

In the previous section, the problem of a particle moving in the potential provided by a fixed, perfect lattice was discussed. An allied problem consists of the description of the small oscillations of the atoms comprising the lattice about their equilibrium positions. Small oscillations of a system about an equilibrium position can be discussed on the basis of classical mechanics. In the classical treatment, the *normal modes* of the system are introduced, the motion corresponding to the excitation of a normal mode being a harmonic motion with a frequency characteristic of the mode. All the atoms of the lattice will be involved in any given normal mode. The feature which distinguishes a regular lattice from an irregular assemblage of particles is the wavelike nature of the normal modes, enabling us to classify them according to a wave vector as well as according to frequency. This occurs because in a uniform medium a wave is not reflected or scattered.

The classical transformation which gives the description of the vibrating system in terms of normal modes is a linear transformation of coordinates. Associated with the coordinate transformation is a linear transformation of the momenta. This type of transformation may be carried out before introducing the quantum features of the description because such a transformation cannot introduce any ambiguities about the order of factors q and p, which were not already present before the transformation. Thus, the normal modes occurring in the quantum mechanics of a system are identical with the classical normal modes. The harmonic oscillation associated with a given mode can then be discussed in just the same way that the one dimensional was discussed in Section 6. The chief task is to describe the normal modes in a classical way.

Many features of lattice vibrations are brought out in a very simple model, the linear chain with nearest neighbor interactions only. We confine our treatment to this case. Consider a linear array of atoms of kind A with spacing a, with an atom of a different kind, B, halfway in between each pair of adjacent A atoms. This is illustrated in Fig. 34–1. The classical equation of

Fig. 34-1

motion for particle A_i, the ith atom of type A, with coordinate ψ_i, may be written as

$$m\ddot{\psi}_i = -m\omega_\sigma^2\psi_i = K[(\phi_i - \psi_i) + (\phi_{i+1} - \psi_i)] \tag{34.1}$$

if only the normal mode σ with frequency ω_σ is excited. The corresponding equation of motion for particle B_i, the ith atom of type B, with coordinate ϕ_i is

$$M\ddot{\phi}_i = -M\omega_\sigma^2\phi_i = K[(\psi_i - \phi_i) + (\psi_{i-1} - \phi_i)]\,. \tag{34.2}$$

These equations are real linear difference equations. They are most easily solved in terms of imaginary exponentials, the desired solution being either the real or imaginary part of the complex solution. We assume a solution of the form

$$\begin{aligned} \psi_i &= \alpha_\sigma \exp[i\gamma_\sigma]\phi_i\,, \\ \phi_{i+1} &= \frac{1}{\alpha_\sigma}\exp[i\delta_\sigma]\psi_i\,, \end{aligned} \tag{34.3}$$

where γ_ρ is the phase difference between the motion of B_i and A_i, δ_ρ is a similar phase difference between the motions of A_i and B_{i+1}, and α_σ is the ratio of the amplitudes of motion of the two types of atoms. Insertion of this in (34.1) and in (34.2) leads to

$$\begin{aligned} -\omega_\sigma^2 &= \frac{K}{m}\left[\frac{1}{\alpha_\sigma}\exp(-i\gamma_\sigma) + \frac{1}{\alpha_\sigma}\exp(i\delta_\sigma) - 2\right], \\ -\omega_\sigma^2 &= \frac{K}{M}\left[\alpha_\sigma \exp(-i\delta_\sigma) + \alpha_\sigma \exp(i\gamma_\sigma) - 2\right]. \end{aligned} \tag{34.4}$$

The value of ω_σ^2 being real, the imaginary part on the right must vanish, which yields

$$\sin \gamma_\sigma = \sin \delta_\sigma\,, \qquad \gamma_\sigma = \delta_\sigma, \text{ or } \pi - \delta_\sigma\,. \tag{34.5}$$

The latter solution leads to

$$\omega_\sigma^2 = \frac{2K}{m} = \frac{2K}{M}\,,$$

which is not permissible when $m \neq M$, the case we consider. Equation (34.4) becomes

$$\begin{aligned}\omega_\sigma^2 &= \frac{2K}{m}\left(1 - \frac{1}{\alpha_\sigma}\cos\gamma_\sigma\right)\\ &= \frac{2K}{M}(1 - \alpha_\sigma \cos\gamma_\sigma)\,.\end{aligned}$$

Elimination of α_σ then gives

$$\left(1 - \frac{m\omega_\sigma^2}{2K}\right)\left(1 - \frac{M\omega_\sigma^2}{2K}\right) = \cos^2\gamma_\sigma\,, \tag{34.6}$$

or

$$\omega_\sigma^2 = K\left[\left(\frac{1}{m} + \frac{1}{M}\right) \pm \left\{\left(\frac{1}{m} + \frac{1}{M}\right)^2 - \frac{4\sin^2\gamma_\sigma}{mM}\right\}^{1/2}\right], \tag{34.7}$$

which specifies ω_σ^2 as a function of γ_σ.

The phase difference between adjacent atoms is determined by the boundary conditions imposed. If these are periodic boundary conditions, the phase difference between atom A_0 and atom A_N, where $N+1$ is the number of A atoms in the chain, must be a multiple of 2π. Thus

$$\begin{aligned}2N\gamma_\sigma &= 2\pi\nu_\sigma\,, &\quad \nu_\sigma &\text{ integer}\,,\\ \gamma_\sigma &= \frac{\pi\nu_\sigma}{N}\,, &\quad -\frac{N}{2} \leq &\ \nu_\sigma \leq \frac{N}{2}\,.\end{aligned} \tag{34.8}$$

For large N values, γ_σ can be considered as a continuous variable, and it is convenient to introduce the wavenumber k, defined by

$$k = 2\gamma_\sigma/a\,, \tag{34.9}$$

and to replace the label j of the various atoms by the coordinate x.

$$\begin{aligned}\psi_j &= \psi(x)\,, &\quad x &= (j + \tfrac{1}{2})a\,,\\ \phi_j &= \phi(x)\,, &\quad x &= ja\,.\end{aligned} \tag{34.10}$$

The solution (34.3) now assumes the form

$$\psi(x) = C \exp[i(kx - \omega(k)t)], \qquad (34.11)$$
$$\phi(x) = \frac{C}{\alpha} \exp[i(kx - \omega(k)t)],$$

which represents two waves of the same frequency and wavelength but with different amplitudes. The relation (34.7) now becomes the *dispersion equation* relating ω and k,

$$\omega^2(k) = K\left[\left(\frac{1}{m} + \frac{1}{M}\right) \pm \left(\frac{1}{m^2} + \frac{1}{M^2} + \frac{2\cos ka}{mM}\right)^{1/2}\right]. \qquad (34.12)$$

For each k there are two values of $\omega(k)$ as given by (34.12). [We always take $\omega(k) \geqslant 0$, with no loss of generality.] The plot of ω vs k is shown in Figure 34–2. The upper branch corresponds to the upper sign in (34.7),

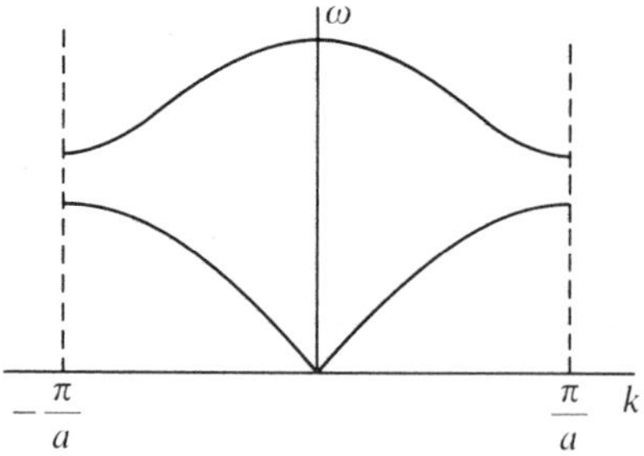

Fig. 34-2

the lower branch to the lower sign. It is easy to verify that for normal modes on the lower branch of this curve the two kinds of atoms oscillate in phase, the amplitude ratio being positive, while for modes on the upper branch α is negative and the oscillations are π out of phase. The latter type of oscillation can, because of the possibly different charges on atoms A and B, give rise to an oscillating electric dipole moment, and is therefore called an *optical mode*. The modes on the lower branch are *acoustic modes*.

The similarity between Figure 34–2 and 33–3 is striking. There are two essential differences. Figure 33–3 contains many branches, while Figure 34–2 contains but two. This limit is due to the existence of only two kinds of atoms in our chain and is not really essential. The other difference is the curvature of lowest branch at the origin. In the graph of electron energy versus k_b this curvature is the reciprocal of the effective mass m^*. In Figure 34–2 this curvature is infinite. If, therefore, we want to regard Figure 34–2 as a plot of the energy of some particle as a function of its momentum, this particle has zero mass. It is useful to introduce a zero mass particle, the phonon, whose energy is a linear function of its momentum. This is then written

$$E = \hbar\omega, \qquad \mathbf{p} = \hbar\mathbf{k}, \qquad E = v|\mathbf{p}|. \qquad (34.13)$$

v is here the velocity of sound in the crystal. We assume this to be the same in all directions. Only those frequencies will be considered for which v is independent of ω, so that we remain always on the linear part of the dispersion curve.

Every normal mode of the crystal which is on the linear portion of the dispersion curve is uniquely characterized by its wave vector $\mathbf{k}$, or by the momentum $\mathbf{p}$. A normal mode can be regarded as a harmonic oscillator with frequency $\omega(\mathbf{k})$, this harmonic oscillator being described like any other quantum oscillator. It is possible, as in Section 8, to introduce the raising and lowering operators, $a^\dagger(\mathbf{k})$ and $a(\mathbf{k})$. $a^\dagger(\mathbf{k})$ changes the state of the normal mode labelled by $\mathbf{k}$, increasing its energy by $\hbar\omega(\mathbf{k})$ and its momentum by $\hbar\mathbf{k}$. This latter effect did not occur in Section 8 as there the oscillator was a single particle rather than a collective motion of many particles. The momentum arises here because the collective motion has been described by travelling waves. Similarly, $a(\mathbf{k})$ decreases the energy associated with this mode by $\hbar\omega(\mathbf{k})$, and the momentum by $\hbar\mathbf{k}$. No other modes are affected.

If we introduce the phonon as a particle, then it is natural to speak of $a^\dagger(\mathbf{k})$ as a *creation operator*, and of $a(\mathbf{k})$ as an *annihilation operator* for phonons of wave vector $\mathbf{k}$. The vibrational state of the crystal can be specified by giving the number of phonons associated with each of the normal modes. Phonons are indistinguishable particles which do not obey the exclusion principle, and are therefore bosons. The operator giving the number of phonons of wave vector $\mathbf{k}$ is

$$N(\mathbf{k}) = a^\dagger(\mathbf{k})a(\mathbf{k}), \tag{34.14}$$

in analogy with (8.14). The total vibrational energy of the crystal, aside from the zero-point energy, is given by

$$E = \sum_k N(\mathbf{k})\hbar\omega(\mathbf{k}), \tag{34.15}$$

and the total momentum associated with this vibration is

$$\mathbf{P} = \sum_k N(\mathbf{k})\hbar\mathbf{k}. \tag{34.16}$$

These expressions are valid for any normal modes. The restriction to the low-lying modes comes about if $\omega(k)$ is taken to be a linear function of $|\mathbf{k}|$.

If the crystal is in the form of a cube of edge L, the periodic boundary conditions used to get travelling wave normal modes lead to

$$k_j = (2\pi/L)n_j,$$

with n_j an integer. Just as in Section 26, this results in the number of normal modes with wave vectors in the range d^3k being given by

$$dN = \frac{d^3k}{(2\pi)^3} L^3 . \tag{34.17}$$

Now a system of N_0 particles has $3N_0$ degrees of freedom, of which $3N_0 - 6$ are internal degrees of freedom. The other six are associated with rigid motions of the crystal. For large N_0 the difference between N_0 and $N_0 - 6$ may be ignored. There is, therefore, a maximum value of k given by

$$3N_0 = \frac{L^3}{(2\pi)^3} \int_0^{k_{\max}} 4\pi k^2 \, dk . \tag{34.18}$$

The frequency associated with $k_{\max}$ is called the Debye frequency. It is clearly off the linear part of the dispersion curve.

The crystal lattice now is seen to house two kinds of particles, namely, electrons and phonons. The state of the electron is described in the previous section for the case when the crystal is perfectly regular, the equivalent single particle potential being assumed to have perfect periodicity. The presence of phonons destroys this perfect periodicity, thus affecting the electron state. The reaction to this change in the electron's state may involve the creation or annihilation of phonons. Thus, there is in general an electron–phonon interaction. This interaction can be neatly described by means of creation and annihilation operators. As is explained in Section 40, the scattering of an electron can be described by saying that an electron initially in the state with momentum $\mathbf{p}$ is annihilated while an electron with the final momentum $\mathbf{p}'$ is created. A phonon is created or annihilated at the same time. We may, therefore, write the interaction between the electron and the phonon field as

$$V = \sum_{p,p',k} \{ W_{p,p'} \alpha^\dagger(\mathbf{p}')\alpha(\mathbf{p})a(\mathbf{k})(2\pi\hbar)^3 \, \delta(\mathbf{p}' - \mathbf{p} - \hbar\mathbf{k}) + W_{p,p'}{}^* \alpha^\dagger(\mathbf{p}')\alpha(\mathbf{p})a^\dagger(\mathbf{k})(2\pi\hbar)^3 \, \delta(\mathbf{p}' - \mathbf{p} + \hbar\mathbf{k}) . \tag{34.19}$$

Here $\alpha^\dagger(p')$ creates an electron of momentum p', spin σ, and $\alpha(p)$ annihilates an electron of momentum p and spin σ. The spin index is not written explicitly. The occurrence of these operators in pairs insures that the number of electrons remains constant. Electrons obey the exclusion principle, so that the α's must have different commutation relations from the phonon operators a and $a^\dagger$. These are described in Section 40.

The analysis of the consequences of the electron–phonon interaction is of great interest for solid state physics, but goes far beyond the limits of what can be discussed here. Related ideas are, however, introduced in Sections 40 and 41.

PROBLEMS

1. The perturbation of atomic states produced by a uniform electric field is the *Stark effect*. Show that in first order there is no Stark effect unless the unperturbed system has degenerate levels of opposite parity.
2. Show that the Stark effect is the same for states with $j_z' = m\hbar$ and $j_z' = -m\hbar$.
3. Calculate the lowest non-vanishing order of the Stark effect for the first excited states of (a) the hydrogen atom, (b) the three-dimensional harmonic oscillator.
4. In hydrogen the $2p_{1/2}$ and $2p_{3/2}$ levels are split by approximately 11,000 Mc/sec. Can spin-orbit coupling account for most of this splitting? Use first-order perturbation theory.
5. One may consider the wave vector **k** associated with a lattice vibration as in (34.9) to be a momentum variable. If this is done, show that the energy of the lattice vibration is a periodic function of **k,** and relate this to the remarks made in Section 9 concerning the occurrence of a discrete spectrum for the coordinate **x**.
6. The interaction between an atom and light assumed in (27.10) is only a first approximation. The next two terms are a magnetic dipole and an electric quadrupole interaction. Show that the matrix elements of them are small in comparison with matrix elements of the electric dipole by a factor of the atomic radius divided by the wavelength of the light. Obtain the selection rules for these types of radiation.
7. A system possesses g degenerate energy eigenstates. Show that if a perturbation reduces or removes this degeneracy only in the second order, the $g \times g$ matrix U_0 must be chosen so that the second-order perturbation operator $V_0^{(2)}$ of (26.22) has no off-diagonal elements. (Note that the E_2' as given by (24.18) is a diagonal matrix element of $V_0^{(2)}$, except that terms with vanishing denominators are to be omitted from the sum in (26.22).)
8. Consider an even phase integral approximation wave function for the two minimum potential of Figure 25–4, corresponding to an energy for which the central hump is classically forbidden. The solution in this region is of the form

$$C \cosh \int_0^x |k(x')|dx' .$$

Find the phase of the approximate wave function in the classically allowed region by using (25.17) as it stands. Find the expression equivalent to (25.26) for this system.
9. Repeating the argument of Problem 8 for an odd wave function, find an expression for the energy difference between the odd and even states in terms of the penetrability of the central barrier. Interpret this in terms of the frequency with which a particle, initially localized in one of the two wells, will oscillate between the two wells.

VI

Scattering

35. SCATTERING BY A CENTRAL POTENTIAL

A schematic diagram of a typical scattering experiment is given in Figure 35–1. Particles from a source (e.g., synchrotron) are collimated and impinge on a target. Particles emerging from the target at angle θ are detected. Several idealizations are made in giving the mathematical description of this experiment.

The target is considered to be an assembly of independent, identical scatterers. For atomic collision studies it must therefore be a gas. For nuclear studies it can be a solid. For some fundamental particle studies it must be free nucleons, which means some form of hydrogen.

The source is supposed to furnish mono-energetic particles. The collimator is supposed to select only those with a given direction of motion, so that the incident particle is in a momentum eigenstate. This is certainly a good approximation, as the collimator slits are very wide in terms of the de Broglie wavelength of the beam particles so that diffraction is negligible. The detector is supposed to be screened from the incident particles so that it detects only scattered particles. This is contradictory to the supposed momentum definition, which precludes localization of the incident particle. The range of momenta, however, needed to construct a wave packet for the incident particles which vanishes at the detector is extremely small and is of no practical importance. The exception to this that arises when the scattering angle θ is

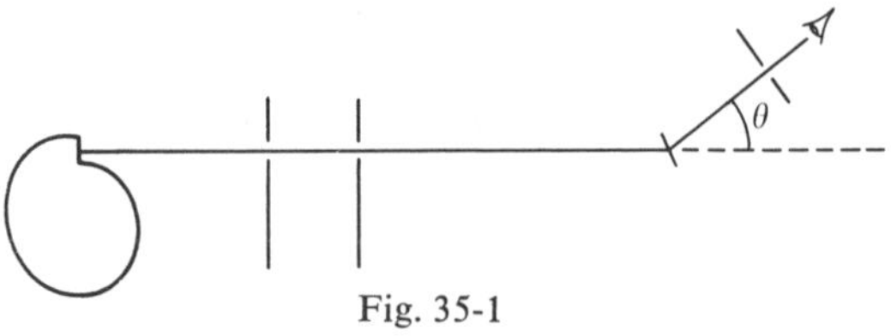

Fig. 35-1

vanishingly small is very important as we shall see in connection with the optical theorem (35.21).

The assumption, that the incident and scattered particles are in definite momentum states, involves an assumption about the range of the interaction which produces the scattering. If the interaction is a central potential, $V(r)$, the wave function of the relative motion of an incident particle and a target particle satisfies the radial wave equation.

$$\frac{d^2u}{dr^2} + \left[k^2 - \frac{l(l+1)}{r^2} - \frac{2mV(r)}{\hbar^2}\right]u = 0 . \tag{35.1}$$

For large r, we want the solution to be of the form $\exp[ikr]$. Let

$$u(r) = f(r)\exp[ikr] . \tag{35.2}$$

Then

$$f'' + 2ikf' - \left[\frac{l(l+1)}{r^2} + \frac{2mV}{\hbar^2}\right]f = 0. \tag{35.3}$$

At large r, the second derivative term is to be small compared with the others, as we want f to tend to a constant. Neglecting this term the equation becomes

$$\frac{f'}{f} = \frac{1}{2ik}\left[\frac{l(l+1)}{r^2} + \frac{2mV(r)}{\hbar^2}\right].$$

Integrating this from a to r yields

$$\ln\frac{f(r)}{f(a)} = \frac{1}{2ik}\int_a^r \left[\frac{l(l+1)}{r^2} + \frac{2mV(r)}{\hbar^2}\right]dr . \tag{35.4}$$

The integral on the right approaches a constant only if

$$rV(r) \to 0 \text{ as } r \to \infty . \tag{35.5}$$

If, therefore, the potential decreases faster than r^{-1}, our assumptions are justified.

This excludes the Coulomb potential. The Schrödinger equation can be solved exactly in the Coulomb case and the scattering of charged particles can be treated exactly in spite of the long range of the force. We do this in Section 36. Another approach is to replace the Coulomb potential by a screened Coulomb potential such as a Yukawa potential,

$$V(r) = e^{-\mu r}/r , \tag{35.6}$$

which has an exponential behavior at infinity but which, for small μ, is very like a Coulomb potential near the origin. We use this device in connection with the Born approximation.

We discuss here only the case where the interaction of incident particle with target particle is described by a central potential. The modifications needed for inclusion of spin-orbit coupling and some other non-central potentials can be made, but are complicated. Inelastic scattering, in which the internal states of the particles change or radiation of some kind is emitted, is still more complicated, and is discussed in Section 38.

The wave function of the relative motion of the two particles involved is taken to be

$$\psi(\mathbf{r}) \approx e^{ikz} + \frac{f(\theta, \phi)}{r} e^{ikr}, \quad r \to \infty . \tag{35.7}$$

The first term describes the unscattered wave, the second term the scattered wave. $f(\theta, \phi)$ is called the *scattering amplitude*. It is independent of the azimuthal angle ϕ under our assumptions. According to this wave function the number dN of scattered particles per unit time entering the element of solid angle $d\Omega$ is

$$dN = \frac{\hbar k}{m} \, | f(\theta, \phi) |^2 \, d\Omega .$$

The ratio of this to the flux of incident particles on the target particle is the differential cross section $d\sigma$ for scattering. According to (35.7) the incident flux φ is given by

$$\varphi = \frac{\hbar k}{m} = \frac{p}{m} .$$

Thus,

$$d\sigma = \frac{dV}{\varphi} = | f(\theta, \phi) |^2 \, d\Omega . \tag{35.8}$$

The angles θ and ϕ are measured here in the center of mass system. In order to compare with experiment these angles must be transformed to the laboratory system.

When the scattering is due to a central potential, the orbital angular momentum is conserved and one can discuss the scattering for each value of the orbital angular momentum quantum number l separately. We have already seen, in Section 16, that a plane wave can be expanded in eigenstates of orbital angular momentum. According to (16.20) we have

$$e^{ikz} \approx \frac{1}{2ikr} \sum_{l=0}^{\infty} (2l + 1) P_l(\cos \theta) \, [e^{ikr} - (-)^l e^{-ikr}] . \tag{35.9}$$

This expresses the unscattered wave as a superposition of outgoing and ingoing spherical waves.

For $r \to \infty$, the ingoing spherical waves are unaffected by the potential. The scattering must be described by a modification of the outgoing wave. Because l is a good quantum number, the flux of particles of a given l must be zero, the ingoing flux equalling the outgoing. The amplitude of the outgoing wave cannot be altered in magnitude, but only by a phase factor for each l. Therefore we write

$$\begin{aligned} \psi(\mathbf{x}) &\approx e^{ikz} + \frac{f(\theta)}{r} e^{ikr} \\ &= \frac{1}{2ikr} \sum_{l=0}^{\infty} (2l+1) P_l(\cos\theta) \left[e^{2i\delta_l} e^{ikr} - (-)^l e^{-ikr} \right], \end{aligned} \tag{35.10}$$

where δ_l is the *phase shift* of the lth *partial wave*. δ_l is a real number.

Subtracting (35.9) from (35.10) we obtain

$$\begin{aligned} f(\theta) &= \frac{1}{2ik} \sum_{l=0}^{\infty} (2l+1)(e^{2i\delta_l} - 1) P_l(\cos\theta) \\ &= \frac{1}{k} \sum_{l=0}^{\infty} (2l+1) e^{i\delta_l} \sin\delta_l P_l(\cos\theta). \end{aligned} \tag{35.11}$$

The phase shift δ_l represents a phase shift of the solution of the radial equation containing the potential $V(r)$ relative to the solution of the free particle radial equation. To see this we rewrite the quantity in the square bracket in (35.10).

$$[e^{2i\delta_l} e^{ikr} - (-)^l e^{-ikr}] = e^{i\delta_l} [e^{i(kr+\delta_l)} - (-)^l e^{-i(kr+\delta_l)}]. \tag{35.12}$$

The quantity in square brackets on the right is just the asymptotic form of

$$j_l(kr + \delta_l) \approx \cos[kr - (l+1)\pi/2 + \delta_l], \tag{35.13}$$

or of

$$\cos\delta_l \hat{j}_l(kr) - \sin\delta_l \hat{n}_l(kr).$$

The functions $\hat{j}_l(z)$, $\hat{n}_l(z)$ are the Ricatti–Bessel functions, defined by

$$\begin{aligned} \hat{j}_l(z) &= z j_l(z) \\ &= \left(\frac{\pi z}{2}\right)^{1/2} J_{l+1/2}(z), \end{aligned} \tag{35.14}$$

and similarly for $\hat{n}_l(z)$.

This result provides a means for finding δ_l. The radial equation is integrated (numerically or otherwise) from the origin out to a value of r for which the interaction is negligible. At this radius the solution must be a linear combination of the two independent solutions of the free particle equation, which is just what (35.13) is. The ratio of the coefficients in the linear combination is $(-\cot \delta_l)$.

The phase shifts can be evaluated analytically in some cases. If the potential is a square well, or a cutoff harmonic oscillator potential, or a cutoff Coulomb potential, the wave function inside the cutoff radius is known. It can be matched at the cutoff radius to a free particle wave function of the form (35.13). (By a cutoff potential, we mean one of the specified form for $r < a$, and zero for $r > a$.)

The phase shifts δ_l constitute a convenient set of parameters to describe scattering, especially if only a few phase shifts differ much from zero. If the potential is of short range and the bombarding energy is not too high, one would expect only a few δ_l to be large. This can be seen semiclassically. To get a large l-value for a given linear momentum, the classical *impact parameter* must be large. If the impact parameter is larger than the range of the potential, there will be little scattering. The quantum mechanical version of this is that the wave function near the origin behaves as r^l. For large l, therefore, the wave function is small in the region where the potential is large and little scattering results.

Expressed in terms of phase shifts, the differential scattering cross section is

$$\frac{d\sigma}{d\Omega} = \frac{1}{k^2}\left|\sum_{l=0}^{\infty}(2l+1)e^{i\delta_l}\sin\delta_l P_l(\cos\theta)\right|^2 \tag{35.15}$$

If L is the largest value of l for which δ_l is appreciably different from zero, the largest power of $\cos\theta$ appearing in the cross section is $(\cos\theta)^{2L}$. Thus, a cross section which can fitted with a formula like

$$\frac{d\sigma}{d\Omega} = a + b\cos\theta + c\cos^2\theta \tag{35.16}$$

is likely to arise from scattering in the S and P states only, with $l = 0$ and $l = 1$.

The total cross section is obtained from the differential cross section by integrating over all solid angles. The cross products of the Legendre polynomials integrate to zero because of orthogonality. Hence

$$\begin{aligned}\sigma &= \int \frac{d\sigma}{d\Omega}\,d\Omega \\ &= \frac{4\pi}{k^2}\sum_{l=0}^{\infty}(2l+1)\sin^2\delta_l\,.\end{aligned} \tag{35.17}$$

This puts a limit on the total cross section associated with any one partial wave of

$$\frac{4\pi}{k^2}(2l+1)\,. \tag{35.18}$$

This is sometimes called a *unitarity limit*. It arises from the reality of the phase shift δ_l. This, in turn, comes from the general requirement that probability be conserved so that the ingoing and outgoing fluxes together give zero net flux when integrated over a closed surface. The name *unitarity* is applied to this because probabilities have been defined in terms of scalar products of state vectors, and these are invariant under unitary transformations. For example, the total cross section associated with the differential cross section (35.16) is

$$\sigma = 4\pi(a + \tfrac{1}{3}c)\,. \tag{35.19}$$

If $(a + c/3) > (1 + 3)/k^2$, where the right side is the contribution from partial waves with $l = 0$ and $l = 1$, then higher partial waves contribute but the measurement did not detect the rapid variations with θ.

The unitarity condition also requires that all particles scattered through finite angles be missing from the unscattered beam. To accomplish this, there must be interference between the unscattered wave and the wave which is scattered in the forward direction. This interference involves the forward scattering amplitude, and not the square of this amplitude. To see this we use the form (16.24) for the plane wave function for large r, namely

$$e^{ikz} \approx \frac{2\pi}{ikr}[\,\delta(\mathbf{n} - \mathbf{n}_z)e^{ikr} - \delta(\mathbf{n} + \mathbf{n}_z)e^{-ikr}]\,. \tag{35.20}$$

In the region behind the scattering center, then, the total wave function may be written

$$\psi(\mathbf{x}) \approx \left[\frac{f(\theta)}{r} + \frac{2\pi}{ikr}\,\delta(\mathbf{n} - \mathbf{n}_z)\right]e^{ikr}\,, \quad kz \gg 1\,. \tag{35.21}$$

The current described by this wave function is

$$\begin{aligned} j_r &= \frac{\hbar}{2mi}\left[\psi^* \frac{\partial\psi}{\partial r} - \left(\frac{\partial\psi^*}{\partial r}\right)\psi\right] \\ &= \frac{\hbar k}{mr^2}\left[f^*f + \frac{4\pi^2}{k^2}(\delta(\mathbf{n} - \mathbf{n}_z))^2 - \frac{2\pi}{ik}\,\delta(\mathbf{n} - \mathbf{n}_z)\,(f - f^*)\right]. \end{aligned} \tag{35.22}$$

Now integrate this over a surface perpendicular to $\mathbf{n}_z$ which subtends the arbitrarily small but finite solid angle $\Delta\Omega$ including the z direction. The first term gives a contribution proportional to $\Delta\Omega$ which is negligible. The second term gives an infinite total current corresponding to the original plane wave which is infinite in extent. The last term is the interference term. It gives a negative contribution of

$$j_{\text{interference}} = -\frac{4\pi\hbar}{m}\operatorname{Im} f(0)\,. \tag{35.23}$$

Dividing this by the incident flux gives the total cross section for removal from the beam:

$$\begin{aligned}\sigma_{\text{tot}} &= -\frac{j_{\text{interference}}}{\hbar k/m} \\ &= \frac{4\pi}{k}\operatorname{Im} f(0)\,.\end{aligned} \tag{35.24}$$

The result (35.24) holds for any scattering process described by quantum mechanics, whether or not the scattering can be ascribed to a potential. It is called the *optical theorem.* It is easily checked for the scattering by a central potential. From (35.11) we see that

$$\operatorname{Im} f(\theta) = \frac{1}{k}\sum_{l=0}^{\infty}(2l+1)\sin^2\delta_l P_l(\cos\theta)\,. \tag{35.25}$$

Because $P_l(1) = 1$, it follows that

$$\begin{aligned}\frac{4\pi}{k}\operatorname{Im} f(0) &= \frac{4\pi}{k^2}\sum_{l=0}^{\infty}(2l+1)\sin^2\delta_l \\ &= \sigma\,,\end{aligned} \tag{35.26}$$

according to (35.17).

The phase shifts δ_l are functions of the energy of the incident particle. The dependence on energy can be understood qualitatively by use of the phase integral approximation. This approximation can give quantitative results also under many conditions. For simplicity let us consider only S states, so that there is no centrifugal potential.

The wave function vanishes at the origin. If there is no classically forbidden region we may write the phase integral approximation to the wave function as

$$\begin{aligned}u(r) &= Ak(r)^{-1/2}\sin\int_0^r k(r)\,dr\,, \\ k(r) &= \left[\frac{2m[E-V(r)]}{\hbar^2}\right]^{1/2},\end{aligned} \tag{35.27}$$

with $k(r)$ everywhere real and positive. The free particle wave function at the same energy is

$$u_0(r) = Ak_0^{1/2} \sin k_0 r \,, \qquad k_0 = \left[\frac{2mE}{\hbar^2}\right]^{1/2} \tag{35.28}$$

The phase shift $\delta_0(E)$ is given by

$$\delta_0(E) = \int_0^\infty [k(r) - k_0(r)]\, dr \,. \tag{35.29}$$

As E increases toward infinity δ_0 decreases toward zero. Expanding this in powers of V/E, to first order

$$\delta_0(E) \approx \int_0^\infty -\frac{V(r)}{2E}\, dr \,. \tag{35.30}$$

For attractive potentials $\delta_0(E)$ approaches zero through positive values, and for repulsive potentials through negative values. Equation (35.29) shows that $\delta_0(E)$ is always negative for repulsive potentials.

At low energy, the behavior of the phase shift is very different for attractive and repulsive potentials. According to Figure 35–2, for a repulsive potential there is an energy below which the origin is in a classically forbidden region. For a very strong repulsion of effective radius a, it is clear that the phase shift is of the order of magnitude ka. This would be exact if the wave

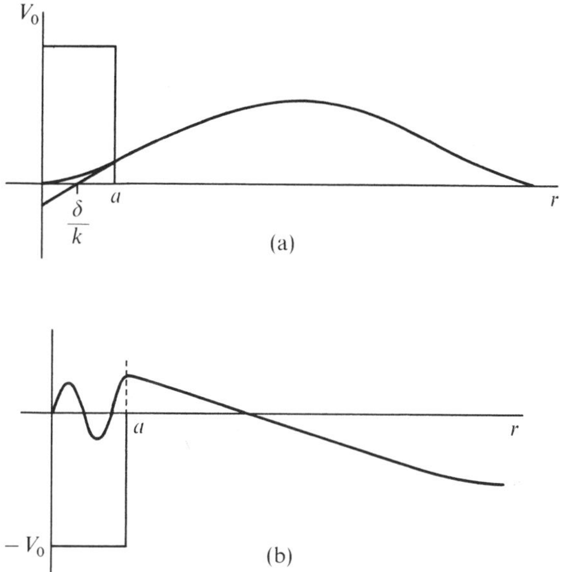

Fig. 35-2

function had to vanish at $r = a$, as for an infinite repulsive square-well potential. Thus, the phase shift approaches zero as $E \to 0$.

For an attractive potential, at low incident energy we have

$$\delta_0(E) \xrightarrow[E\to 0]{} \int_0^\infty \left[\frac{2m|V(r)|}{\hbar^2}\right]^{1/2} dr\,. \tag{35.31}$$

This can be related to the number of bound states of this particular angular momentum, $l = 0$. The bound state with the highest energy is determined, in this approximation, by the condition

$$\int_0^{r_0} \left[\frac{2m(E - V(r))}{\hbar^2}\right]^{1/2} = (N + \tfrac{1}{4})\pi\,. \tag{35.32}$$

The factor on the right is $N + \frac{1}{4}$ instead of $N + \frac{1}{2}$, because there is only one matching at a turning point, as in (25.22). The wave function must vanish at the origin. Both E and $V(r)$ are here negative. N has its maximum value when the energy obtained by replacing N by $N + 1$ leads to no real turning point r_0, i.e., if as N is increased continuously $r_0 \to \infty$ before N reaches $N + 1$. We conclude that

$$(N + \tfrac{1}{4})\pi < \delta_0(E = 0) < (N + \tfrac{5}{4})\pi\,.$$

This result is not exact. It may be shown that under very general conditions

$$\delta_l(E = 0) = N_l\pi\,. \tag{35.33}$$

Here N_l is the number of bound states with orbital angular momentum l. This is called *Levinson's theorem.*

If the potential is such as to have a classically forbidden region between the origin and infinity, more complicated behavior of the phase shift as a function of energy occurs. This forbidden region may arise because of the centrifugal potential in states other than S states. We give a purely qualitative discussion based on the phase integral approximation.

Consider the potential $V(r)$ shown in Figure 35–3. Let $u(E_0, r)$ be the wave function which matches a purely decaying exponential in the forbidden region. It is shown as a solid curve in the figure. This matching corresponds to $\theta = 0$ in (25.21). An increase in the energy to $E_0 + \epsilon$ is equivalent to giving ϕ a small negative value in (25.21). This brings in an increasing exponential in the forbidden region with a negative coefficient. The wave function corresponding to this is drawn as a dashed curve. Similarly replacing E_0 by $E_0 - \epsilon$ brings in an increasing exponential with positive coefficient. This is shown as a dotted curve.

Two things emerge from this discussion: At energy E_0 the wave function inside the barrier is very large compared with that of wave functions for some-

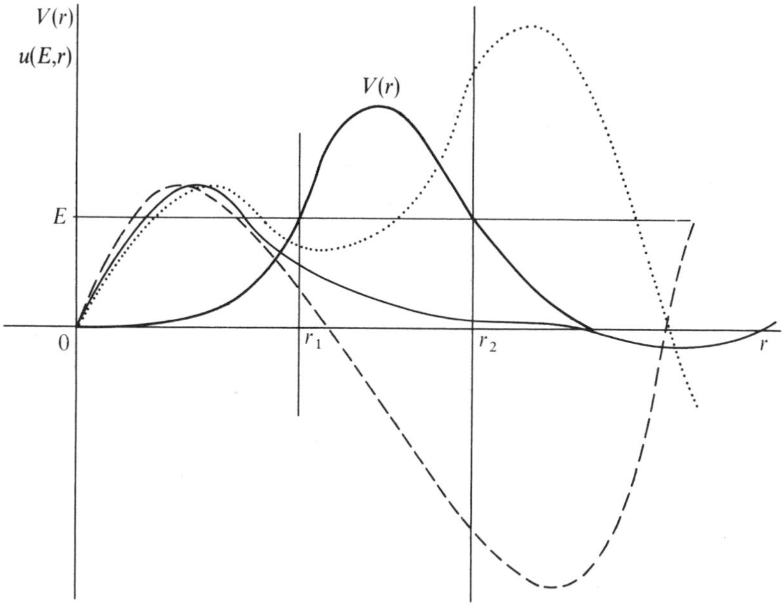

Fig. 35-3

what different energies when the amplitude outside the barrier is the same. On changing the energy from below E_0 to above E_0, the phase of the external wave function increases by π. These two features characterize a *resonance*. The approximation used here is not a very reliable one for calculating the position of the resonant energy. It is clear that the range over which the energy must be varied to produce the change π in the phase shift gets smaller the more impenetrable the barrier is, as this increases the ratio of the growing to the decaying exponential. This energy spread is called the *width* of the resonance.

The amplitude inside the barrier may be related to that outside by

$$A_{\text{in}} = \frac{1}{(E - E_0) + i\Gamma/2} A_{\text{out}} . \tag{35.34}$$

This is the simplest dependence on E which shows the desired behavior. Here Γ is the width mentioned above. It is customary to regard Γ as a constant for each resonance, but it may actually depend on the energy E rather than just on E_0. Any process which depends on an interaction inside the barrier, be it scattering by a potential or something else, will have a probability depending on energy through the factor

$$P(E) \sim \frac{1}{(E - E_0)^2 + \frac{1}{4}\Gamma^2} . \tag{35.35}$$

Such a factor is called a *Breit–Wigner* factor. If there is more than one resonance, the resonant behavior is described in the above way only when the resonances are well separated, so that the widths Γ are much smaller than the energy separation of the resonances.

Another approach to the subject of resonances is to consider them as eigenstates of the Hamiltonian including the scattering interaction but with complex eigenvalues

$$W = E - i\Gamma/2\,. \tag{35.36}$$

These are not true eigenvalues, which must be real as the Hamiltonian is hermitian as applied to acceptable wave functions. W is determined by the condition that the wave function at large r contain only outgoing spherical waves. This formulation is clearly connected with the uncertainty principle for energy $\times$ time. The time factor associated with an eigenvalue W is

$$\exp\,[-iWt/\hbar] = \exp\,[-iEt/\hbar]\,\exp\,[-\Gamma t/2\hbar]\,,$$

of which the second factor is a damping factor. The probability of finding the initial state decreases according to

$$P(t) \sim \exp\,[-\Gamma t/\hbar]\,,$$

which is the result expected for a decaying state. The mean life $\hbar/\Gamma$ is now identified with Δt in the uncertainty relation

$$\Delta E\,\Delta t \leq \hbar$$

to yield

$$\Delta E \simeq \Gamma\,.$$

Hence the name *width* for Γ. This approach is called the *Wigner–Weisskopf method.*

36. COULOMB SCATTERING

The scattering of one charged particle by another was used by Rutherford to investigate the charge distribution in atoms. Rutherford used alpha particles as incident particles and gold atoms as targets. He compared the scattering observed with that to be expected on the basis of the classical mechanical description of the scattering of two point particles with appropriate charges and found excellent agreement. This led him to propose the nuclear model of the atom.

The classical Rutherford formula for the scattering cross section of particles with charges Ze and $Z'e$ in the center of mass system is

$$\frac{d\sigma}{d\Omega} = \left(\frac{ZZ'e^2}{2\mu v_0^2}\right)^2 \frac{1}{\sin^4\theta/2}\,. \tag{36.1}$$

μ is the reduced mass of the two particles and v_0 the relative velocity of the particles at large separation. Because of the long tail of the Coulomb potential, particles with very large impact parameters still contribute essentially to the scattering cross section and the total cross section is infinite.

In this section we discuss the quantum mechanical derivation of the Rutherford formula, the result being the same as the classical one. In many cases of interest, however, the Coulomb potential does not extend all the way into the origin or all the way to infinity, but is modified by short range effects such as the nuclear force between two protons and by screening of the central charge. To treat the modification of the Rutherford result caused by these additional forces we require a complete quantum treatment of the Coulomb scattering by itself. A partial wave approach to pure Coulomb scattering is not advantageous because all l values contribute essentially to the cross section, but it is advantageous in studying the modification of Coulomb scattering by a short range potential which affects only a few partial waves. We use both approaches here.

The problem of pure Coulomb scattering is best solved using parabolic coordinates. These coordinates, ξ, η, ϕ, are defined in terms of spherical coordinates by

$$\begin{aligned} \xi &= r - z = r(1 - \cos\theta)\,, \\ \eta &= r + z = r(1 + \cos\theta)\,, \\ \phi &= \phi\,. \end{aligned} \tag{36.2}$$

In these variables the Schrödinger equation is separable and for a Coulomb potential is soluble in terms of known functions. It reads*

$$\left\{\frac{4}{\xi+\eta}\left[\frac{\partial}{\partial\xi}\left(\xi\frac{\partial}{\partial\xi}\right)+\frac{\partial}{\partial\eta}\left(\eta\frac{\partial}{\partial\eta}\right)+\frac{1}{\xi\eta}\frac{\partial^2}{\partial\phi^2}\right] + \frac{2\mu}{\hbar^2}\left[E-\frac{2ZZ'e^2}{\xi+\eta}\right]\right\}\psi(\xi,\eta,\phi)=0\,. \tag{36.3}$$

The ϕ dependence is separable by multiplying through with $\xi\eta$. ϕ is the same coordinate as occurs in the spherical system, so we treat it in the same way as there and set

$$\frac{\partial^2}{\partial\phi^2} = -m^2$$

with m an integer. Multiplying the resulting equation by $\xi + \eta$ separates the dependence on these two variables. Writing

$$\psi(\xi,\eta,\phi) = NF(\xi)G(\eta)\exp\,[im\phi]\,, \tag{36.4}$$

*See footnote, p. 68.

with N a normalization constant to be chosen later, we obtain the separated equations

(36.5)
$$(\xi F')' + \left(-\frac{m^2}{4\xi} + \frac{\mu E}{2\hbar^2}\xi + \frac{\mu ZZ'e^2}{\hbar^2} - \lambda\right)F = 0\,,$$
$$(\eta G')' + \left(-\frac{m^2}{4\eta} + \frac{\mu E}{2\hbar^2}\eta + \lambda\right)G = 0\,.$$

These two are of the same form, differing only in the constant in the second parenthesis.

Equation (36.3) is to be solved subject to certain conditions. The solution must be regular at the origin $r = 0$ and must be axially symmetric about the incident direction (chosen as the z axis). Because in the Coulomb case $rV(r)$ does not tend to zero as $r \to \infty$, (35.5) shows that we cannot expect to find plane wave solutions at infinity. In order to identify the incident wave, however, we look for a solution in the form of a modified plane wave.

(36.6)
$$\psi(\xi, \eta) = N \exp[ikz] f(\xi)\,,$$
$$= N \exp\left[ik\frac{\eta - \xi}{2}\right] f(\xi)\,,$$

which is of the form (36.4) with $m = 0$ and with

(36.7)
$$F(\xi) = \exp[-\tfrac{1}{2}ik\xi]\; f(\xi)\,,$$
$$G(\eta) = \exp[\tfrac{1}{2}ik\eta]\,.$$

This $G(\eta)$ satisfies the second of (36.5) provided that

(36.8)
$$\lambda = -\frac{ik}{2}\,, \qquad k^2 = \frac{2\mu E}{\hbar^2}\,.$$

This leads to the differential equation for $f(\xi)$:

(36.9)
$$\xi f'' + (1 - ik\xi)f' - \alpha k f = 0\,,$$

with

(36.10)
$$\alpha = \frac{ZZ'e^2}{\hbar v_0}\,.$$

Equation (36.9) is a special case of the confluent hypergeometric equation whose canonical form is

(36.11)
$$zy'' + (b - z)y' - ay = 0\,.$$

The solution of (36.11) regular at the origin $z = 0$ is written as*

*See J. Mathews and R. L. Walker, *Mathematical Methods of Physics*, Benjamin, New York, 1964.

$$y(z) = {}_1F_1(a, b; z) \tag{36.12}$$
$$= 1 + \frac{a}{b \cdot 1} z + \frac{a(a+1)}{b(b+1)2!} z^2 + \cdots .$$

Comparison of (36.9) and (36.11) shows that

$$f(\xi) = {}_1F_1(-i\alpha, 1; ik\xi) . \tag{36.13}$$

To obtain the scattering cross section it is necessary to find the asymptotic form of $f(\xi)$. We do this by studying the canonical equation (36.11).

A solution of (36.11) is provided by the contour integral

$$y(z) = \frac{\Gamma(b)}{2\pi i} \int_C e^{zt} t^{a-1} (t-1)^{b-a-1} \, dt , \tag{36.14}$$

provided the contour C in the complex t-plane is properly chosen. To see this we insert the integral into (36.11) and obtain

$$0 = \int_C e^{zt} t^{a-1} (t-1)^{b-a-1} \{ zt(t-1) + bt - a \} \, dt$$
$$= \int_C \left[e^{zt} t^{a-1} (t-1)^{b-a-1} (bt - a) - \left(\frac{d}{dt} e^{zt} \right) t^a (t-1)^{b-a} \right] dt \tag{36.15}$$
$$= - \left[e^{zt} t^a (t-1)^{b-a} \right]_A^B ,$$

where A and B are the endpoints of the contour C. If, therefore, the quantity in the bracket takes on the same values at A and at B, $y(z)$ given by (36.14) is a solution of (36.11).

A more convenient integral representation is obtained by noting that if

$$y = y_1 z^{1-b}$$

satisfies (36.11), then $y_1(z)$ satisfies the equation

$$z y_1'' + (2 - b - z) y_1' - (a - b + 1) y_1 = 0 ,$$

which is again a confluent hypergeometric equation. The solution of this can be written as a contour integral like (36.16). For $y(z)$ we get

$$y(z) = \frac{\Gamma(b)}{2\pi i} z^{1-b} \int_C e^{zt} t^{a-b} (t-1)^{-a} \, dt .$$

On letting $zt \to t$ this becomes

$$y(z) = \frac{\Gamma(b)}{2\pi i} \int_C e^t t^{a-b} (t-z)^{-a} \, dt , \tag{36.16}$$

provided that

$$\left[e^t t^{-b} (t-z)^{1-a} \right]_A^B = 0. \tag{36.17}$$

For the values a and b which interest us, neither a nor $a - b$ is an integer, so that the integrand in (36.16) has two branch points lying at $t = 0$ and $t = z$. The integrand can be made single valued by introducing cuts into the t plane from $t = 0$ and $t = z$ as shown in Figure 36–1. The contour C can now be chosen to be either C_1 or C_2 of the figure, as both of these satisfy (36.17). The integral (36.16) over $C_{1,2}$ is denoted by $W_{1,2}(a, b; z)$. As $z \to 0$, the two branch points come together, pinching the contour C_1 between them. The contour cannot stay a distance ϵ away from the singularity of the integrand so that the function $W_1(a, b; z)$ acquires a singularity as $z \to 0$. W_2 becomes singular at the origin for the same reason. A solution regular at the origin is obtained by taking a contour going around both branch points.

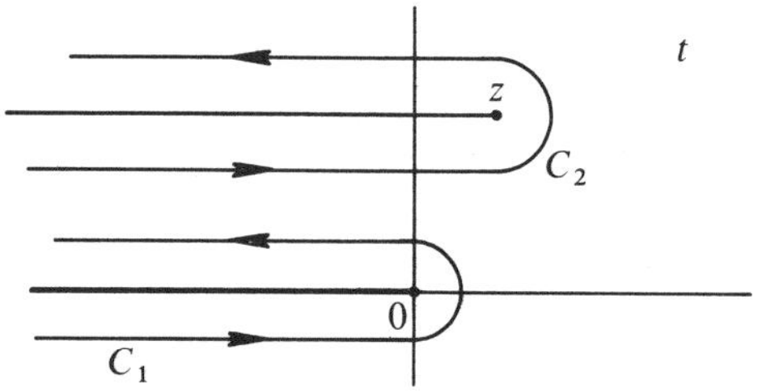

Fig. 36-1

This solution is $W_1 + W_2$, as the troublesome parts of C_1 and C_2 then give cancelling contributions. We write

$$y(z) = W_1(a, b; z) + W_2(a, b; z)\,. \tag{36.18}$$

It will appear below that W_1 describes the incident wave and W_2 the scattered wave, which is the reason for making this split. By making the change of variable $t - z \to t$, W_2 is written as an integral over the contour C_1. Then

$$\begin{aligned} W_1(a, b; z) &= \frac{\Gamma(b)}{2\pi i} \int_{C_1} e^t t^{a-b}(t - z)^{-a}\, dt\,, \\ W_2(a, b; z) &= \frac{\Gamma(b)}{2\pi i} \int_{C_1} e^{z+t} t^{-a}(t + z)^{a-b}\, dt\,. \end{aligned} \qquad z \neq 0 \tag{36.19}$$

When $z = 0$, the contour going around both branch points reduces to the contour C_1, so that at this point the value of $W_1 + W_2$ is given by either of (36.19) with $z = 0$. The integral satisfies the equation

$$\int_{C1} e^t t^{-b}\, dt = \frac{1}{b-1} \int_{C1} e^t t^{-(b-1)}\, dt$$

as is seen by integrating by parts. Recalling that the Γ-function satisfies the functional equation

$$\Gamma(b) = (b - 1)\Gamma(b - 1)\,,$$

we see that the integral is proportional to $1/\Gamma(b)$. The proportionality factor is found by putting $b = 1$, in which case the branch cut is not present and C_1 can be shrunk to a circle around the origin to yield the value $2\pi i$. Thus finally, the integral above is $2\pi i/\Gamma(b)$, and we obtain

$$W_1(a, b; 0) + W_2(a, b; 0) = 1 . \tag{36.20}$$

The wave function describing the scattering involves $W_{1,2}(-i\alpha, 1; ik\xi)$, and to obtain the scattering cross section we need the asymptotic behavior of the wave function. This is easily obtained from the integral representation (36.19). We have only to expand the binomial in powers of t/z and integrate term by term. This yields only an asymptotic expansion rather than a convergent series because the t integration goes to $|t| = \infty$ making the binomial expansion divergent over part of the integration range. For large $|z|$, however, this occurs only where the exponential is very small, and in the limit $|z| \to \infty$ the procedure becomes strictly valid. To order $1/\xi$

$$\begin{aligned} W_1(-i\alpha, 1; ik\xi) &\approx \frac{1}{2\pi i}\int_{C_1} e^t t^{-(1+i\alpha)}(-ik\xi)^{i\alpha}\left(1 - \frac{\alpha t}{k\xi}\right) dt \\ &= (-ik\xi)^{i\alpha}\left[\frac{1}{\Gamma(1 + i\alpha)} - \frac{\alpha}{k\xi}\frac{1}{\Gamma(i\alpha)}\right] \\ &= \frac{(-ik\xi)^{i\alpha}}{\Gamma(1 + i\alpha)}\left(1 - \frac{\alpha^2}{ik\xi}\right) \end{aligned} \tag{36.21}$$

We have used the result (36.20) and the property of the gamma function $z\Gamma(z) = \Gamma(1 + z)$. Similarly,

$$W_2(-i\alpha, 1; ik\xi) \approx \frac{(ik\xi)^{-(1+i\alpha)}}{\Gamma(-i\alpha)} e^{ik\xi} . \tag{36.22}$$

Now, we can write out the wave function (36.6) in the asymptotic region. It is

$$\begin{aligned} \psi(\xi, \eta) &\approx N \exp\left[ik\frac{\eta - \xi}{2}\right](W_1 + W_2) \\ &= N\frac{e^{\alpha\pi/2}}{\Gamma(1 + i\alpha)}\left\{\left(1 - \frac{\alpha^2}{ik\xi}\right)\exp\left[i\alpha \ln(1 - \cos\theta)\right]\right. \\ &\quad \times \exp\left[i(kz - \alpha \ln kr)\right] \\ &\quad + \frac{-\alpha}{k(1 - \cos\theta)}\frac{\Gamma(1 + i\alpha)}{\Gamma(1 - i\alpha)}\exp\left[-i\alpha \ln(1 - \cos\theta)\right] \\ &\quad \left. \times \frac{\exp\left[i(kr - \alpha \ln kr)\right]}{r}\right\} . \end{aligned} \tag{36.23}$$

This form is that expected for a scattering problem with a short range potential except for the phase distortion proportional to α and therefore to e^2 caused by the long tail of the Coulomb potential. We choose N to make the factor in front of the curly bracket unity and then write

$$\psi(r, \theta) = I + f(\theta)S\,. \tag{36.24}$$

Comparison of (36.24) with (36.23) shows that

$$I = \left(1 - \frac{\alpha^2}{ikr(1 - \cos\theta)}\right) \exp[i\alpha \ln(1 - \cos\theta)] \exp[i(kz - \alpha \ln kr)]\,, \tag{36.25}$$

$$S = \frac{\exp[i(kr - \alpha \ln kr)]}{r} \tag{36.26}$$

$$f(\theta) = \frac{ZZ'e^2}{\mu v_0^2} \frac{1}{\sin^2 \frac{1}{2}\theta} \exp[i(-\alpha \ln(1 - \cos\theta) + \pi + 2\sigma_0)]\,, \tag{36.27}$$

with σ_0 given by

$$\exp[2i\sigma_0] = \frac{\Gamma(1 + i\alpha)}{\Gamma(1 - i\alpha)}\,, \tag{36.28}$$

which is a number of modulus unity.

The cross section is the absolute square of the scattering amplitude $f(\theta)$. The phase factor here makes no difference and the result is clearly the Rutherford formula (36.1).

The amplitude of the wave function at large distance from the scattering center approaches unity. It is of interest to find the factor by which the wave function at the origin differs from this. To evaluate this we need the value of N, determined by comparing (36.25) and (36.23), and the value of $W_1 + W_2$ at the origin. The latter was given by (36.20) to be unity. We therefore have

$$|\psi(0)| = e^{-\alpha\pi/2}|\Gamma(1 + i\alpha)|\,. \tag{36.29}$$

For $\alpha > 0$ this is a reduced amplitude relative to the amplitude in the absence of the Coulomb potential, a result to be expected since the potential is repulsive. For $\alpha < 0$ the amplitude is enhanced. The enhancement factor $|\psi(0)|^2$ is used to estimate the effect of the Coulomb potential on the probability of an event such as a nuclear reaction which can take place when two charged particles are close together. It is essentially a barrier penetrability when $\alpha > 0$, as discussed in Section 25.

37. SCATTERING BY A MODIFIED COULOMB POTENTIAL

The Coulomb potential occurs in nature always in a modified form. There are two important kinds of modification which occur, those at long range and those at short range. The long range modification is produced by the screening of the central charge by charges of the opposite sign. It acts to eliminate the complications of the formulation given in the last section by eliminating the long Coulomb tail. It also eliminates the solubility of the Schrödinger equation in terms of known functions and is therefore of no advantage in those problems where extremely small angle scattering is not important. If the distance over which the potential is accurately a Coulomb potential is of the order of magnitude of, or less than, the de Broglie wavelength of the scattered particles, or if very small angle scattering is of interest, so that impact parameters of the order of the screening radius are important, then one must solve the problem using the screened potential. If one is solving the Coulomb problem by approximation methods such as the Born approximation, very great mathematical convenience is gained by using an exponentially screened potential with a long screening radius. In this way, Coulomb effects on processes such as bremsstrahlung can be calculated.

The modification we consider here is in the short range potential. For example, proton–proton scattering can be described by a pure Coulomb potential only at very low energies. At a few hundred keV the nuclear force between the protons becomes very important, though collisions in the higher partial waves, corresponding to large impact parameters, remain essentially pure Coulomb collisions. In order to describe combined Coulomb and nuclear scattering, we must have a description of Coulomb scattering in terms of partial waves. If the short range potential affects only the partial waves up to $l = L$, we write the total scattering amplitude in the form

$$f(\theta) = f^{(c)}(\theta) + \sum_{l=0}^{L} [f_l^{(M)} - f_l^{(c)}](2l+1)P_l(\cos\theta) \tag{37.1}$$

where $f_l^{(c)}$ is the lth Coulomb partial amplitude and $f_l^{(M)}$ the lth modified one. We obtain the expression for $f_l^{(c)}$ here and show how $f_l^{(M)}$ is obtained in terms of the short range potential.

The radial part of the Schrödinger equation for the pure Coulomb potential is

$$\frac{1}{r^2}\frac{d}{dr}(r^2F_l') + \frac{2\mu}{\hbar^2}\left[E - \frac{l(l+1)}{2\mu r^2} - \frac{ZZ'e^2}{r}\right]F_l = 0\,. \tag{37.2}$$

Introducing the independent variable z defined by

$$kr = \tfrac{1}{2}iz \tag{37.3}$$

with k defined by $2\mu E = \hbar^2k^2$ as usual, and defining the new function $u(z)$ by

$$F_l(r) = N(kr)^l e^{ikr}u(z)\,, \tag{37.4}$$

with the normalization N to be determined, the radial equation becomes

(37.5) $$zu'' + (2l + 2 - z)u' - (i\alpha + l + 1)u = 0\,.$$

This we recognize as the confluent hypergeometric equation. The solution regular at the origin is

(37.6) $$\begin{aligned} u(z) &= {}_1F_1(l + 1 + i\alpha, 2l + 2; -2ikr) \\ &= W_1 + W_2\,, \end{aligned}$$

where $W_{1,2}$ are the functions defined in (36.19).

The asymptotic expressions for $W_{1,2}$ with the present arguments are obtained in the same manner as (36.21). We need only the leading term in each:

(37.7) $$\begin{aligned} W_1(l + 1 + i\alpha, 2l + 2; -2ikr) &\approx \frac{\Gamma(2l + 2)}{\Gamma(l + 1 - i\alpha)}(2ikr)^{-l-1-i\alpha}\,, \\ W_2(l + 1 + i\alpha, 2l + 2; -2ikr) &\approx \frac{\Gamma(2l + 2)}{\Gamma(l + 1 + i\alpha)}(-2ikr)^{-l-1+i\alpha}e^{-2ikr}\,. \end{aligned}$$

These are now inserted in (37.4) to yield

(37.8) $$\begin{aligned} F_l(r) \approx{}& Ne^{\alpha\pi/2}i^{l+1}\frac{\Gamma(2l + 2)}{\Gamma(l + 1 + i\alpha)} \\ &\times\left[\frac{\Gamma(l + 1 + i\alpha)}{\Gamma(l + 1 - i\alpha)}\frac{e^{i(kr-\alpha\ln 2kr)}}{kr} - (-)^l\frac{e^{-i(kr-\alpha\ln 2kr)}}{kr}\right], \end{aligned}$$

which is of the form of an ingoing spherical wave plus an outgoing spherical wave except for the logarithmic phase distortion proportional to α. From this we can identify the Coulomb phase shift which we denote by σ_l, [cf., Equation (35.10)]

(37.9) $$\begin{aligned} \exp[2i\sigma_l] &= \frac{\Gamma(l + 1 + i\alpha)}{\Gamma(l + 1 - i\alpha)}\,, \\ \sigma_l &= \arg\Gamma(l + 1 + i\alpha)\,. \end{aligned}$$

Finally, we choose N so as to obtain

(37.10) $$F_l(r) \approx \frac{\sin(kr - \alpha\ln 2kr - l\pi/2 + \sigma_l)}{kr}\,.$$

This expression can be used to obtain the total Coulomb scattering amplitude by summing over l, as the Coulomb phase distortion is independent of l though it goes to infinity as $r \to \infty$.

In the presence of an additional short range potential, the radial function $R_l(r)$ is no longer given at large radius by the regular Coulomb function alone although it satisfies (37.2) in this region. We need an irregular solution of the Coulomb radial equation, and for convenience we choose it to have an asymptotic behavior $\pi/2$ out of phase with $F_l(r)$. This function is denoted by $G_l(r)$.

(37.11) $$G_l(r) \approx -\frac{\cos(kr - \alpha \ln 2kr - l\pi/2 + \sigma_l)}{kr}.$$

It is easily verified that

(37.12) $$G_l(r) = N(kr)^l e^{ikr} v(z)$$

with

(37.13) $$v(z) = (W_1 - W_2)/i\,.$$

The radial function in the presence of the short range potential is now written as a linear combination of the fundamental solutions F_l and G_l.

(37.14) $$R_l(r) = \cos \nu_l F_l(r) - \sin \nu_l G_l(r)\,,$$

where ν_l are the "nuclear" phase shifts. In the asymptotic region this amounts to adding the phase shift ν_l to the Coulomb phase shift σ_l. The corresponding scattering amplitude is written as in (35.11), with neglect of the common phase factor,

(37.15) $$\begin{aligned} f(\theta) &= \sum_l \frac{2l+1}{2ik}(e^{2i(\sigma_l+\nu_l)} - 1)P_l(\cos\theta) \\ &= \sum_l \frac{2l+1}{2ik}[(e^{2i\sigma_l} - 1) + e^{2i\sigma_l}(e^{2i\nu_l} - 1)]P_l(\cos\theta) \\ &= f^{(c)}(\theta) + f^{(nuc)}(\theta)\,, \end{aligned}$$

where

(37.16) $$f^{(nuc)}(\theta) = \frac{1}{2ik}\sum_l (2l+1)e^{2i\sigma_l}(e^{2i\nu_l} - 1)P_l(\cos\theta)\,.$$

The form obtained here is just that specified at the start of this section since ν_l vanishes for all partial waves not affected by the short range potential.

The method used to determine the nuclear phase shifts is to integrate, numerically or otherwise, the radial equation containing both Coulomb and short range potentials outward from the origin until the short range potential has negligible effect on the wave function. The resulting function is then a combination of the regular and irregular Coulomb functions as in (37.14) with an over-all amplitude factor added to allow for the arbitrary value used in starting the integration at the origin. The ratio of the coefficients in this combination determines the phase shift.

The cross section, being the square of the scattering amplitude, contains interference terms between the two types of scattering.

$$\frac{d\sigma}{d\Omega} = |f^{(c)}(\theta) + f^{(\mathrm{nuc})}(\theta)|^2$$

(37.17)

$$= |f^{(c)}(\theta)|^2 + |f^{(\mathrm{nuc})}(\theta)|^2 + 2\mathrm{Re}\, f^{(c)}(\theta)^* f^{(\mathrm{nuc})}(\theta) .$$

For very small angles of scattering the Coulomb term will dominate, since it diverges as $\theta \to 0$ and the nuclear interaction is assumed to affect only a few partial waves. If the nuclear effect is to be important at all, it must be so in the backward angles, θ near π, at least, and at high energies the nuclear part usually dominates here. In between, then, there is a region where the two amplitudes are comparable, which gives the possibility of determining the phase of the nuclear scattering amplitude by use of the interference term. Note, however, that this phase is not the phase the nuclear amplitude would have in the absence of the Coulomb field since according to the definition (37.15) of $f^{(nuc)}(\theta)$, this depends also on the Coulomb phase shift σ_l. One can still find the phase shift that $f^{(nuc)}(\theta)$ would have in the absence of the Coulomb field since the σ_l are known. At energies so high that the Coulomb scattering is restricted to importance only very near the forward direction, the individual Coulomb phase shifts become small, as is seen in (37.9). The large cross section results from the slow decrease of σ_l with l. At these energies, therefore, the nuclear phase shift ν_l is related to the nuclear scattering amplitude as if the Coulomb potential were absent, the factor $\exp[2i\sigma_l]$ in the definition being near unity for the low values of l, and the factor $\exp[2i\nu_l] - 1$ being negligible for the higher values of l.

38. THE GENERAL DESCRIPTION OF SCATTERING

In Section 35 a brief discussion was given of the way a scattering experiment is carried out. That discussion was adequate for the purpose of that section, the description of potential scattering. In this section we want to study a more general scattering problem and must repeat the previous discussion in more detail. We consider here a reaction of the type

$$A + B \to C + D . \tag{38.1}$$

Both the initial and final states contain two particles, though now these "particles" may be complex systems of other, more elementary particles in bound states. We restrict our attention to non-relativistic processes so that no particles are created or destroyed. The pair of particles in the final state, C and D, must therefore consist of the same more elementary particles as do A and B. We call these more elementary particles *permanent particles*. They themselves may be bound states of still more elementary particles. A typical example of the kind of reaction being discussed is the pickup reaction much studied in nuclear physics,

$$d + N^{14} \rightarrow N^{13} + t \tag{38.2}$$

in which a deuteron picks up a neutron from a nucleus to become a triton.

The permanent particles may be grouped into complex particles in a variety of ways. We are concerned only with groupings into two complex particles. Consider the initial state of the reaction (38.1). Particle A consists of some bound state of a set of the permanent particles, this state being labelled with an energy E_A, a spin J_A, and various other quantum numbers. The same is true for particle B, which contains all the remaining permanent particles, the labels being E_B, J_B, etc. Each of these bound states is described in the center of mass coordinate system for that particle. The initial state of the system is specified by giving the two sets of quantum numbers E, J, etc., the way these are combined, and the state of relative motion of the two mass centers. In combining the internal states the energies simply add, but the angular momenta can be combined in several ways unless one of them is zero. There are other variables such as isospin which are not simply additive.

Each set of internal quantum numbers of A and of B which are combined in a specified way defines a *channel* for the reaction. The initial state of the system is specified by giving the *entrance channel* I and the state of relative motion of the particles in that channel. Under the conditions of any scattering experiment the initial state relative motion must be described in terms of two non-overlapping wave packets. Similarly, the final state which is detected by the experimental equipment is specified by giving the *exit channel* F and the state of relative motion in that channel. Of course there are channels containing three or more particles, but we do not consider them here. If, for example, A and B are protons, there are four possible entrance channels, three triplet channels and one singlet channel, differing in how the two proton spins are combined.

The entire system is described by a Hamiltonian H which depends on the relative coordinates of all the permanent particles. The presence of only relative coordinates assures that momentum is conserved. To each channel c corresponds a splitting of H into two terms,

$$H = K_c + V_c\,. \tag{38.3}$$

K_c is the sum of the Hamiltonians describing the internal structure of each of the particles in channel c and the kinetic energy of their motion. V_c gives the interaction of the two particles in this channel. In the initial state of a scattering experiment the value of V_{I} is zero, as is that of V_{F} after the scattering.

The target particle, B, in a scattering experiment is localized on the macroscopic scale of slits and foils, but not on the microscopic scale of atomic spacings. We write its wave function as $\psi_B(\mathbf{x}_B,\xi_B)$, where ξ_B are the internal coordinates of B and $\mathbf{x}_B$ is the coordinate of the center of mass:

$$\psi_B(\mathbf{x}_B, \xi_B) = \int \frac{d^3p}{(2\pi\hbar)^3}\, \phi_B(\mathbf{p})\chi_B(\xi_B) \exp\,[i\mathbf{p}\cdot\mathbf{x}_B/\hbar]\,. \tag{38.4}$$

This wave packet is centered on the origin and $\mathbf{p}$ has zero expectation value:

$$\begin{aligned}\langle\mathbf{p}\rangle &= \frac{1}{N_B}\int \frac{d^3p}{(2\pi\hbar)^3}\, \phi_B{}^*(\mathbf{p})\mathbf{p}\phi_B(\mathbf{p}) \\ &= 0\,.\end{aligned} \tag{38.5}$$

ϕ_B has been normalized to the number of scatterers in the target. The incident particle is localized to a similar extent.

$$\psi_A(\mathbf{x}_A, \xi_A) = \int \frac{d^3p}{(2\pi\hbar)^3}\, \phi_A(\mathbf{p})\chi_A(\xi_A) \exp\,[i\mathbf{p}\cdot\mathbf{x}_A/\hbar]\,. \tag{38.6}$$

This packet is centered on a point remote from the origin and has a mean momentum in the general direction of the origin. ϕ_A is normalized to the number of particles in an incident pulse.

Let us now introduce the center of mass coordinate system for the two particles A and B.

$$\begin{aligned}\mathbf{X} &= \frac{m_A\mathbf{x}_A + m_B\mathbf{x}_B}{m_A + m_B} = M\left(\frac{\mathbf{x}_A}{m_B} + \frac{\mathbf{x}_B}{m_A}\right), \\ \mathbf{p} &= \frac{m_B\mathbf{p}_A - m_A\mathbf{p}_B}{m_A + m_B} = M\left(\frac{\mathbf{p}_A}{m_A} - \frac{\mathbf{p}_B}{m_B}\right), \\ \mathbf{x} &= \mathbf{x}_A - \mathbf{x}_B\,, \qquad \mathbf{P} = \mathbf{p}_A + \mathbf{p}_B\,, \qquad M = \frac{m_A m_B}{m_A + m_B}\,.\end{aligned} \tag{38.7}$$

The wave function Ψ_{I} at the initial time t_0, long before A and B interact, is

$$\begin{aligned}\Psi_{\mathrm{I}}(x) &= \chi_A(\xi_A)\chi_B(\xi_B)\int \frac{d^3p}{(2\pi\hbar)^3}\frac{d^3P}{(2\pi\hbar)^3} \\ &\times \phi_A\left(\mathbf{p} + \frac{M}{m_B}\mathbf{P}\right)\phi_B\left(-\mathbf{p} + \frac{M}{m_A}\mathbf{P}\right)\exp\,[i(\mathbf{P}\cdot\mathbf{X} + \mathbf{p}\cdot\mathbf{x})/\hbar]\,.\end{aligned} \tag{38.8}$$

The function

$$\chi_A(\xi_A)\chi_B(\xi_B) \exp\,[i\mathbf{p}\cdot\mathbf{x}/\hbar] \tag{38.9}$$

is an eigenfunction of the Hamiltonian K_{I} with total momentum zero. Thus,

(38.8) is an expansion of the initial state in eigenfunctions of K_{I}. The time dependence of the wave function is given by adding the exponential factor

$$\exp\left[-i\left(E_{\mathrm{I}}(\mathbf{p}) + \frac{\mathbf{p}^2}{2M}\right)\left(\frac{t - t_0}{\hbar}\right)\right]$$

to the integrand in (38.8). This is correct only for times before the particles A and B have begun to interact.

The time-dependent wave function, valid for all times, can be obtained from (38.8) by replacing the functions (38.9) appearing there by appropriate eigenfunctions of H. The eigenfunctions of H are complicated, as H contains interactions between all the permanent particles. Among these eigenfunctions is a set each of whose members $\psi_{c\mathbf{p}}^{(+)}(x)$ is asymptotically a plane wave in channel c plus outgoing waves in all channels. Another set exists each of whose

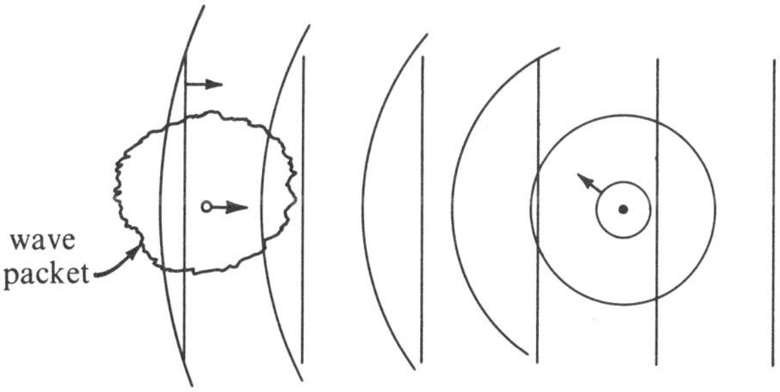

Fig. 38-1

members $\psi_{c\mathbf{p}}^{(-)}(x)$ is asymptotically a plane wave in channel c plus ingoing waves in all channels. Neither set is complete if more than one channel exists.

The state of the system at $t = t_0$, the initial state, can be expressed as a superposition of states $\psi_{c\mathbf{p}}^{(+)}(x)$ because these functions have the right ingoing waves, i.e., those coming from the plane wave. Not only is the expansion possible, but the expansion coefficients are just the same as those occurring in (38.8). To see this, we look at the geometry of the situation. Figure 38–1 illustrates what is going on. The $\psi^{(+)}$ wave function is a plane wave in the relative coordinate x plus outgoing spherical waves centered on the origin. Initially the wave packet is remote from the origin but is moving toward the origin without spreading much. When expanded in plane waves alone, only momenta in a rather small range of magnitudes and directions contribute essentially to the wave packet. At the initial location of the wave packet, the outgoing spherical waves associated with $\psi^{(+)}$ look like plane waves travelling in the direction opposite to that of the packet. They do not, therefore, contribute appreciably to the integral which gives the expansion coefficient, so this coefficient is that determined by plane waves alone.

The wave function for the scattering system can now be written for all times:

$$\Psi_{\mathrm{I}}(x, t) = \int \frac{d^3P}{(2\pi\hbar)^3} \frac{d^3p}{(2\pi\hbar)^3} \phi_A\left(\mathbf{p} + \frac{M\mathbf{P}}{m_B}\right)\phi_B\left(-\mathbf{p} + \frac{M\mathbf{P}}{m_A}\right)$$

$$\times\, \psi_{\mathrm{I}\mathbf{p}}^{(+)}(x) \exp\left[i\frac{\mathbf{P}\cdot\mathbf{x}}{\hbar}\right] \tag{38.10}$$

$$\times \exp\left[-i\left(E_{\mathrm{I}}(\mathbf{p}) + \frac{\mathbf{P}^2}{2M}\right)\frac{(t - t_0)}{\hbar}\right]$$

We imagine that the experimenter has provided two detectors. The first detector will register if a particle of the kind C traverses it, and not otherwise, while the second will respond to a particle of the kind D only. These counters are localized in space relative to the wave packets describing the target particle B and the incident particle A so that the registration of a detector implies the existence of a wave packet with a mean momentum pointing from the origin of coordinates to the counter. The registration of the counter does not give detailed information about the shape of the wave packet, and the relative phase of the wave packets associated with the two counters is not detected either. For any ordinary scattering experiment these are irrelevant. What is important is that we can construct a wave packet which we know will register a count even though we cannot deduce the form of the packet from the count.

Let the wave packet

$$\chi_c(\xi_c) \int \frac{d^3p}{(2\pi\hbar)^3} \phi_c(\mathbf{p}_c) \exp\left[i\, \mathbf{p}_c \cdot \mathbf{x}_c/\hbar\right] \tag{38.11}$$

cause counter one to register, and the wave packet

$$\chi_D(\xi_D) \int \frac{d^3p}{(2\pi\hbar)^3} \phi_D(\mathbf{p}_D) \exp\left[i\, \mathbf{p}_D \cdot \mathbf{x}_D/\hbar\right] \tag{38.12}$$

cause counter two to register. If the final state is given by the product of these two wave packets, then both counters will register.

The final state described above is expressed as a superposition of eigenfunctions of K_{F}. By an argument like that given for the entrance channel, this wave function can be expressed as a superposition of eigenfunctions of H of the kind $\Psi_{\mathrm{F}\mathbf{p}'}^{(-)}(x)$. We must use plane waves plus ingoing waves here because the wave packets are moving apart, and the outgoing part of the wave function must correspond to just the plane wave of the relative motion. Again, the replacement of the plane waves by the exact eigenfunctions does not change the expansion coefficients. Thus, we write a possible final state wave function as

(38.13)
$$\Psi_F(x) = \int \frac{d^3P'}{(2\pi\hbar)^3}\frac{d^3p'}{(2\pi\hbar)^3}\phi_c\left(\mathbf{p}' + \frac{M'}{m_D}\mathbf{P}'\right)\phi_D\left(-\mathbf{p}' + \frac{M}{m_c}\mathbf{P}'\right) \times \psi_{\mathrm{F}\mathbf{p}'}{}^{(-)}(x)\exp\left[i\,\mathbf{P}'\cdot\mathbf{X}/\hbar\right].$$

The center of mass coordinate **X** is common to all channels. The relative coordinate x is constructed out of the coordinates of the permanent particles in a way which depends on the channel.

The probability amplitude for this final state to occur in the state which the initial state has become at time t_1 is the scalar product of the wave functions. It is

(38.14)
$$\begin{aligned} A_{\mathrm{FI}} = \int d^3X\, d(x) & \frac{d^3P}{(2\pi\hbar)^3}\frac{d^3P'}{(2\pi\hbar)^3}\frac{d^3p}{(2\pi\hbar)^3}\frac{d^3p'}{(2\pi\hbar)^3} \\ & \times \exp\left[i(\mathbf{P}' - \mathbf{P})\cdot\mathbf{X}/\hbar\right] \\ & \times \phi_c{}^*\phi_D{}^*\phi_A\phi_B\psi_{\mathrm{F}\mathbf{p}'}{}^{(-)*}(x)\psi_{\mathrm{I}\mathbf{p}}{}^{(+)}(x) \\ & \times \exp\left[-i\left(E_{\mathrm{I}}(\mathbf{p}) + \frac{\mathbf{P}'}{2M_{\mathrm{I}}}\right)\frac{(t_1 - t_0)}{\hbar}\right] \end{aligned}$$

The integration over (x) means integration and summation over all coordinates other than the center of mass coordinate **X**. This expression shows that momentum and energy are conserved. Momentum conservation follows from the integration over **X**, which yields $(2\pi\hbar)^3\delta(\mathbf{P}' - \mathbf{P})$. Energy conservation follows from the orthogonality of the eigenfunctions $\psi_{\mathrm{I}\mathbf{p}}{}^{(+)}(x)$ and $\psi_{\mathrm{F}\mathbf{p}'}{}^{(-)}(x)$ for different eigenvalues of H.

The only place that the interaction between the particles enters this expression is in the quantity

(38.15)
$$S_{\mathrm{FI}}(\mathbf{p}', \mathbf{p}) = \int d(x)\,\psi_{\mathrm{F}\mathbf{p}'}{}^{(-)*}(x)\psi_{\mathrm{I}\mathbf{p}}{}^{(+)}(x)\,.$$

The remainder involves the shape of the initial and final wave packets, and this is, as we have seen, only partially determined by the experimental arrangement. The details of the energy resolution and collimation achieved by the source and detectors are described by these packets, and these are accurately described by classical mechanics. We therefore restrict our discussion to the interpretation of $S_{\mathrm{FI}}(\mathbf{p}', \mathbf{p})$ as given in (38.15). This expression is very difficult to arrive at without using the idea of wave packets.

The quantity $S_{\mathrm{FI}}(\mathbf{p}', \mathbf{p})$ is called an element of the *S-matrix*. From its definition (38.15) it is the expansion coefficient of $\psi_{\mathrm{I}\mathbf{p}}{}^{(+)}(x)$ in terms of eigenfunctions $\psi_{\mathrm{F}\mathbf{p}'}{}^{(-)}(x)$. If the two particle channels alone are considered, these wave functions do not constitute complete sets of states. If they are generalized to complete sets, then S becomes a unitary matrix. We need not make this generalization in detail here.

The incident beam is represented by $\psi_{\mathrm{I}\mathbf{p}}^{(+)}(x)$. For large values of the relative coordinate $\mathbf{x}$, only the plane wave part is large, so the incident beam is given by the plane wave part of $\psi_{\mathrm{I}\mathbf{p}}^{(+)}(x)$. The scattered beam is given likewise by the plane wave part of $\psi_{\mathrm{F}\mathbf{p}'}^{(-)}(x)$. The amplitude of the former is unity, while the amplitude of the latter is $S_{\mathrm{FI}}(\mathbf{p}', \mathbf{p})$. The incident flux is the initial relative velocity p/M. We calculate the scattered current in a solid angle $d\Omega$ in a region where there is no incident beam.

It is useful to split S into two parts. One part gives the unscattered beam, the other the scattered beam. The conservation of energy is taken explicitly into account by writing

$$S_{\mathrm{FI}}(\mathbf{p}', \mathbf{p}) = (2\pi\hbar)^3\delta(\mathbf{p}' - \mathbf{p})\,\delta_{\mathrm{FI}} - 2\pi\hbar i\delta\,(E_{\mathrm{F}}(\mathbf{p}') - E_{\mathrm{I}}(\mathbf{p}))T_{\mathrm{FI}}(\mathbf{p}', \mathbf{p})\,. \tag{38.16}$$

In the region to which the incident beam does not penetrate, the first term gives nothing. $T_{\mathrm{FI}}(\mathbf{p}', \mathbf{p})$ is now a continuous function of its arguments, defined only for momenta which conserve energy. Its continuation to other momenta by establishing that it is an analytic function of its arguments is the subject of dispersion theory. It is of great interest at the present time, but we do not enter into this here.

The contributions to $\psi_{\mathrm{I}\mathbf{p}}^{(+)}(x)$ from states $\psi_{\mathrm{F}\mathbf{p}'}^{(-)}(x)$ with momenta in the direction $\mathbf{p}'$ are

$$\begin{aligned}
&\int S_{\mathrm{FI}}(\mathbf{p}', \mathbf{p})\psi_{\mathrm{F}\mathbf{p}'}^{(-)}(x)\frac{dp'}{2\pi\hbar} \\
&= \int -2\pi\hbar i\,\delta\left(\frac{p'^2}{2M'} - E_{\mathrm{F}}^{kin}\right)T_{\mathrm{FI}}(\mathbf{p}', \mathbf{p})\psi_{\mathrm{F}\mathbf{p}'}^{(-)}(x)\frac{dp'}{(2\pi\hbar)} \\
&= -\left[\frac{iM'}{p'}T_{\mathrm{FI}}(\mathbf{p}', \mathbf{p})\psi_{\mathrm{F}\mathbf{p}'}^{(-)}(x)\right]_{E_{\mathrm{F}}(p') = E_{\mathrm{I}}(p)}\,.
\end{aligned} \tag{38.17}$$

In the asymptotic region, the amplitude of $\psi_{\mathrm{F}\mathbf{p}'}^{(-)}$ is unity, so that the current carried in this direction is the absolute square of the coefficient of $\psi_{\mathrm{F}\mathbf{p}'}^{(-)}$ times the velocity p'/M' in the exit channel.

$$j_{\mathbf{p}'} = \frac{M'}{p'}\,|\,T_{\mathrm{FI}}(\mathbf{p}', \mathbf{p})\,|^2\,. \tag{38.18}$$

The total current carried into the solid angle $d\Omega$ is the current $j_{\mathbf{p}'}$ multiplied by the "number of states" with momentum vectors in the solid angle, namely $p'^2\,d\Omega/(2\pi\hbar)^2$, obtained from (26.17). Thus, the scattered current per unit solid angle is

$$j = \frac{1}{(2\pi\hbar)^2}M'p'\,|\,T_{\mathrm{FI}}(\mathbf{p}', \mathbf{p})\,|^2\,. \tag{38.19}$$

The differential cross section for scattering from channel I into a solid angle

$d\Omega$ in channel F, the channel F momentum being such as to conserve energy, is

$$\frac{d\sigma}{d\Omega} = \frac{j}{p/M} = \frac{1}{(2\pi\hbar)^2}\frac{MM'p'}{P}\,|\,T_{\mathrm{FI}}(\mathbf{p}', \mathbf{p})\,|^2\,. \tag{38.20}$$

The expression (38.20) for the cross section is very similar to (35.8) derived for potential scattering. The only difference lies in the numerical factors in front of $|T|^2$ and $|f|^2$. For this reason, $T_{\mathrm{FI}}(\mathbf{p}', \mathbf{p})$ is called a scattering amplitude. It is instructive to relate the development given here to that given in Section 35, and, hence, to find the connection between T and the phase shifts used in potential scattering.

In potential scattering there is only one channel so that no channel index is needed. The eigenfunctions of H were written in (35.7) as plane waves plus outgoing spherical waves in the asymptotic region. This we now denote by $\psi_{\mathbf{p}}^{(+)}(\mathbf{r})$. Expanded in partial waves, it is given by (35.10) which reads

$$\psi_{\mathbf{p}}^{(+)}(\mathbf{r}) \approx \frac{1}{2ikr}\sum_{l=0}^{\infty}(2l+1)P_l(\cos\theta)[e^{2i\delta_l}e^{ikr} - (-)^l e^{-ikr}]\,. \tag{38.21}$$

We now want to construct the corresponding $\psi_{\mathbf{p}}^{(-)}$. This is related to $\psi_{\mathbf{p}}^{(+)}$ by time reversal, which involves (as shown in Section 23) taking the complex conjugate and replacing $\cos\theta$ by $-\cos\theta$. The latter reverses the sign of $\mathbf{p}$. Of course $p = |\mathbf{p}|$ remains positive. The expression for $\psi_{\mathbf{p}}^{(-)}$ is then

$$\begin{aligned}\psi_{\mathbf{p}}^{(-)}(\mathbf{r}) &\approx \frac{1}{-2ikr}\sum_{l=0}^{\infty}(2l+1)P_l(-\cos\theta)[e^{-2i\delta_l}e^{-ikr} - (-)^l e^{ikr}]\\ &= \frac{1}{2ikr}\sum_{l=0}^{\infty}(2l+1)P_l(\cos\theta)\,[e^{ikr} - (-)^l e^{-2i\delta_l}\,e^{-ikr}]\\ &= \frac{1}{2ikr}\sum_{l=0}^{\infty}(2l+1)P_l(\cos\theta)\,e^{-2i\delta_l}[e^{2i\delta_l}e^{ikr} - (-)^l e^{-ikr}]\,.\end{aligned} \tag{38.22}$$

In the notation of kets the S-matrix is defined by

$$S_{\mathrm{FI}}(\mathbf{p}', \mathbf{p}) = \langle F, \mathbf{p}'|S|\mathrm{I}, \mathbf{p}\rangle\,, \tag{38.23}$$

where the states are pure plane wave states. The entire effect of the interaction is contained in S. In our present case of potential scattering the channel indices are superfluous. Thus,

$$\langle\mathbf{p}'|S|\mathbf{p}\rangle = \langle\mathbf{p}', -\,|\mathbf{p}, +\rangle\,. \tag{38.24}$$

In order to evaluate the right side, we must express the wave functions whose asymptotic forms are given in (38.21) and (38.22) in the same coordinate system. As they stand, in $\psi_{\mathbf{p}}^{(+)}(\mathbf{r})$, θ is measured away from $\mathbf{p}$, and in $\psi_{\mathbf{p}'}^{(-)}(\mathbf{r})$, θ is measured away from $\mathbf{p}'$. The spherical harmonic addition theorem enables us to rewrite the Legendre polynomials. This theorem states that

$$\frac{2l+1}{4\pi} P_l(\cos\Theta) = \sum_{m=-l}^{l} Y_{lm}(\theta,\phi) Y_{lm}^*(\theta',\phi'), \tag{38.25}$$

where Θ is the angle between two directions whose polar angles are θ, ϕ and θ', ϕ'.

$$\cos\Theta = \cos\theta\cos\theta' + \sin\theta\sin\theta'\cos(\phi-\phi'). \tag{38.26}$$

The arguments of a spherical harmonic are represented by a unit vector, denoted by a caret. The argument of the Legendre polynomial in $\psi_{\mathbf{p}}^{(+)}(\mathbf{r})$ is $\hat{\mathbf{r}}\cdot\hat{\mathbf{p}}$. We may write

$$(2l+1)P_l(\hat{\mathbf{r}}\cdot\hat{\mathbf{p}}) = 4\pi \sum_{m=-l}^{l} Y_{lm}(\hat{\mathbf{r}}) Y_{lm}^*(\hat{\mathbf{p}}), \tag{38.27}$$

and similarly for $P_l(\hat{\mathbf{r}}\cdot\hat{\mathbf{p}}')$. Thus, the scalar product on the right of (38.24) may be written out as

$$\begin{aligned} &\int d^3x \frac{4\pi\hbar}{-2ip'r} \sum_{l'=0}^{\infty} \sum_{m'=-l'}^{l'} Y_{l'm'}(\hat{\mathbf{p}}') Y_{l'm'}^*(\hat{\mathbf{r}} e)^{2i\delta_l} u_{p'l'}^*(r) \\ &\times \frac{4\pi\hbar}{2ipr} \sum_{l=0}^{\infty} \sum_{m=-l}^{l} Y_{lm}^*(\hat{\mathbf{p}}) Y_{lm}(\hat{\mathbf{r}}) u_{pl}(r). \end{aligned} \tag{38.28}$$

Here $u_{pl}(r)$ is the exact, normalized, radial wave function whose asymptotic form is $[e^{2i\delta_l}e^{ikr} - (-)^l e^{-ikr}]$. This is normalized according to the convention of Section 16. The radial integration therefore yields $2\pi\hbar\,\delta(p'-p)$. The spherical harmonics are normalized to unity and yield $\delta_{l'l}\,\delta_{m'm}$. Thus,

$$\begin{aligned} \langle \mathbf{p}'|S|\mathbf{p}\rangle &= \frac{4\pi^2\hbar^2}{p^2} \sum_{l=0}^{\infty} \sum_{m=-l}^{l} Y_{lm}(\hat{\mathbf{p}}') Y_{lm}^*(\hat{\mathbf{p}} e)^{2i\delta_l}\, 2\pi\hbar\,\delta(p'-p) \\ &= \frac{\pi\hbar^2}{p^2} 2\pi\hbar\,\delta(p'-p) \sum_l (2l+1) P_l(\hat{\mathbf{p}}'\cdot\hat{\mathbf{p}}) e^{2i\delta_l}. \end{aligned} \tag{38.29}$$

The constants may be checked by letting $\delta_l = 0$. Then, according to (16.22), the sum becomes just $4\pi\,\delta(\hat{\mathbf{p}}' - \hat{\mathbf{p}})$ so that the whole right side becomes

$$\frac{(2\pi\hbar)^3}{p^2} \delta(p'-p)\,\delta(\hat{\mathbf{p}}'-\hat{\mathbf{p}}) = (2\pi\hbar)^3\,\delta(\mathbf{p}'-\mathbf{p}) \tag{38.30}$$

as it should.

In the one channel case, S must be unitary. In many-channel problems S is also unitary, but all channels must be included once and only once. The unitary condition is a statement that a system prepared in any way, in particular in a two particle channel, must end up in some final state. Thus

$$\sum_{F,\,\alpha_F} \langle I, \alpha_I|S^\dagger|F, \alpha_F\rangle \langle F, \alpha_F|S|I, \alpha_I\rangle = \sum_{F,\,\alpha_F} |\langle F, \alpha_F|S|I, \alpha_I\rangle|^2 = 1\,, \tag{38.31}$$

where F, α_F label a complete set of states. We have given an explicit definition of S only for two particle channels.

It is often useful to have a partial wave decomposition of an operator which commutes with $\mathbf{l}^2$ and which is therefore diagonal in l. The partial wave decomposition of S is given essentially by (38.21) and (38.22), where one sees that within a partial wave the state $|\mathbf{p}, -\rangle$ differs from $|\mathbf{p}, +\rangle$ only by the factor $\exp[-2i\,\delta_l]$. Since $|\mathbf{p}', -\rangle$ appears as a bra, we define the lth component of S, S_l, by

$$S_l = e^{2i\delta_l}\,. \tag{38.32}$$

Thus,

$$\langle \mathbf{p}'|S|\mathbf{p}\rangle = \frac{\pi\hbar^2}{p^2}\, 2\pi\hbar\, \delta(p' - p) \sum_{l=0}^{\infty} (2l+1) P_l(\hat{\mathbf{p}}' \cdot \hat{\mathbf{p}}) S_l\,. \tag{38.33}$$

A similar expansion can be made for any A diagonal in l. It has a somewhat more complicated angular dependence than (38.33) if A is not also diagonal in m, as, for example, if A is a spin-orbit coupling $\mathbf{l} \cdot \boldsymbol{\sigma}$. We can also make a partial wave decomposition of T as defined by (38.16). We obtain, using (38.30),

$$\langle \mathbf{p}'|S|\mathbf{p}\rangle = (2\pi\hbar)^3\, \delta(\mathbf{p}' - \mathbf{p}) + \frac{\pi\hbar^2}{p^2}\, 2\pi\hbar\, \delta(E' - E) \frac{m}{p} \times \sum_{l=0}^{\infty} (2l+1) P_l(\hat{\mathbf{p}}' \cdot \hat{\mathbf{p}})(e^{2i\delta_l} - 1)\,. \tag{38.34}$$

Thus,

$$\langle \mathbf{p}'|T|\mathbf{p}\rangle = \frac{i\pi\hbar^2}{p^2} \frac{m}{p} \sum_{l=0}^{\infty} (2l+1) P_l(\hat{\mathbf{p}}' \cdot \hat{\mathbf{p}})(e^{2i\delta_l} - 1)\,. \tag{38.35}$$

Comparing this with the defining equation (38.29) for a partial wave decomposition, we see that

$$T_l = \frac{im}{p}(e^{2i\delta_l} - 1) \tag{38.36}$$
$$= -\frac{2m}{p} e^{i\delta_l} \sin \delta_l .$$

This exhibits T as a function of the phase shifts.

In the development given so far, the permanent particles have been treated as distinguishable, since no requirement of symmetry or of antisymmetry has been placed upon the states of the system. If there are identical particles among those making up the particle A, for example, then the initial wave packet describing particle A must be constructed with the proper symmetry. The same goes for the other particles. If there are identical permanent particles, say of type α, in both A and B, there is no need to symmetrize the product of the initial wave packets in the coordinates of these particles because in the initial state they belong to non-overlapping wave packets and can be regarded as distinguished by the packet to which they belong. These identical permanent particles will also be present in C and D. There is, however, no way to tell whether a permanent particle of type α, which was initially in A, ends up in C or in D, if both of these contain permanent particles of this type. Thus, the final state may be arrived at in more than one way, depending on how the identical permanent particles from A and B are distributed in C and D. This multiplicity is automatically included if the final state has the proper symmetry under permutation of *all* identical permanent particles.

A simple example will illustrate what has been said above. Let A and B be single, identical particles, and let C and D be the same as A and B. According to the above, the initial state need not be symmetrized, but the final state must be. The scattering amplitude then contains the following possibilities:

(i) $A \to C$ and $B \to D$,

(ii) $A \to D$ and $B \to C$.

The amplitudes for these individual possibilities are to be added if the final state is symmetric and subtracted if it is antisymmetric. When A, B, C, D are alpha particles, the final state must be symmetric, as these are bosons. In the Coulomb scattering of two alpha particles, then, the scattering amplitude for detecting an alpha particle at angle θ in the center of mass system is the sum of the amplitudes for angle θ and for $\pi - \theta$ as given in (36.27). If the particles are protons, the result is dependent on the channel involved. In the singlet channel where the spin state is antisymmetric, the spatial state is symmetric and the amplitudes for θ and $\pi - \theta$ are added. In the triplet channels they are subtracted. The Coulomb interaction does not cause any singlet–triplet transitions. For unpolarized protons the cross section is

$$\frac{d\sigma}{d\Omega} = \tfrac{1}{4}|f(\theta)+f(\pi-\theta)|^2 + \tfrac{3}{4}|f(\theta)-f(\pi-\theta)|^2 \tag{38.37}$$

$$= |f(\theta)|^2 + |f(\pi-\theta)|^2 - \mathrm{Re}\, f^*(\theta)f(\pi-\theta)\,,$$

since there are three triplet channels and one singlet channel.

Symmetrization questions can become complicated. For example, is it correct to treat alpha particles as single bosons when they consist of four fermions? It is, but we do not justify it here. (Such questions are discussed in Goldberger and Watson.*)

39. THE INTEGRAL EQUATIONS OF SCATTERING THEORY

The scattering of a particle by a central potential is described by the phase shifts δ_l. The connection between the dynamics of the system and the phase shifts is established by integrating the radial Schrödinger equation by one means or another. When a more general scattering process is to be described, the phase shifts are replaced by elements of the T-matrix as in the previous section, and then the connection between the dynamics and these T-matrix elements must be established. To do this in a way with any claims to mathematical rigor is difficult and we forego any such attempt. We try to make the formulation given seem plausible, but go no further.

The problem facing us is to calculate the elements of the S- or T-matrix starting from the Hamiltonian describing the system. The Schrödinger equation must be solved subject to the boundary condition that for $r \to \infty$ the solution consists of a plane wave plus outgoing waves. This boundary condition is separate from the Schrödinger equation and cannot be included in it. It is possible to construct an integral equation which is equivalent to the Schrödinger equation together with the boundary condition, which is a great advantage. We do this in detail when the system is a particle in a potential. The result is then extrapolated to much more complicated systems without proof.

The equation to be discussed first is written

$$(E - K(\mathbf{p}))\psi^{(+)}(\mathbf{x}) = V(\mathbf{x})\psi^{(+)}(\mathbf{x})\,, \tag{39.1}$$

where $K(\mathbf{p})$ is the kinetic energy and $V(\mathbf{x})$ the potential. For simplicity we assume that there are no bound states of the system, and that to every eigenvalue of K there corresponds one of $H = K + V$ and vice versa. $\psi(\mathbf{x})$ is to behave asymptotically like a plane wave and an outgoing spherical wave. It is therefore denoted by $\psi^{(+)}(\mathbf{x})$. The purely outgoing character is only possible

*M. L. Goldberger and K. M. Watson, *Collision Theory*, John Wiley and Sons, New York, 1964.

for $r \longrightarrow \infty$ where the potential is negligible, and so can be specified in connection with the free particle Hamiltonian $K(\mathbf{p})$.

If $V(\mathbf{x})\psi^{(+)}(\mathbf{x})$ were a known function, $f(\mathbf{x})$ say, then (39.1) would be an inhomogeneous equation with a source term $f(\mathbf{x})$.

(39.2) $$[E - K(\mathbf{p})]\psi^{(+)}(\mathbf{x}) = f(\mathbf{x}) .$$

This source is to yield outgoing waves, so we write the solution as

(39.3) $$\psi^{(+)}(\mathbf{x}) = \phi(\mathbf{x}) + \int d^3x\, G^{(+)}(\mathbf{x}, \mathbf{x}')f(\mathbf{x}') ,$$

where $G^{(+)}(\mathbf{x}, \mathbf{x}')$ is a Green's function. It satisfies the differential equation

(39.4) $$[E - K(\mathbf{p})]G^{(+)}(\mathbf{x}, \mathbf{x}') = \delta(\mathbf{x} - \mathbf{x}') .$$

Since the coordinates appear only in the combination $\mathbf{x} - \mathbf{x}'$, G is a function of $\mathbf{x} - \mathbf{x}'$. $\phi(\mathbf{x})$ is a solution of the homogeneous equation. If $\phi(\mathbf{x}) = \exp [i\mathbf{p} \cdot \mathbf{x}/\hbar]$ (a plane wave of momentum $\mathbf{p}$), and if $G^{(+)}(\mathbf{x} - \mathbf{x}')$ contains only outgoing waves for large values of $|\mathbf{x}|$, the solution (39.2) would be the desired one. Equation (39.1) is, however, not inhomogeneous. The right side is unknown. Hence, instead of (39.3) which gives an explicit solution of the inhomogeneous equation (39.2), we obtain the integral equation

(39.5) $$\psi^{(+)}(\mathbf{x}) = \phi(\mathbf{x}) + \int d^3x\, G^{(+)}(\mathbf{x} - \mathbf{x}')V(\mathbf{x}')\psi^{(+)}(\mathbf{x}') .$$

The potential, which is the cause of the scattering, leads to outgoing waves at $r \longrightarrow \infty$ because $G^{(+)}(\mathbf{x} - \mathbf{x}')$ is chosen to do this. We must find $G^{(+)}(\mathbf{x} - \mathbf{x}')$ before the solution of (39.5) can be discussed.

The free particle Green's functions are very simple in momentum space, but must be expressed in coordinate space to be interpreted. In momentum space, (39.4) reads

(39.6) $$[E - K(\mathbf{p})]G_E(\mathbf{p}) = 1 .$$

A solution of this is

(39.7) $$G_E(\mathbf{p}) = \frac{1}{E - K(\mathbf{p})} ,$$

where $K(\mathbf{p}) \neq E$. At $K(\mathbf{p}) = E$ the solution is not defined. In the end we want E to be a physical energy which is an eigenvalue of $K(p)$, but for the moment let us replace E by a complex variable z. Since $K(\mathbf{p})$ has only real eigenvalues, $G_z(\mathbf{p})$ is defined for every complex z. We get different Green's functions by letting z approach real, positive values in different ways. Thus, we consider

(39.8) $$G_z(\mathbf{p}) = \frac{1}{z - K(\mathbf{p})} , \qquad K(p) = \frac{\mathbf{p}^2}{2m} .$$

The coordinate space Green's function is now given by

$$G(\mathbf{x}) = \int \frac{d^3p}{(2\pi\hbar)^3} \frac{1}{z - \mathbf{p}^2/2m} \exp[i\mathbf{p}\cdot\mathbf{x}/\hbar]$$

(39.9)
$$= \int_0^\infty \frac{p^2\,dp}{(2\pi\hbar)^3} \int_{-1}^1 2\pi\,d\mu \frac{-2m}{p^2 - 2mz} \exp[ipr\mu/\hbar]$$

$$= \int_0^\infty \frac{p^2\,dp}{(2\pi\hbar)^3} \frac{-4\pi m}{p^2 - 2mz} \left\{ \frac{\exp[ipr/\hbar] - \exp[-ipr/\hbar]}{ipr/\hbar} \right\}.$$

In the integration over the second term, replacing p by $-p$ enables us to write

(39.10)
$$G(\mathbf{x}) = \int_{-\infty}^\infty \frac{p\,dp}{(2\pi\hbar)^2} \frac{2im}{p^2 - 2mz} \frac{1}{r} \exp[ipr/\hbar].$$

The presence of the exponential factor permits us to close the path of integration in the upper half of the complex p-plane. The integrand has two simple poles, at $p = \pm(2mz)^{1/2} = \pm p'$, where p' is chosen to have a positive imaginary part. The situation is shown in Figure 39–1. Clearly only the pole at p' contributes to the integral, and we get

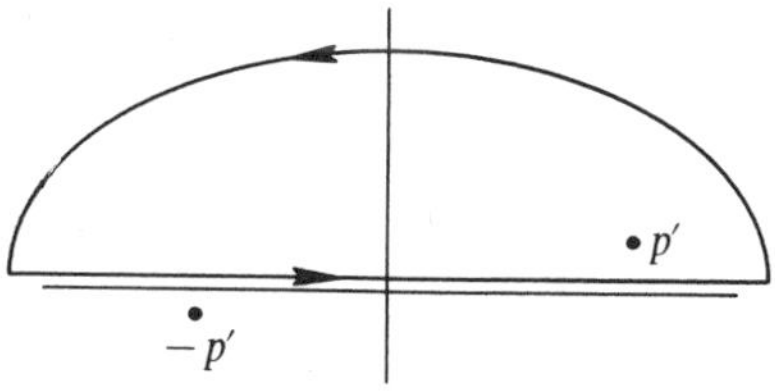

Fig. 39-1

(39.11)
$$G(\mathbf{x}) = 2\pi i \frac{2im}{(2\pi\hbar)^2} \frac{p'}{2p'} \frac{1}{r} \exp[ip'r/\hbar]$$

$$= \frac{-1}{2\pi\hbar^2} \frac{1}{r} \exp[ip'r/\hbar].$$

We now want p' to tend toward a real limit so that z tends toward a positive real number. There are two ways to do this, letting p' have first a positive and then a negative real part. (i) $p' = p + i\eta$, $p, \eta > 0$. As $\eta \to 0$ we obtain

(39.12)
$$G^{(+)}(\mathbf{x}) = \frac{-1}{2\pi\hbar^2} \frac{1}{r} \exp[ipr/\hbar]$$

which does describe an outgoing wave. (ii) $p' = -p + i\eta$, $p, \eta > 0$. Now as $\eta \to 0$ we obtain

$$G^{(-)}(\mathbf{x}) = \frac{-1}{2\pi\hbar^2}\frac{1}{r}\exp\left[-ipr/\hbar\right], \tag{39.13}$$

which describes ingoing waves. The Green's function needed in (39.5) is that given by (39.12), i.e., with $p' = p + i\eta$. When p' is so given, the energy $E = z^2/2m$ has a small positive imaginary part, $i\epsilon$, which tends toward zero. When p' is given by (ii) above, E has a small negative imaginary part, $-i\epsilon$. Thus, we can distinguish the outgoing Green's function in momentum space, $G_E{}^{(+)}(\mathbf{p})$, from the ingoing Green's function $G_E{}^{(-)}(\mathbf{p})$ by writing

$$\begin{aligned} G_E{}^{(+)}(\mathbf{p}) &= \frac{1}{E - K(\mathbf{p}) + i\epsilon}, \\ G_E{}^{(-)}(\mathbf{p}) &= \frac{1}{E - K(\mathbf{p}) - i\epsilon}, \end{aligned} \tag{39.14}$$

with the understanding that E is real and that the limit $\epsilon \to 0^+$ is taken after all momentum integrations have been done.

We now write (39.5) in ket notation.

$$|\mathbf{p}, +\rangle = |\mathbf{p}\rangle + \frac{1}{E - K + i\epsilon} V|\mathbf{p}, +\rangle\,. \tag{39.15}$$

The integration is concealed in the operator products which involve $V(\mathbf{x})$, which is not diagonal in the momentum representation. The corresponding ingoing state is given by

$$|\mathbf{p}, -\rangle = |\mathbf{p}\rangle + \frac{1}{E - K - i\epsilon} V|\mathbf{p}, -\rangle\,. \tag{39.16}$$

In these two equations the Green's function is explicitly known, but the unknown state appears on both sides. Another form of equation equivalent to this is

$$\begin{aligned} |\mathbf{p}, +\rangle &= \left(1 + \frac{1}{E - H + i\epsilon} V\right) |\mathbf{p}\rangle\,, \\ |\mathbf{p}, -\rangle &= \left(1 + \frac{1}{E - H - i\epsilon} V\right) |\mathbf{p}\rangle\,, \end{aligned} \tag{39.17}$$

as is verified by application of $(E - H \pm i\epsilon)$ and recalling that $(E - K)|\mathbf{p}\rangle = 0$. Here the Green's function contains H rather than K and it is therefore complicated, but the state $|\mathbf{p}, +\rangle$ appears only on the left.

We now have expressions for $|\mathbf{p}, +\rangle$ and $|\mathbf{p}, -\rangle$, so that we can construct the elements of the S-matrix. Using (39.17) we get

$$
\begin{aligned}
\langle \mathbf{p}'|S|\mathbf{p}\rangle &= \langle \mathbf{p}', -|\mathbf{p}, +\rangle \\
&= \left\{\langle \mathbf{p}', +| + \langle \mathbf{p}'|V\left(\frac{1}{E' - H + i\epsilon} - \frac{1}{E' - H - i\epsilon}\right)\right\}|\mathbf{p}, +\rangle \\
&= \langle \mathbf{p}', + |\mathbf{p}, +\rangle + \langle \mathbf{p}'|V\frac{-2i\epsilon}{(E' - H)^2 + \epsilon^2}|\mathbf{p}, +\rangle \\
&= \langle \mathbf{p}', + |\mathbf{p}, +\rangle + \frac{-2i\epsilon}{(E' - E)^2 + \epsilon^2}\langle \mathbf{p}'|V|\,\mathbf{p}, +\rangle\,.
\end{aligned} \tag{39.18}
$$

The first scalar product is just $(2\pi\hbar)^3\,\delta(\mathbf{p}' - \mathbf{p})$. It is a consequence of the last part of (9.16) that

$$
\lim_{\epsilon\to 0}\frac{\epsilon}{x^2 + \epsilon^2} = \pi\,\delta(x)\,, \tag{39.19}
$$

so that we may write

$$
\begin{aligned}
\langle \mathbf{p}'|S|\mathbf{p}\rangle &= (2\pi\hbar)^3\,\delta(\mathbf{p}' - \mathbf{p}) - 2\pi i\,\delta(E' - E)\,\langle \mathbf{p}'|V|\mathbf{p}, +\rangle \\
&= (2\pi\hbar)^3\,\delta(\mathbf{p}' - \mathbf{p}) - 2\pi i\,\delta(E' - E)\,\langle \mathbf{p}'|V + V\frac{1}{E - H + i\epsilon}V|\mathbf{p}\rangle\,.
\end{aligned} \tag{39.20}
$$

Comparing this with (38.16) we see that for the single channel case being considered we have an expression for the T-matrix:

$$
\begin{aligned}
T(\mathbf{p}', \mathbf{p}) &= \langle \mathbf{p}'|T|\mathbf{p}\rangle \\
&= \langle \mathbf{p}'|V + V\frac{1}{E - H + i\epsilon}V|\mathbf{p}\rangle
\end{aligned} \tag{39.21}
$$

by use of (39.17). The operator

$$
T = V + V\frac{1}{E - H + i\epsilon}V \tag{39.22}
$$

is therefore called the *scattering operator.*

The expression for T just obtained contains H, the total Hamiltonian, a complete set of whose states $|p, +\rangle$ or $|p, -\rangle$ is not, in general, known. The operator products cannot, therefore, be explicitly evaluated. The easiest way out of this difficulty is to use the identity

$$
\frac{1}{A - a} = \frac{1}{A} + \frac{1}{A}a\frac{1}{A - a}\,, \tag{39.23}
$$

which holds whenever the indicated reciprocals exist. On iteration this gives a geometric series expansion for $(A - a)^{-1}$. We apply this with $A = E - K(p) + i\epsilon$ and $a = V$, to obtain

$$\frac{1}{E - H + i\epsilon} = \frac{1}{E - K + i\epsilon} + \frac{1}{E - K + i\epsilon} V \frac{1}{E - K + i\epsilon} + \cdots \quad (39.24)$$

Inserting this into (39.21) yields the *Born series* for $\langle \mathbf{p}'|T|\mathbf{p}\rangle$:

$$\begin{aligned} \langle \mathbf{p}'|T^{(1)}|\mathbf{p}\rangle &= \langle \mathbf{p}'|V|\mathbf{p}\rangle\,, \\ \langle \mathbf{p}'|T^{(2)}|\mathbf{p}\rangle &= \langle \mathbf{p}'|V \frac{1}{E - K + i\epsilon} V|\mathbf{p}\rangle\,, \end{aligned} \quad (39.25)$$

etc.

To illustrate the use of the Born approximation we use it in first order to calculate the scattering from a Yukawa potential

$$V(r) = g\frac{e^{-\mu r}}{r}\,. \quad (39.26)$$

The matrix element of $T^{(1)}$ is just the Fourier transform of this:

$$\begin{aligned} \langle \mathbf{p}'|T^{(1)}|\mathbf{p}\rangle &= \int d^3x\, d^3x'\, \langle \mathbf{p}'|\mathbf{x}'\rangle \langle \mathbf{x}'|V(r)|\mathbf{x}\rangle \langle \mathbf{x}|\mathbf{p}\rangle \\ &= \int d^3x\, d^3x' \exp[-i\mathbf{p}'\cdot\mathbf{x}'/\hbar]\, \delta(\mathbf{x}' - \mathbf{x})V(r) \exp[i\mathbf{p}\cdot\mathbf{x}/\hbar] \\ &= \int d^3x \exp[i(\mathbf{p} - \mathbf{p}')\cdot\mathbf{x}/\hbar] g\frac{e^{-\mu r}}{r} \\ &= \frac{4\pi\hbar^2 g}{(\mathbf{p}' - \mathbf{p})^2 + \mu^2\hbar^2}\,. \end{aligned} \quad (39.27)$$

If $\mu \to 0$, and if $g = ZZ'e^2$, this potential is the Coulomb potential. On substituting into (38.20), noting that here $M' = M$, $p' = p$, and $(p' - p)^2 = 4p^2 \sin^2(\theta/2)$, we get the Rutherford formula for the cross section again.

We now go back and repeat the steps of the development when more general processes than potential scattering can occur. The result that the outgoing Green's function is obtained by giving E a small positive imaginary part before doing momentum integrals is extrapolated to this more general situation. It can be justified, but this requires a long argument. The analogue of (39.15) is written as

$$\begin{aligned} |\mathrm{I}, \mathbf{p}, +\rangle &= |\mathrm{I}, \mathbf{p}\rangle + \frac{1}{E - K_{\mathrm{I}} + i\epsilon} V_{\mathrm{I}}|\mathrm{I}, \mathbf{p}, +\rangle \\ &= \left(1 + \frac{1}{E - H + i\epsilon} V_{\mathrm{I}}\right)|\mathrm{I}, \mathbf{p}\rangle\,. \end{aligned} \quad (39.28)$$

The second line is the analogue of (39.17). The corresponding equation for the exit channel is

$$|\mathrm{F}, \mathbf{p}', +\rangle = |\mathrm{F}, \mathbf{p}'\rangle + \frac{1}{E - K_{\mathrm{F}} + i\epsilon} V_{\mathrm{F}} |\mathrm{F}, \mathbf{p}', +\rangle$$

(39.29)
$$= \left(1 + \frac{1}{E - H + i\epsilon} V_{\mathrm{F}}\right) |\mathrm{F}, \mathbf{p}'\rangle ,$$

$$|\mathrm{F}, \mathbf{p}', -\rangle = \left(1 + \frac{1}{E - H - i\epsilon} V_{\mathrm{F}}\right) |\mathrm{F}, \mathbf{p}'\rangle .$$

Subtracting the last two equations we get

(39.30)
$$|\mathrm{F}, \mathbf{p}', -\rangle = |\mathrm{F}, \mathbf{p}', +\rangle + \frac{-2i\epsilon}{(E' - H)^2 + \epsilon^2} V_{\mathrm{F}} |\mathrm{F}, \mathbf{p}'\rangle .$$

We can now evaluate the S-matrix element.

(39.31)
$$\begin{aligned}\langle \mathrm{F}, \mathbf{p}' | S | \mathrm{I}, \mathbf{p}\rangle &= \langle \mathrm{F}, \mathbf{p}', - | \mathrm{I}, \mathbf{p}, +\rangle \\ &= \langle \mathrm{F}, \mathbf{p}', + | \mathrm{I}, \mathbf{p}, +\rangle - 2\pi i \delta (E' - E) \langle \mathrm{F}, \mathbf{p}' | V_{\mathrm{F}} | \mathrm{I}, \mathbf{p}, +\rangle ,\end{aligned}$$

which is just like (39.18) after (39.19) has been used. We see that V_{F} must be used for V. In the latter matrix element we now insert the second of (39.28)

(39.32)
$$\begin{aligned}\langle \mathrm{F}, \mathbf{p}' | V_{\mathrm{F}} | \mathrm{I}, \mathbf{p}, +\rangle &= \langle \mathrm{F}, \mathbf{p}' | V_{\mathrm{F}} + V_{\mathrm{F}} \frac{1}{E - H + i\epsilon} V_{\mathrm{I}} | \mathrm{I}, \mathbf{p}\rangle \\ &= \langle \mathrm{F}, \mathbf{p}' | T | \mathrm{I}, \mathbf{p}\rangle .\end{aligned}$$

This T is the generalized scattering matrix.

(39.33)
$$T = V_{\mathrm{F}} + V_{\mathrm{F}} \frac{1}{E - H + i\epsilon} V_{\mathrm{I}} .$$

It clearly reduces to (39.22) when only one channel is present in the system.

The scattering matrix T looks strangely unsymmetrical in I and F, as V_{F} alone appears in the first term. This asymmetry is only apparent because here V_{F} can be replaced by V_{I} or by $\frac{1}{2}(V_{\mathrm{I}} + V_{\mathrm{F}})$. To see this, we note that for the matrix elements of interest here we have

(39.34)
$$\begin{aligned}\langle \mathrm{F}, \mathbf{p}' | V_{\mathrm{F}} - V_{\mathrm{I}} | \mathrm{I}, \mathbf{p}\rangle &= \langle \mathrm{F}, \mathbf{p}' | K_{\mathrm{I}} - K_{\mathrm{F}} | \mathrm{I}, \mathbf{p}\rangle \\ &= (E_{\mathrm{I}} - E_{\mathrm{F}}) \langle \mathrm{F}, \mathbf{p}' | \mathrm{I}, \mathbf{p}\rangle \\ &= 0 .\end{aligned}$$

The term in parentheses vanishes because of energy conservation. In the second term of (39.33) V_{I} and V_{F} are not interchangeable.

Exactly as in potential scattering, the Born series is obtained by expanding the quantity $(E - H + i\epsilon)^{-1}$. The expansion can be made in terms of V_{I} by writing $H = K_{\mathrm{I}} + V_{\mathrm{I}}$, or in terms of V_{F} by writing $H = K_{\mathrm{F}} + V_{\mathrm{F}}$, or in terms of some other splitting of H into a large, simple part and a small part. Using V_{I}, we write

$$T = V_F + V_F \frac{1}{E - K_I + i\epsilon} V_I + V_F \frac{1}{E - K_I + i\epsilon} V_I \frac{1}{E - K_I + i\epsilon} V_I + \cdots . \tag{39.35}$$

We give only one very simple illustration of the use of this theory, the first Born approximation to a stripping reaction such as

$$\mathrm{d} + \mathrm{N}_A{}^Z \to \mathrm{p} + \mathrm{N}_{A+1}{}^Z . \tag{39.36}$$

The nucleus $\mathrm{N}_A{}^Z$ is treated as one of the permanent particles, while the neutron and the proton in the deuteron are the other permanent particles. The complete Hamiltonian is taken to be

$$H = T_p + T_n + T_N + V_{np} + V_{nN} . \tag{39.37}$$

The interaction of the proton with the nucleus is completely ignored, including Coulomb effects. In the entrance channel

$$K_I = (T_p + T_n + V_{np}) + T_N , \quad V_I = V_{nN} , \tag{39.38}$$

while in the exit channel

$$K_F = (T_N + T_n + V_{nN}) + T_p , \quad V_F = V_{np} . \tag{39.39}$$

The entrance channel is specified by having the deuteron in its ground state and by giving the target nucleus. Polarization effects are ignored, so the spins are treated as non-existent. The exit channel is specified by the energy and orbital angular momentum of the neutron captured by the target nucleus. The polarizations are again ignored. We further assume the target nucleus to be infinitely heavy, so that nuclear recoil is zero. This last assumption enables us to put $T_N = 0$, which we do.

In our model, the entrance channel wave function corresponding to (38.9) is

$$\chi_d(\mathbf{r}_n - \mathbf{r}_p) \exp [\tfrac{1}{2} i \mathbf{p}_d \cdot (\mathbf{x}_n + \mathbf{x}_p)/\hbar] \tag{39.40}$$

and the exit channel wave function is

$$u_l(r_n) Y_{l0}(\theta_n, \phi_n) \exp [i \mathbf{p}_p \cdot \mathbf{x}_p/\hbar] . \tag{39.41}$$

The first Born approximation to the scattering matrix is

$$\langle \mathrm{F}, \mathbf{p}' | T^{(1)} | \mathrm{I}, \mathbf{p} \rangle = \langle \mathrm{F}, \mathbf{p}' | V_I | \mathrm{I}, \mathbf{p} \rangle , \tag{39.42}$$

where we have elected to use V_I rather than V_F, as it is simpler, being a function of r_n only. Thus,

$$\langle \mathrm{F}, \mathbf{p}'|T^{(1)}|\mathrm{I}, \mathbf{p}\rangle = \int d^3r_{\mathrm{p}} \int d^3r_{\mathrm{n}}\, u_l^*(r_{\mathrm{n}}) Y_{l0}(\theta_{\mathrm{n}}, \phi_{\mathrm{n}}) \times V(r_{\mathrm{n}}) \chi_{\mathrm{d}}(\mathbf{r}_{\mathrm{n}} - \mathbf{r}_{\mathrm{p}}) \exp\{i[(\tfrac{1}{2}\mathbf{p}_{\mathrm{d}} - \mathbf{p}_{\mathrm{p}}) \cdot \mathbf{r}_{\mathrm{p}} + \tfrac{1}{2}\mathbf{p}_{\mathrm{d}} \cdot \mathbf{r}_{\mathrm{n}}]/\hbar\}\,. \tag{39.43}$$

To evaluate this we need, first of all, the deuteron wave function. This is given in the approximation of a δ-function neutron–proton potential by

$$\chi_{\mathrm{d}} = A \frac{\exp[-\kappa|\mathbf{r}_{\mathrm{n}} - \mathbf{r}_{\mathrm{p}}]}{|\mathbf{r}_{\mathrm{n}} - \mathbf{r}_{\mathrm{p}}|} \tag{39.44}$$

with κ related to the binding energy E_{B} of the deuteron by $\hbar^2\kappa^2/m = E_{\mathrm{B}}$. The integration over $\mathbf{r}_{\mathrm{p}}$ can now be done since $\mathbf{r}_{\mathrm{p}}$ appears only in χ_{d} and a plane wave. The form χ_{d} is just that of a Yukawa potential, so the integration involves evaluating the Fourier transform of a Yukawa potential after a shift of variable from $\mathbf{r}_{\mathrm{p}}$ to $\mathbf{r} = \mathbf{r}_{\mathrm{p}} - \mathbf{r}_{\mathrm{n}}$. This was evaluated in (39.27). We are left with

$$A' \int d^3r_{\mathrm{n}}\, u_l^*(r_{\mathrm{n}}) Y_{l0}(\theta_{\mathrm{n}}, \phi_{\mathrm{n}}) V(r_{\mathrm{n}}) \exp[i(\mathbf{p}_{\mathrm{d}} - \mathbf{p}_{\mathrm{p}}) \cdot \mathbf{r}_{\mathrm{n}}/\hbar] \times \frac{1}{(\tfrac{1}{2}\mathbf{p}_{\mathrm{d}} - \mathbf{p}_{\mathrm{p}})^2 + \kappa^2\hbar^2}\,. \tag{39.45}$$

The angular integration can now be done on choosing the z axis in the direction of $\mathbf{p}_{\mathrm{d}} - \mathbf{p}_{\mathrm{p}}$. This integral is given in (16.18). Using this, we get

$$A'' \frac{\int dr_{\mathrm{n}}\, u_l^*(r_{\mathrm{n}}) V(r_{\mathrm{n}}) j_l(|\mathbf{p}_{\mathrm{d}} - \mathbf{p}_{\mathrm{p}}| r_{\mathrm{n}}/\hbar)}{(\tfrac{1}{2}\mathbf{p}_{\mathrm{d}} - \mathbf{p}_{\mathrm{p}})^2 + \kappa^2\hbar^2}\,. \tag{39.46}$$

To go further, some knowledge of the neutron wave function $u_l(r_{\mathrm{n}})$ and of the potential $V(r_{\mathrm{n}})$ is needed. For the sake of simplicity let us assume that $u^*(r_{\mathrm{n}})V(r_{\mathrm{n}})$ is peaked at a value $r_{\mathrm{n}} = R$ and small in other regions. Then the angular dependence of the proton comes from

$$\frac{j_l(|\mathbf{p}_{\mathrm{d}} - \mathbf{p}_{\mathrm{p}}|R/\hbar)}{(\tfrac{1}{2}\mathbf{p}_{\mathrm{d}} - \mathbf{p}_{\mathrm{p}})^2 + \kappa^2\hbar^2}\,. \tag{39.47}$$

Conservation of energy requires that

$$\frac{\mathbf{p}_{\mathrm{d}}^2}{4m} - E_{\mathrm{B}} = \frac{\mathbf{p}_{\mathrm{p}}^2}{2m} - E_{\mathrm{n}}\,, \tag{39.48}$$

where E_{B} and E_{n} are the binding energies in the entrance and exit channels. To illustrate what happens, we take the extreme case where $|\mathbf{p}_{\mathrm{p}}| = |\mathbf{p}_{\mathrm{d}}| = p$, corresponding to a very large nuclear binding E_{n}. Then the denominator of (39.47) becomes $p^2(5/4 - \cos\theta) + \kappa^2\hbar^2$, and the argument of the Bessel function becomes $2pR \sin\tfrac{1}{2}\theta/\hbar$. The angular dependence is thus a strong function

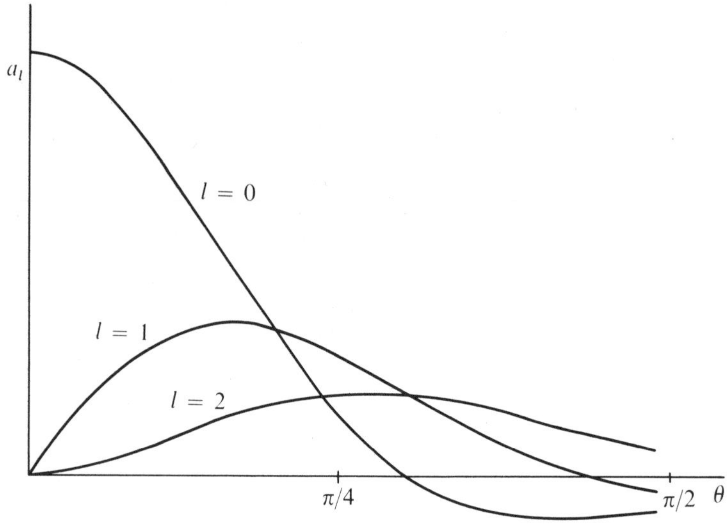

Fig. 39-2

of l, the orbital angular momentum of the neutron about the capturing nucleus. For $l = 0$ there is a large forward amplitude. For $l = 1$ the forward amplitude vanishes and a peak appears at a finite angle.

The amplitude $\mathfrak{a}_l$ is shown in Figure 39–2 for values of the parameters corresponding to 5 Mev deuterons, making the assumptions of the last paragraph. The cross section is proportional to the square of this amplitude. The strong dependence on l is seen. Some scattering processes act qualitatively in this way, so that the proton angular distribution can be interpreted to give the orbital angular momentum of the captured neutron. Clearly, the calculation can be done much more realistically than we have done it here.

PROBLEMS

1. Equations (36.5) are equivalent to the Schrödinger equation for a particle in a Coulomb potential. Solve these equations for the bound states of hydrogen. $\{$Take $\psi(\xi, \eta, \phi) = N \exp[-\kappa r] f(\xi) g(\eta) \exp[im\phi)].\}$ Determine the degeneracy of the levels.
2. Describe the operation of spatial reflection in parabolic coordinates. Are the hydrogen eigenfunctions found in Problem 1 eigenfunctions of this operator? Are the scattering wave functions?
3. By an argument similar to that used in deriving the condition (35.5) on a potential in order that plane waves can describe a particle at infinity, prove that if $r^2V(r) \to 0$ as $r \to \infty$, the solution at infinity of a problem containing a Coulomb potential and the potential $V(r)$ is expressible by means of Coulomb wave functions.

4. By using the continuity of the logarithmic derivative of the wave function across a sphere of radius R outside of which the scattering potential vanishes, show that

$$k \cot(kR + \delta_0) = -\frac{1}{a} + O(k^2)\,;$$

a is the *scattering length.*

5. At very low energy the result of Ex. 4 becomes

$$k \cot \delta_0 = -\frac{1}{a}\,.$$

Show that if a is positive, there exists a bound state in the potential while if a is negative there is none.

6. Neutron–proton scattering takes place in both the singlet and triplet states. Assuming there are two central potentials, V_s and V_t, it is known from the existence of the deuteron with spin unity that there is a bound triplet state, so that $a_t > 0$. To find the sign of a_s, and thus to find if there is a bound singlet state, one scatters very slow neutrons from parahydrogen (hydrogen molecules in a nuclear singlet state). Write down the expression for the coherent scattering amplitude for the neutron in terms of a_t and a_s and hence show how the sign of a_s can be determined.

7. Show that the scattering phase shifts caused by an attractive square well potential of radius R and depth V_0 ($V_0 > 0$) are given by

$$\frac{k\,[\cos\delta_l \hat{j}_l'(kR) - \sin\delta_l \hat{n}_l'(kR)]}{\cos\delta_l \hat{j}_l(kR) - \sin\delta_l \hat{n}_l(kR)} = \frac{K\hat{j}_l'(KR)}{\hat{j}_l(KR)}$$

with $\hbar^2 k^2 = 2mE$, $\hbar^2 K^2 = 2m(E + V_0)$.

VII

Many particle systems

40. OCCUPATION NUMBER REPRESENTATION

When a system contains many identical particles, its description in coordinate space becomes very awkward because of the large number of dimensions needed, three per particle, and because of the need to symmetrize or antisymmetrize the wave function. The complication is largely gratuitous because the particles cannot even in principle be identified. A coordinate representation first treats the particles as distinguishable and then destroys their distinguishability by symmetrizing. A much more compact and useful representation is developed here, a representation which never treats the particles as distinguishable. The complete equivalence of the *occupation number representation* to be developed and the coordinate representation with symmetrization has been established by Fock. We confine our attention here to the occupation number representation.

In the study of the harmonic oscillator it was seen that there exist raising and lowering operators, $a^\dagger$ and a, which obey the commutation relation

$$[a, a^\dagger] = 1 \tag{40.1}$$

and which combine into a positive definite operator

$$N = a^\dagger a \tag{40.2}$$

with integer eigenvalues. We wish to use these operators in a different context similar to that mentioned in Section 34 where phonons were introduced. The new meaning is connected with the old through the quantum theory of fields.

The eigenvalue spectrum of N follows from the above equations. Let

$$N|n\rangle = n|n\rangle\,. \tag{40.3}$$

Then

(40.4)
$$\begin{aligned} Na^\dagger|n\rangle &= a^\dagger a a^\dagger|n\rangle \\ &= a^\dagger(a^\dagger a + 1)|n\rangle \\ &= (n+1)a^\dagger|n\rangle\,. \end{aligned}$$

Similarly,

(40.5)
$$Na|n\rangle = (n-1)a|n\rangle\,.$$

Because of its definition,

(40.6)
$$\begin{aligned} n = \langle n|N|n\rangle &= \langle n|a^\dagger a|n\rangle \\ &\geqslant 0\,. \end{aligned}$$

The equality holds only when $a|n\rangle = 0$, that is, for the state $|0\rangle$. The operator a operating on an eigenstate of N produces another eigenstate of N with eigenvalue lower by unity or annihilates the state. Let $|\nu\rangle$ be an eigenstate of N with eigenvalue ν. By successive applications of a we get a sequence of eigenstates of N, $|\nu\rangle$, $|\nu - 1\rangle$, $\cdots$, $|\nu - m\rangle$, such that

(40.7)
$$|\nu - m\rangle \neq 0\,, \qquad a|\nu - m\rangle = 0\,,$$

because otherwise N would acquire a negative eigenvalue. Now

(40.8)
$$\begin{aligned} N|\nu - m\rangle &= a^\dagger a|\nu - m\rangle \\ &= 0\,, \end{aligned}$$

so that $\nu - m = 0$ and ν is an integer.

We are going to interpret N as the operator giving the number of particles of a certain kind present in a system. Thus $a^\dagger$ becomes a *creation operator* and a becomes an *annihilation operator* for this kind of particle. If our system consists of particles of mass m confined in a cubic box of edge L, so that there exists a complete set of one particle states labelled by the momentum $\mathbf{p} = \hbar\mathbf{k}$, then the operator $N_{\mathbf{k}}$ is the number operator for particles of mass m and momentum $\mathbf{k}$; $a_{\mathbf{k}}^\dagger$ is the creation operator and $a_{\mathbf{k}}$ the annihilation operator for these particles. (For the rest of this section and all of Section 41 we use units such that $\hbar = 1$, so that momenta $\mathbf{p}$ and wave vectors $\mathbf{k}$ are the same thing.)

The particles which are created and annihilated by these operators are non-interacting particles. We assume that the creation and annihilation operators for particles of different momenta commute, writing the commutation relations as

(40.9)
$$\begin{aligned} [a_{\mathbf{k}}, a_{\mathbf{k}'}^\dagger] &= \delta_{\mathbf{k}\mathbf{k}'}\,, \\ [a_{\mathbf{k}}, a_{\mathbf{k}'}] = 0 &= [a_{\mathbf{k}}^\dagger, a_{\mathbf{k}'}^\dagger]\,. \end{aligned}$$

The particles so described are *bosons*. To see this we look at the two particle state

(40.10)
$$a_{\mathbf{k}}^\dagger a_{\mathbf{k}'}^\dagger|0\rangle = a_{\mathbf{k}'}^\dagger a_{\mathbf{k}}^\dagger|0\rangle\,,$$

which is symmetric in $\mathbf{k}$ and $\mathbf{k}'$, the labels of the single particle states of the particles considered separately.

The systems of interest need not be composed of bosons but may consist of fermions. A single particle state can either be empty or be occupied by one fermion, but cannot be occupied by more than one fermion. The formalism just given allows a single particle state to be occupied by an arbitrary number of particles, which are necessarily bosons. It was shown by Jordan and Wigner that a formalism suitable for fermions is obtained by replacing the commutators of creation and annihilation operators in (40.9) by *anticommutators*. Thus, we prescribe the following equations for fermion creation and annihilation operators. If $\{a, b\} = ab + ba$, then

$$\begin{aligned} \{\alpha_{\boldsymbol{k}}, \alpha_{\boldsymbol{k}'}{}^\dagger\} &= \delta_{\boldsymbol{k}\boldsymbol{k}'} , \\ \{\alpha_{\boldsymbol{k}}, \alpha_{\boldsymbol{k}'}\} = 0 &= \{\alpha_{\boldsymbol{k}}{}^\dagger, \alpha_{\boldsymbol{k}'}{}^\dagger\} . \end{aligned} \tag{40.11}$$

Again, defining the occupation number operator by

$$N_{\boldsymbol{k}} = \alpha_{\boldsymbol{k}}{}^\dagger \alpha_{\boldsymbol{k}} , \tag{40.12}$$

we see immediately that

$$\begin{aligned} N_{\boldsymbol{k}}{}^2 &= \alpha_{\boldsymbol{k}}{}^\dagger \alpha_{\boldsymbol{k}} \alpha_{\boldsymbol{k}}{}^\dagger \alpha_{\boldsymbol{k}} \\ &= \alpha_{\boldsymbol{k}}{}^\dagger \alpha_{\boldsymbol{k}}(1 - \alpha_{\boldsymbol{k}} \alpha_{\boldsymbol{k}}{}^\dagger) \\ &= \alpha_{\boldsymbol{k}}{}^\dagger \alpha_{\boldsymbol{k}} . \\ &= N_{\boldsymbol{k}} . \end{aligned} \tag{40.13}$$

Thus,

$$N_{\boldsymbol{k}}(N_{\boldsymbol{k}} - 1) = 0 , \tag{40.14}$$

so that $N_{\boldsymbol{k}}$ can have eigenvalues zero and unity and no others. This establishes the exclusion principle. The fact that $\alpha_{\boldsymbol{k}}{}^\dagger$ is the creation operator and $\alpha_{\boldsymbol{k}}$ the annihilation operator depends on the order of factors in $N_{\boldsymbol{k}}$.

$$\begin{aligned} N_{\boldsymbol{k}} \alpha_{\boldsymbol{k}} &= \alpha_{\boldsymbol{k}}{}^\dagger \alpha_{\boldsymbol{k}} \alpha_{\boldsymbol{k}} \\ &= 0 . \end{aligned} \tag{40.15}$$

The effect of $\alpha_{\boldsymbol{k}}$ is either to annihilate the state or to produce an eigenstate of $N_{\boldsymbol{k}}$ with eigenvalue zero, so $\alpha_{\boldsymbol{k}}$ is an annihilation operator. Similarly,

$$\begin{aligned} N_{\boldsymbol{k}} \alpha^\dagger &= {}_{\boldsymbol{k}}\alpha_{\boldsymbol{k}}{}^\dagger \alpha_{\boldsymbol{k}} \alpha_{\boldsymbol{k}}{}^\dagger \\ &= \alpha_{\boldsymbol{k}}{}^\dagger(1 - \alpha_{\boldsymbol{k}}{}^\dagger \alpha_{\boldsymbol{k}}) \\ &= \alpha_{\boldsymbol{k}}{}^\dagger . \end{aligned} \tag{40.16}$$

The effect of $\alpha_{\boldsymbol{k}}{}^\dagger$ is to annihilate the state on which it operates, or to produce an eigenstate of $N_{\boldsymbol{k}}$ with eigenvalue unity, so it is a creation operator.

The magnitudes of the matrix elements of $\alpha_{\boldsymbol{k}}$ and $\alpha_{\boldsymbol{k}}{}^\dagger$ are unity or zero. We choose the phases of the states so that the matrix elements between a state containing one particle of any kind and a state containing no particle of any kind, the empty state, are positive real:

(40.17)
$$\langle \mathbf{k}|\alpha_k^\dagger|0\rangle = 1\,, \qquad \langle 0|\alpha_k|\mathbf{k}\rangle = 1\,.$$

All other matrix elements vanish. If more than one particle is present, the sign must be watched carefully. When M particles are present, the state may be written

(40.18)
$$|\mathbf{k}_M\,, \ldots, \mathbf{k}_2, \mathbf{k}_1\rangle = \alpha_{k_M}{}^\dagger \cdots \alpha_{k_2}{}^\dagger \alpha_{k_1}{}^\dagger|0\rangle\,,$$

where the order of the labels $\mathbf{k}_j$ shows the order of application of creation operators to the empty state. The bra dual to this is

(40.19)
$$\langle \mathbf{k}_1, \mathbf{k}_2, \ldots, \mathbf{k}_M\,| = \langle 0|\alpha_{k_1}, \alpha_{k_2} \cdots \alpha_{k_M}\,.$$

Now the matrix element of an annihilation operator α_{k_l} is

(40.20)
$$\begin{aligned}\langle \mathbf{k}_1, \mathbf{k}_2, \ldots (\mathbf{k}_l = 0) \ldots \mathbf{k}_M|\alpha_{k_l}|\mathbf{k}_M \ldots (\mathbf{k}_l = 1) \ldots \mathbf{k}_1\rangle \\ = \langle 0|\alpha_{k_1}\alpha_{k_2} \cdots \alpha_{k_M}\alpha_{k_l}\alpha_{k_M}{}^\dagger \cdots \alpha_{k_l}{}^\dagger \cdots \alpha_{k_1}{}^\dagger|0\rangle \\ = \delta_P(= \pm 1)\,.\end{aligned}$$

Whether the result is ± 1 depends on the number of operators $\alpha^\dagger$ standing between α_{k_l} and $\alpha_{k_l}{}^\dagger$. It is $+1$ if this number is even, -1 if it is odd. This results from bringing the operator α_{k_l} up to $\alpha_{k_l}{}^\dagger$. The product $\alpha_k\alpha_k{}^\dagger$ commutes with all the other $\alpha^\dagger$'s and so can be brought up to the ket $|0\rangle$, where we have

$$\begin{aligned}\alpha_{k_l}\alpha_{k_l}{}^\dagger|0\rangle &= (1 - \alpha_{k_l}{}^\dagger\alpha_{k_l})|0\rangle \\ &= |0\rangle\,.\end{aligned}$$

The signs of the matrix elements thus depend on the order in which the particles in the given states are created. This order must, therefore, be specified in each case. δ_P is the signature of the permutation necessary to bring α_{k_l} next to $\alpha_{k_l}{}^\dagger$.

The two particle state

(40.21)
$$\alpha_k{}^\dagger\alpha_{k'}{}^\dagger|0\rangle = -\alpha_{k'}{}^\dagger\alpha_k{}^\dagger|0\rangle$$

is antisymmetric in the single particle labels $\mathbf{k}$ and $\mathbf{k}'$, as is to be expected of fermions. This can be extended to any number of particles.

From this point on we discuss only systems of fermions. The Hamiltonian of a system of non-interacting fermions is just the energy of the system expressed in terms of occupation numbers.

(40.22)
$$\begin{aligned}H_0 &= \sum_k \alpha_k{}^\dagger\alpha_k \frac{\mathbf{k}^2}{2m} \\ &= \sum_k N_k \frac{\mathbf{k}^2}{2m}\,,\end{aligned}$$

which expresses the total energy as the sum of the kinetic energies of the individual particles present. If we want to change from box normalization to delta-function normalization, we replace α_k by

$$\xi(\mathbf{k}) = L^{3/2}\alpha_{k} . \tag{40.23}$$

This $\xi(\mathbf{k})$ annihilates one particle per unit volume rather than one particle in the box of volume L^3. The Hamiltonian becomes

$$H_0 = \int \frac{d^3k}{(2\pi)^3}\, \xi^\dagger(\mathbf{k})\xi(\mathbf{k})\frac{\mathbf{k}^2}{2m} . \tag{40.24}$$

Correspondingly the anticommutation relations (40.11) become

$$\begin{aligned} \{\xi(\mathbf{k}), \xi^\dagger(\mathbf{k}')\} &= (2\pi)^3\, \delta(\mathbf{k} - \mathbf{k}') , \\ \{\xi(\mathbf{k}), \xi(\mathbf{k}')\} = 0 &= \{\xi^\dagger(\mathbf{k}), \xi^\dagger(\mathbf{k}')\} . \end{aligned} \tag{40.25}$$

Physically interesting systems consist of interacting particles. The simplest kind of interaction involves just two particles. Such an interaction can be written in the occupation number representation as

$$V = \tfrac{1}{4}\int \frac{d^3k_A\, d^3k_B\, d^3k_C\, d^3k_D}{(2\pi)^{12}}\, \mathcal{V}(\mathbf{k}_C, \mathbf{k}_D; \mathbf{k}_B, \mathbf{k}_A)\xi^\dagger(\mathbf{k}_C)\xi^\dagger(\mathbf{k}_D)\xi(\mathbf{k}_B)\xi(\mathbf{k}_A) . \tag{40.26}$$

This annihilates two particles with momenta $\mathbf{k}_A$ and $\mathbf{k}_B$ and replaces them with two other particles with momenta $\mathbf{k}_C$, $\mathbf{k}_D$. For V to be hermitian we must have

$$\mathcal{V}^*(\mathbf{k}_A, \mathbf{k}_B; \mathbf{k}_D, \mathbf{k}_C) = \mathcal{V}(\mathbf{k}_C, \mathbf{k}_D, \mathbf{k}_B, \mathbf{k}_A) . \tag{40.27}$$

A two body interaction conserves momentum, so that $\mathcal{V}$ contains a factor $(2\pi)^3\delta(\mathbf{k}_A + \mathbf{k}_B - \mathbf{k}_C - \mathbf{k}_D)$. It is also antisymmetric in $\mathbf{k}_C$, $\mathbf{k}_D$ and in $\mathbf{k}_A$, $\mathbf{k}_B$, as a symmetric part would not contribute to V because of the anticommutation of $\xi^\dagger(\mathbf{k}_C)$, $\xi^\dagger(\mathbf{k}_D)$ and of $\xi(\mathbf{k}_B)$, $\xi(\mathbf{k}_A)$.

If V is given in the coordinate representation by a potential depending on the relative coordinates of two particles, $U(\mathbf{r})$, $\mathcal{V}$ can be expressed in terms of its Fourier transform. To establish the connection we compare matrix elements of V between two particle states with those of $U(\mathbf{r})$ between antisymmetrized two particle coordinate representation states. Thus, the former is

$$\langle 0|\xi(\mathbf{k}_3)\xi(\mathbf{k}_4)\, |V|\xi^\dagger(\mathbf{k}_2)\xi^\dagger(\mathbf{k}_1)\, |0\rangle . \tag{40.28}$$

To evaluate this, we look at two integrations that occur in V, say those over $\mathbf{k}_A$ and $\mathbf{k}_B$. The relevant factors are

$$\int \frac{d^3k_B}{(2\pi)^3}\frac{d^3k_A}{(2\pi)^3}\, \mathcal{V}(\mathbf{k}_C, \mathbf{k}_D; \mathbf{k}_B, \mathbf{k}_A)\xi(\mathbf{k}_B)\xi(\mathbf{k}_A)\xi^\dagger(\mathbf{k}_2)\xi^\dagger(\mathbf{k}_1)\, |0\rangle .$$

Now,

$$\begin{aligned}&\xi(\mathbf{k}_B)\xi(\mathbf{k}_A)\xi^\dagger(\mathbf{k}_2)\xi^\dagger(\mathbf{k}_1)\,|0\rangle\\ &\quad= \xi(\mathbf{k}_B)[-\xi^\dagger(\mathbf{k}_2)\xi(\mathbf{k}_A) + (2\pi)^3\,\delta(\mathbf{k}_A - \mathbf{k}_3)]\xi^\dagger(\mathbf{k}_1)\,|0\rangle\\ &\quad= \xi(\mathbf{k}_B)(2\pi)^3[-\delta(\mathbf{k}_A - \mathbf{k}_1)\xi^\dagger(\mathbf{k}_2) + \delta(\mathbf{k}_A - \mathbf{k}_2)\xi^\dagger(\mathbf{k}_1)]\,|0\rangle\\ &\quad= (2\pi)^6[-\delta(\mathbf{k}_A - \mathbf{k}_1)\,\delta(\mathbf{k}_B - \mathbf{k}_2) + \delta(\mathbf{k}_A - \mathbf{k}_2)\,\delta(\mathbf{k}_B - \mathbf{k}_1)]\,|0\rangle\,,\end{aligned}$$

so that the above integral becomes

$$[\mathcal{V}(\mathbf{k}_C, \mathbf{k}_D; \mathbf{k}_1, \mathbf{k}_2) - \mathcal{V}(\mathbf{k}_C, \mathbf{k}_D; \mathbf{k}_2, \mathbf{k}_1)]\,|0\rangle\,.$$

By a similar argument the integrals over $\mathbf{k}_C$, $\mathbf{k}_D$ lead to a net result for the entire matrix element of

$$\begin{aligned}&\tfrac{1}{4}[\mathcal{V}(\mathbf{k}_4, \mathbf{k}_3; \mathbf{k}_1, \mathbf{k}_2) + \mathcal{V}(\mathbf{k}_3, \mathbf{k}_4; \mathbf{k}_2, \mathbf{k}_1)\\ &\qquad - \mathcal{V}(\mathbf{k}_3, \mathbf{k}_4; \mathbf{k}_1, \mathbf{k}_2) - \mathcal{V}(\mathbf{k}_4, \mathbf{k}_3; \mathbf{k}_2, \mathbf{k}_1)]\,.\end{aligned} \tag{40.29}$$

The initial coordinate space wave function is

$$\tfrac{1}{2}\Big(\exp\,[i(\mathbf{k}_1\cdot\mathbf{r}_1 + \mathbf{k}_2\cdot\mathbf{r}_2)] - \exp\,[i(\mathbf{k}_1\cdot\mathbf{r}_2 + \mathbf{k}_2\cdot\mathbf{r}_1)]\Big)\,. \tag{40.30}$$

The factor $\frac{1}{2}$ rather than $(1/2)^{1/2}$ appears because integration over all r_1, r_2 covers the configuration space of two indistinguishable particles twice. Thus

$$\begin{aligned}\langle\mathbf{k}_3, \mathbf{k}_4|\,U(\mathbf{r})\,|\mathbf{k}_2, \mathbf{k}_1\rangle &= \tfrac{1}{4}\int d^3r_1\,d^3r_2\\ &\quad\times \{\exp\,[-i(\mathbf{k}_3\cdot\mathbf{r}_1 + \mathbf{k}_4\cdot\mathbf{r}_2)] - \exp\,[-i(\mathbf{k}_3\cdot\mathbf{r}_2 + \mathbf{k}_4\cdot\mathbf{r}_1)]\}\\ &\quad\times U(\mathbf{r}_1 - \mathbf{r}_2)\{\exp\,[i(\mathbf{k}_1\cdot\mathbf{r}_1 + \mathbf{k}_2\cdot\mathbf{r}_2)] - \exp\,[i(\mathbf{k}_1\cdot\mathbf{r}_2 + \mathbf{k}_2\cdot\mathbf{r}_1)]\}\,.\end{aligned}$$

Introducing center of mass coordinates so that

$$\mathbf{r}_1 = \mathbf{R} + \tfrac{1}{2}\mathbf{r}\,, \qquad \mathbf{r}_2 = \mathbf{R} - \tfrac{1}{2}\mathbf{r}$$

this becomes

$$\begin{aligned}&\tfrac{1}{4}(2\pi)^3\,\delta(\mathbf{k}_1 + \mathbf{k}_2 - \mathbf{k}_3 - \mathbf{k}_4)\left\{U\left(\frac{\mathbf{k}_4 - \mathbf{k}_3 + \mathbf{k}_1 - \mathbf{k}_2}{2}\right)\right.\\ &\quad - U\left(\frac{\mathbf{k}_3 - \mathbf{k}_4 + \mathbf{k}_1 - \mathbf{k}_2}{2}\right) - U\left(\frac{\mathbf{k}_4 - \mathbf{k}_3 + \mathbf{k}_2 - \mathbf{k}_1}{2}\right)\\ &\qquad\left. + U\left(\frac{\mathbf{k}_3 - \mathbf{k}_4 + \mathbf{k}_2 - \mathbf{k}_1}{2}\right)\right\}.\end{aligned} \tag{40.31}$$

We can now correlate the terms as follows:

(40.32)

$$\mathcal{V}(\mathbf{k}_C, \mathbf{k}_D; \mathbf{k}_B, \mathbf{k}_A) = (2\pi)^3\,\delta(\mathbf{k}_A + \mathbf{k}_B - \mathbf{k}_C - \mathbf{k}_D)U\left(\frac{\mathbf{k}_C - \mathbf{k}_D + \mathbf{k}_B - \mathbf{k}_A}{2}\right).$$

Because of the δ-function, the argument of the Fourier transform $U(\mathbf{k})$ can be simplified.

$$U\left(\frac{\mathbf{k}_4 - \mathbf{k}_3 + \mathbf{k}_1 - \mathbf{k}_2}{2}\right) = U(\mathbf{k}_1 - \mathbf{k}_3) = U(\mathbf{k}_4 - \mathbf{k}_2)\,, \tag{40.33}$$

and the matrix element (40.28) can be written

$$\begin{aligned}\frac{(2\pi)^3}{4}\,&\delta(\mathbf{k}_1 + \mathbf{k}_2 - \mathbf{k}_3 - \mathbf{k}_4) \\ &\times [U(\mathbf{k}_4 - \mathbf{k}_2) + U(\mathbf{k}_3 - \mathbf{k}_1) - U(\mathbf{k}_4 - \mathbf{k}_1) - U(\mathbf{k}_3 - \mathbf{k}_2)]\,,\end{aligned} \tag{40.34}$$

which exhibits the antisymmetry in $\mathbf{k}_1$, $\mathbf{k}_2$ and in $\mathbf{k}_3$, $\mathbf{k}_4$. Another form of writing this uses the fact that since $U(\mathbf{r})$ is real, $U(-\mathbf{k}) = U^*(\mathbf{k})$, which yields for the matrix element

$$\tfrac{1}{2}(2\pi)^3\,\delta(\mathbf{k}_1 + \mathbf{k}_2 - \mathbf{k}_3 - \mathbf{k}_4)\mathrm{Re}[U(\mathbf{k}_3 - \mathbf{k}_1) - U(\mathbf{k}_4 - \mathbf{k}_1)]. \tag{40.35}$$

Every interaction of the form (40.26) is not equivalent to a potential $U(\mathbf{r})$. When there is a potential, (40.35) shows that the interaction falls naturally into two parts, one where the particle of momentum $\mathbf{k}_1$ is scattered to momentum $\mathbf{k}_3$, and one where it is scattered to momentum $\mathbf{k}_4$. Even in the general case, (40.29) can be interpreted in this way. The first and last momenta in $\mathcal{V}(k_C, k_D; k_B, k_A)$ can be associated with one scattering, the other two momenta being related to these by momentum conservation. Then together the two terms with plus signs in (40.29) describe the scattering of the particle with momentum $\mathbf{k}_1$ to momentum $\mathbf{k}_3$, and the two terms with minus signs its scattering to momentum $\mathbf{k}_4$. From now on we assume the existence of a potential, so that we may use the simpler form (40.35).

Any state of the non-interacting particles can be written as the empty state acted on by the appropriate creation operators. This is convenient as long as only a few particles are of interest, but if the system of fermions contains very many particles, it is not. A typical system of fermions consists of the electrons in a solid, where the number is very large indeed. In such cases it is advantageous to use a state other than the empty state as the starting point of the discussion. The starting point used is the state with all possible particles with kinetic energies less than E_F present, all higher energy states being unoccupied. This state is called the unperturbed ground state and is denoted by $|F\rangle$. The density of particles in this state is given by

$$\rho = \int_0^{K_F} \frac{d^3k}{(2\pi)^3} = \frac{K_F{}^3}{6\pi^2}\,, \tag{40.36}$$

K_F being the momentum corresponding to the kinetic energy E_F. The energy density of the unperturbed ground state is

$$U_F = \int_0^{K_F} \frac{4\pi k^2\, dk}{(2\pi)^3} \frac{k^2}{2m} \tag{40.37}$$
$$= \frac{K_F^5}{20\pi^2 m} .$$

The particles present in the unperturbed ground state are called collectively the *Fermi sea*, illustrated in Figure 40–1.

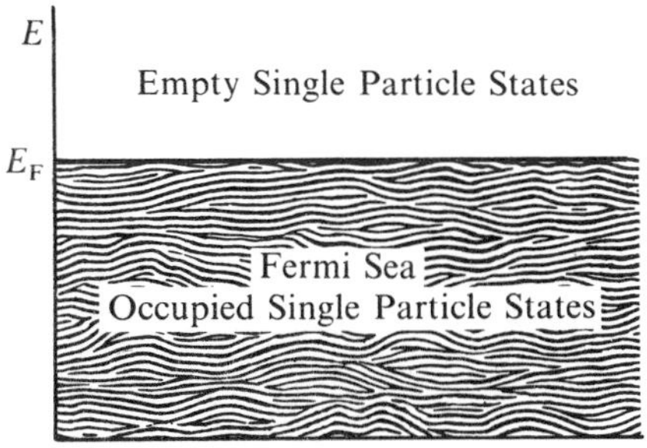

Fig. 40-1

Interactions of the type just discussed couple the state $|\mathbf{F}\rangle$ to excited states in which a number of particles in the Fermi sea have been annihilated, and an equal number of particles have been created above the Fermi sea. A vacant state within the sea is called a *hole*. An occupied state above the sea is called a particle. Then

(40.38)
$\xi^\dagger(\mathbf{k})$ creates a particle if $|\mathbf{k}| > K_F$,
$\xi^\dagger(\mathbf{k})$ annihilates a hole if $|\mathbf{k}| < K_F$,
$\xi(\mathbf{k})$ annihilates a particle if $|\mathbf{k}| > K_F$,
$\xi(\mathbf{k})$ creates a hole if $|\mathbf{k}| < K_F$.

The states with which we shall be concerned contain relatively few particles and holes.

The effect of the interaction V can be described either by time dependent perturbation theory or by time independent perturbation theory. We need both methods. The time dependent method is carried out in the interaction picture as in Section 26, of which we give a recapitulation.

In the interaction picture the equations of motion are, with units chosen so that $\hbar = 1$,

$$\frac{i d\alpha}{dt} = [\alpha, H_0] , \qquad i\frac{d|t\rangle}{dt} = V(t)|t\rangle , \tag{40.39}$$

where

$$H = H_0 + V , \qquad V(t) = e^{iH_0t}Ve^{-iH_0t} . \tag{40.40}$$

Writing

(40.41)
$$|t\rangle = U(t)\,|0\rangle\,, \qquad U(0) = 1\,,$$

we see that

(40.42)
$$i\frac{dU}{dt} = V(t)U\,.$$

This is satisfied by

(40.43)
$$\begin{aligned} U(t) &= e^{iH_0t}e^{-iHt} \\ &= e^{iH_0t}\sum_n |n\rangle e^{-iE_nt}\langle n|\,, \end{aligned}$$

where $|n\rangle$ is one of a complete set of eigenstates of H with eigenvalue E_n.

$U(t)$ also satisfies the integral equation

$$U(t) = 1 - i\int_0^t dt'\,V(t')U(t')\,.$$

This equation may be iterated to give

(40.44)
$$\begin{aligned} U(t) &= \sum_n U^{(n)}(t) \\ U^{(n)}(t) &= (-i)^n\int_0^t dt'\int_0^{t'} dt''\cdots\int_0^{t^{(n-1)}} dt^{(n)}V(t')V(t'')\cdots V(t^{(n)})\,, \end{aligned}$$

which is the result we want.

The time independent theory is carried out in any picture as the time dependence does not enter. We use the Heisenberg picture. The state $|\,\rangle$ in the presence of the interaction is related to the state in the absence of the interaction, $|\phi_0\rangle$, by

(40.45)
$$|\,\rangle = |\phi_0\rangle + \frac{1}{E-H}V|\phi_0\rangle\,,$$

where E may have a small positive imaginary part to define the behavior at the poles. Then with

(40.46)
$$\begin{aligned} G(E) &= \frac{1}{E-H} \\ &= \frac{1}{E-H_0} + \frac{1}{E-H_0}V\frac{1}{E-H_0} + \frac{1}{E-H_0}V\frac{1}{E-H_0}V\frac{1}{E-H_0} + \cdots \\ &= \frac{1}{E-H_0} + \frac{1}{E-H_0}T(E)\frac{1}{E-H_0}\,, \end{aligned}$$

(40.47)
$$T(E) = V + V\frac{1}{E - H_0}V + \cdots$$

and we have

(40.48)
$$G(E) = \sum_n |n\rangle \frac{1}{E - E_n} \langle n| \,.$$

Comparing (40.43) and (40.48) we find that $U(t)$ can be expressed in terms of $G(E)$ by means of the contour integral

(40.49)
$$U(t) = \frac{1}{2\pi i}\int_C \exp\,[i\,(H_0 - E)t]G(E)\,dE\,,$$

where the contour goes from right to left above the real axis in the E-plane and from left to right below the real axis, thus enclosing all the poles of $G(E)$. The inverse transformation is

(40.50)
$$\begin{aligned} G(E) &= -i\int_0^{\infty} \exp\,[i\,(E - H_0)t]U(t)\,dt\,, \qquad \operatorname{Im} E > 0\,, \\ &= -i\int_0^{-\infty} \exp\,[i\,(E - H_0)t]U(t)\,dt\,, \qquad \operatorname{Im} E < 0\,. \end{aligned}$$

The above is quite general. We wish to apply it to the many fermion problem in which the unperturbed state is a state of the non-interacting particles and the perturbation is the two particle interaction given by (40.26). This type of interaction can be described by the technique of Feynman diagrams. These may be founded on either (40.47) or (40.44). The latter yields a needed result more easily than the former, so we use it here, developing the diagrammatic method for $U(t)$.

We are concerned with the amplitude for finding the system in state $|B\rangle$ at time T if at time $t = 0$ it was in state $|A\rangle$. The transition is to occur as a result of a two particle interaction V, as given by (40.26). The difference between the number of particles and the number of holes is unchanged by this interaction, so that $|A\rangle$ and $|B\rangle$ must have the same value for this difference. In the nth order of perturbation theory there are exactly n scatterings of pairs of particles or holes, ordered in time according to (40.44). These are represented by n points called vertices, the time of the interaction being plotted vertically. At each vertex two operators ξ and two operators $\xi^\dagger$ act. Consider the ξ operators first. Each can give a non-zero result by annihilating a particle or by creating a hole. If a particle is annihilated, it may either have been in the initial state or have been created at an earlier vertex. If a hole is created, it may either be a hole present in the final state or one to be annihilated at a later vertex. The $\xi^\dagger$ operators act similarly. Each can give a non-zero result by

Fig. 40-2

creating a particle, either present in $|B\rangle$ or to be annihilated at a later vertex, or by annihilating a hole present in the initial state $|A\rangle$ or created at an earlier vertex.

Each vertex is associated with a combination of particles and holes, four in all. If particles are represented by lines going up the paper and holes by lines running down the paper, four lines meet at a vertex. Figure 40–2 shows a first order diagram connecting a state $|A\rangle$ containing two particles with a state $|B\rangle$ also containing two particles. The lines entering the vertex are associated with operators ξ in V, and those leaving the vertex with operators $\xi^\dagger$.

It is often advantageous to draw this diagram somewhat differently, as shown in Figure 40–3. Here the two possible ways of pairing the operators occurring in V with the particles and holes to be annihilated or created are shown separately. The minus sign between them indicates that the entire matrix element is the difference between the quantities corresponding to the two graphs. The matrix element associated with the diagram of Figure 40–2 is

$$\begin{aligned} \langle B|V|A\rangle &= \langle \mathbf{F}|\xi(\mathbf{k}_3)\xi(\mathbf{k}_4)V\xi^\dagger(\mathbf{k}_2)\xi^\dagger(\mathbf{k}_1)\,|\mathbf{F}\rangle \\ &= \tfrac{1}{4}\{[\mathcal{V}(\mathbf{k}_4, \mathbf{k}_3; \mathbf{k}_1, \mathbf{k}_2) + \mathcal{V}(\mathbf{k}_3, \mathbf{k}_4; \mathbf{k}_2, \mathbf{k}_1)] \\ &\quad - [\mathcal{V}(\mathbf{k}_3, \mathbf{k}_4; \mathbf{k}_1, \mathbf{k}_2) + \mathcal{V}(\mathbf{k}_4, \mathbf{k}_3; \mathbf{k}_2, \mathbf{k}_1)]\}\ . \end{aligned} \tag{40.51}$$

The left diagram of Figure 40–3 is associated with the first term in square brackets above, the right diagram with the second term in square brackets. In lowest order, all integrations coming from V can be carried out using only the delta functions coming from the vertex. In higher order, some of the integrations must be carried out using the dependence of the $\mathcal{V}(k_A, k_B; k_C, k_D)$ on its arguments.

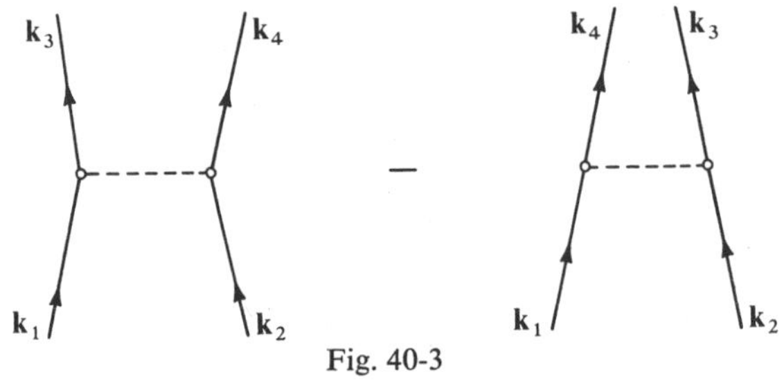

Fig. 40-3

The dashed lines in Figure 40–3 represent the momentum transfer $\mathbf{q}$ between the two particles. It can be assigned either direction. We can consider $\mathbf{q}$ as a new integration variable and associate a δ-function with each three-line vertex, for example

$$\delta(\mathbf{k}_1 - \mathbf{k}_3 - \mathbf{q})$$

with the left vertex of the left part of Figure 40–3. The numerical factor associated with the interaction is a function of $\mathbf{q}$. For the left diagram of Figure 40–3 it is, according to (40.35),

$$\tfrac{1}{4}[U(\mathbf{q}) + U(-\mathbf{q})] = \tfrac{1}{2}\mathrm{Re}\, U(\mathbf{q})\,. \tag{40.52}$$

The factor for the right diagram is also Re $U(\mathbf{q})$, but as the δ-function has a different argument here, the values of $\mathbf{q}$ which appear are different in the two diagrams.

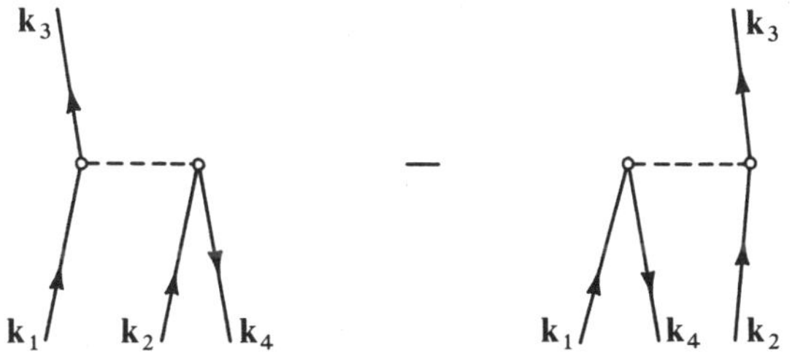

Fig. 40-4

In the discussion just given, all the momenta $\mathbf{k}_1, \ldots, \mathbf{k}_4$ were greater than K_F, so that only particles were involved. Now consider the situation when $\mathbf{k}_1, \mathbf{k}_2, \mathbf{k}_3$, are greater than K_F, but $\mathbf{k}_4$ is less than K_F, so that it represents a hole. The diagram of Figure 40–3 now becomes that of Figure 40–4. The interpretation is that state $|A\rangle$ containing two particles and a hole makes a transition to a state containing just one particle. The initial state is here

$$|A\rangle = \xi(\mathbf{k}_4)\xi^\dagger(\mathbf{k}_2)\xi^\dagger(\mathbf{k}_1)\,|\mathrm{F}\rangle \tag{40.53}$$

and the final state is

$$|B\rangle = \xi^\dagger(\mathbf{k}_3)\,|\mathrm{F}\rangle\,. \tag{40.54}$$

The matrix element coming from the diagram of Figure 40–4 is therefore

$$\begin{aligned}
&\langle \mathrm{F}|\xi(\mathbf{k}_3)V\xi(\mathbf{k}_4)\xi^\dagger(\mathbf{k}_2)\xi^\dagger(\mathbf{k}_1)\,|\mathrm{F}\rangle \\
&= \langle \mathrm{F}|\xi(\mathbf{k}_3)\{\xi^\dagger(\mathbf{k}_3)\xi^\dagger(\mathbf{k}_4)\xi(\mathbf{k}_2)\xi(\mathbf{k}_1)\}\xi(\mathbf{k}_4)\xi^\dagger(\mathbf{k}_2)\xi^\dagger(\mathbf{k}_1)\,|\mathrm{F}\rangle \\
&\quad\times \tfrac{1}{4}[U(\mathbf{k}_2 - \mathbf{k}_3) + U(\mathbf{k}_1 - \mathbf{k}_4) - U(\mathbf{k}_2 - \mathbf{k}_4) - U(\mathbf{k}_1 - \mathbf{k}_3)] \\
&\quad\times (2\pi)^3\,\delta(\mathbf{k}_1 + \mathbf{k}_2 - \mathbf{k}_3 - \mathbf{k}_4) \\
&= \tfrac{1}{2}[\mathrm{Re}\, U(\mathbf{k}_1 - \mathbf{k}_3) - \mathrm{Re}\, U(\mathbf{k}_1 - \mathbf{k}_4)](2\pi)^3\,\delta(\mathbf{k}_1 + \mathbf{k}_2 - \mathbf{k}_3 - \mathbf{k}_4)\,,
\end{aligned} \tag{40.55}$$

which is of exactly the same form as that obtained before, only with a different value of $\mathbf{k}_4$. In any matrix element, the replacement of a momentum $\mathbf{k}$,

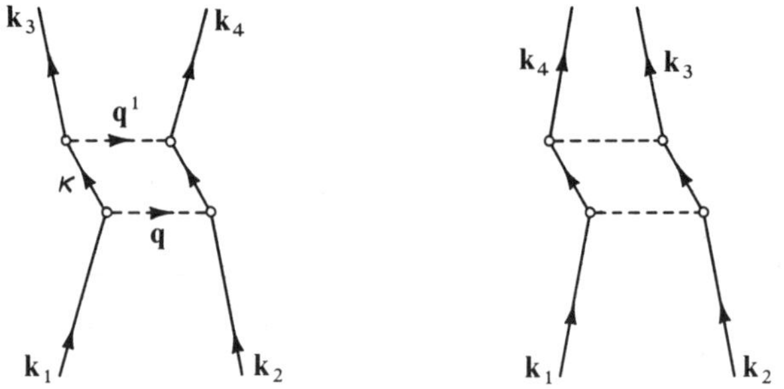

Fig. 40-5

$|\mathbf{k}| > K_F$, of a final particle by a momentum $\mathbf{k}'$, $|\mathbf{k}'| < K_F$, yields the matrix element of the process in which the final particle has been replaced by an initial hole. The same holds for an initial particle and a final hole. This invariance of form is known as *crossing symmetry*. We do not give the general proof for its existence.

Higher-order processes involve more complicated diagrams. The second-order matrix element for particle–particle scattering involves four distinct time orderings. The V which acts earlier can annihilate the initial state particles and that which acts later can create the final state particles. The intermediate state then contains two particles. This is diagrammed in Figure 40–5. In each of these diagrams there are four *external* lines representing particles in the initial or final state. There are also two *internal* lines which connect vertices. A given physical process involves certain fixed external lines. The number and kind of internal lines depend on the process and on the order of perturbation theory being used.

The second time ordering is diagrammed in Figure 40–6. Here the earlier interaction produces two particle–hole pairs, the particles being the final state particles. The latter interaction then annihilates the holes and the initial state particles. The momenta of the internal lines must here be less than K_F in magnitude. The δ-function associated with a three-line vertex such as the extreme left one in Figure 40–6 is

$$\delta(\mathbf{k}_1 - \boldsymbol{\kappa} - \mathbf{q}')$$

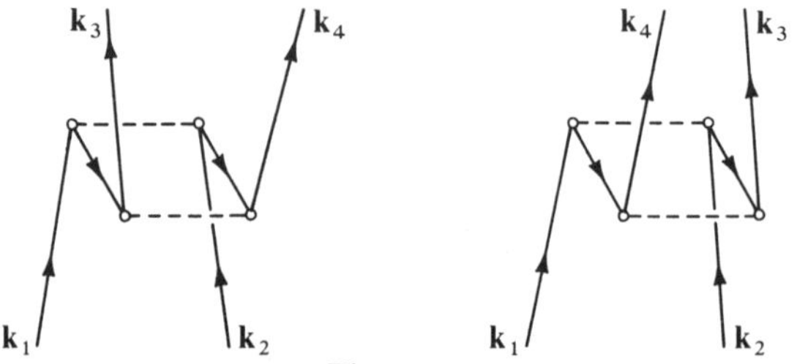

Fig. 40-6

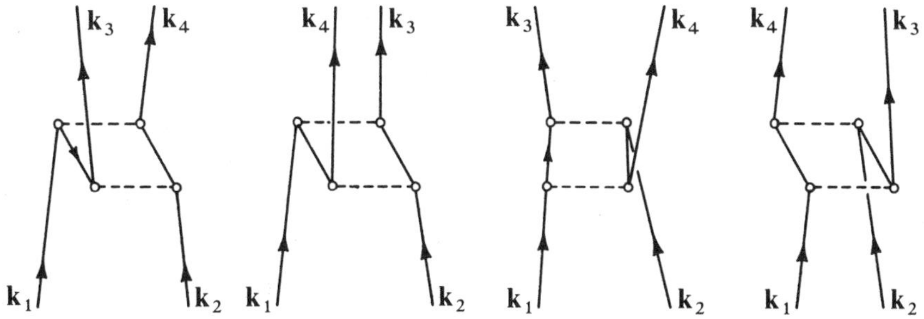

Fig. 40-7

even though the hole is spoken of as going upward. This is because a hole represents missing momentum. The other two time orderings are shown in Figure 40–7. Their description in terms of particles and holes is evident.

The effect of the various time orderings is to arrange the creation and annihilation operators in various orders, and as these do not commute, to change the relative signs of the contributions of the different diagrams.

There are other diagrams, called *tadpoles*, which can occur in first order in the amplitude for a single particle to remain in its single particle state. Such a diagram is shown in Figure 40–8. It involves the forward scattering of the particle with a fermion of the Fermi sea. Clearly such a diagram can be added to any particle or hole line in any diagram. The two operators associated with the tadpole vertex must annihilate and create a fermion within the sea, so the momentum is less than K_F and the closed loop is to be considered as a hole line. Going along with the tadpole is the right diagram of the figure in which the particle is exchanged with a fermion of the sea.

In the second-order diagrams just given, the total momentum transfer $\mathbf{q} + \mathbf{q}'$ is fixed by the initial and final states, but the sharing of this total between $\mathbf{q}$ and $\mathbf{q}'$ is not. Thus $\mathbf{q}$ is a non-trivial integration variable and the second-order scattering amplitude involves $U(\mathbf{q})$ for a range of $\mathbf{q}$. Higher-order matrix elements are much more complicated than the lowest order which can contribute to a given process.

There are diagrams with no external lines. The lowest-order one is shown in Figure 40–9. The left part shows a pair of particles which are in the Fermi

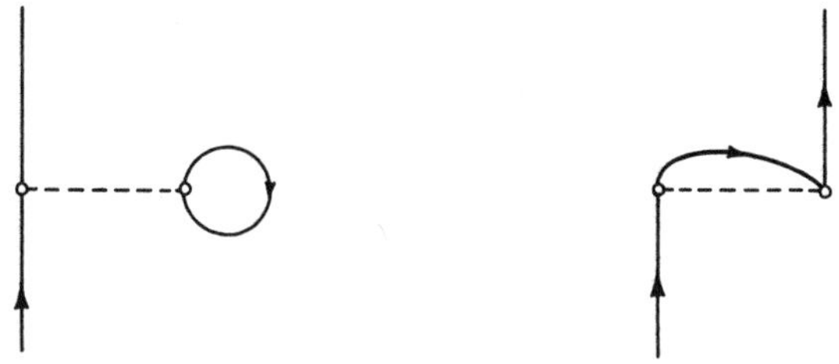

Fig. 40-8

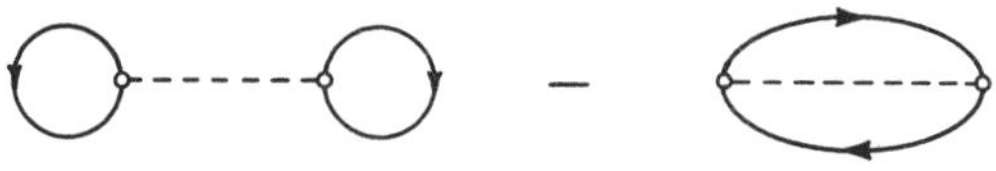

Fig. 40-9

sea which are forward scattered, remaining in the sea. The right part shows the exchange of two particles in the sea. Higher-order processes of this kind exist, such as those of Figure 40–10. The processes described by these diagrams do not correspond to scatterings or to particle–hole pair formation or annihilation as real physical processes. They reflect a modification of the Fermi sea by virtual processes caused by the interaction V. Any ground-state to ground-state diagram can be introduced alongside any diagram involving external lines. In a perturbation approach such diagrams can always be ignored as they give equal contributions to all processes, including the process in which nothing happens to anything. They correspond, therefore, to an unobservable common phase factor in all matrix elements. We see in Section 41 how these diagrams do lead to a change in the energy of the ground state of the system.

Fig. 40-10

Diagrams provide a very useful way of talking about and classifying terms in the perturbation series for $U(t)$. In the end one must go back and use the series to find actual results. There are rules for constructing the mathematical expression for the matrix element directly from the diagrams, but for this we refer the interested reader elsewhere.*

41. THE GROUND STATE OF A MANY FERMION SYSTEM

In this section, we want to show one application of the techniques developed in Section 40, the derivation of the Goldstone expansion for the energy of a system of weakly interacting fermions. This ground state energy is altered from that of the non-interacting fermions by the effect of ground-state to ground-state matrix elements like those discussed at the end of the previous section. We follow a method due to Bloch.

*J. Goldstone, Proc. Roy Soc. (London) **A239**, 267 (1957). C. Bloch, in *Studies in Statistical Mechanics* (J. de Boer and G. E. Uhlenbeck, eds.) North Holland Publishing Co., Amsterdam, 1965, Vol. III.

Equation (40.43) expresses $U(t)$ as an operator involving the eigenstates of the complete Hamiltonian H, namely as

(41.1) $$U(t) = e^{iH_0 t} \sum_n |n\rangle e^{-iE_n t} \langle n| \,,$$

so that

(41.2) $$\langle \mathrm{F}| U(t) |\mathrm{F}\rangle = e^{iE_F t} \sum_n |\langle \mathrm{F}|n\rangle|^2 e^{-iE_n t} \,.$$

This contains all the eigenvalues of H, here taken to be discrete. If in this equation we replace it by β, it reads

(41.3) $$\langle \mathrm{F}| \hat{U}(\beta) |\mathrm{F}\rangle = \sum_n |\langle \mathrm{F}|n\rangle|^2 e^{\beta(E_F - E_n)} \,,$$

where $\hat{U}(\beta) = \hat{U}(it) = U(t)$. For real positive β, the terms in the sum get exponentially smaller with E_n while the number of states within a fixed range of energies increases only as some power of the mean energy of the range, so that as β approaches infinity the contribution of all higher terms relative to that of the first vanishes. We may therefore write, for large positive β,

(41.4) $$\begin{aligned} \langle \mathrm{F}| \hat{U}(\beta) |\mathrm{F}\rangle &\approx | \langle \mathrm{F}|0\rangle |^2 e^{\beta(E_F - E_0)} \\ &= | \langle \mathrm{F}|0\rangle |^2 e^{-\beta \Delta E_0} \,. \end{aligned}$$

This exhibits ΔE_0 as a function of ground-state to ground-state matrix elements of $U(t)$ evaluated at large imaginary time.

There are too many possible diagrams involved in (41.4) to make it useful for calculation, as not only connected but also unconnected diagrams enter. An unconnected diagram is one such as is illustrated in Figure 41–1 where there are two parts not joined by any particle, hole, or momentum transfer line. The one shown is of third order. In higher order, the proliferation of such diagrams complicates the calculation. Fortunately we do not need to consider such diagrams separately, but can include their effect easily once the contribution of the connected diagrams is known. To see this, we note that there are three essentially different time orderings of the interactions in the diagram shown which are possible. They are shown in Figure 41–2. The first-order process, Γ_1, can occur before, during, or after the second-order process Γ_2. All orderings must be considered. In changing the time order of two unconnected parts,

Fig. 41-1

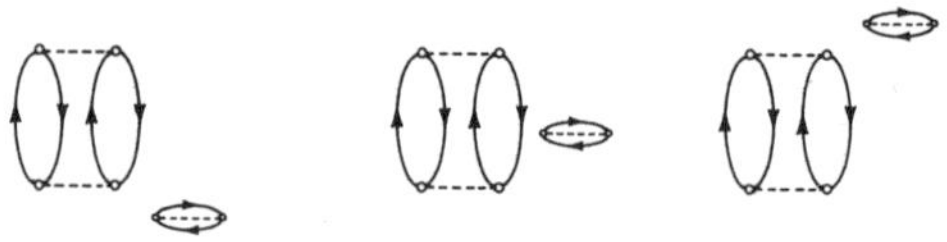

Fig. 41-2

the direction of no line is changed so that no particle becomes a hole or vice versa. Thus, the three diagrams shown give a contribution to $\langle F|U(t)|F\rangle$ which is just what one would get by suppressing the time ordering between operators occurring in Γ_1 relative to those occurring in Γ_2, namely the product of the two separate contributions

$$\langle F|U_{\Gamma_1}(t)|F\rangle\,\langle F|U_{\Gamma_2}(t)|F\rangle\,.$$

If Γ_1 and Γ_2 are diagrams of the same kind, as shown in Figure 41–3, then the above prescription gives double the correct result, because the two time

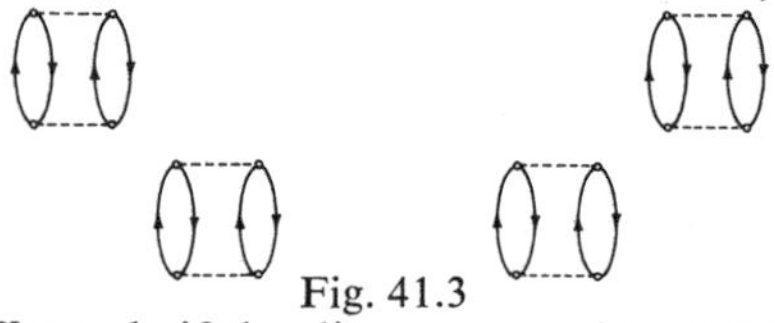

Fig. 41.3

orderings shown differ only if the diagrams are identifiable. Since all momenta involved are integration variables there is no distinction to be made between them and we get a contribution

$$\tfrac{1}{2}\langle F|U_\Gamma(t)|F\rangle^2\,.$$

In general, if a diagram of a given type Γ appears n times, its contribution is

$$\langle F|U_\Gamma(t)|F\rangle^n/n!\,.$$

Therefore, on summing over all possible diagrams we get

$$\begin{aligned}(41.5)\quad \langle F|U(t)|F\rangle &= \sum_{n_1,n_2,\ldots}\frac{1}{n_1!n_2!\cdots}\langle F|U_{\Gamma_1}(t)|F\rangle^{n_1}\langle F|U_{\Gamma_2}(t)|F\rangle^{n_2}\cdots\\ &= \exp\left[\langle F|U_{\Gamma_1}(t)|F\rangle + \langle F|U_{\Gamma_2}(t)|F\rangle + \cdots\right]\\ &= \exp\left[\langle F|U(t)|F\rangle_c\right]\end{aligned}$$

where the subscript c denotes connectedness. We need to consider only connected diagrams.

Comparing (41.5) with (41.4) we see that

$$(41.6)\qquad \begin{aligned}\exp\left[\langle F|\hat{U}(\beta)|F\rangle_c\right] &\approx |\langle F|0\rangle|^2\exp\left[-\beta\Delta E_0\right]\\ \langle F|\hat{U}(\beta)|F\rangle_c &\approx \ln|\langle F|0\rangle|^2 - \beta\Delta E_0\,.\end{aligned}$$

Thus, the problem reduces to finding the term in $\langle F|\hat{U}(\beta)|F\rangle_c$, which, for large β, is proportional to β. This problem is easily solved on using the connection between $U(t)$ and $G(E)$ given by (40.49). Equation (40.49) is also valid when only the connected parts of $\langle F|U(t)|F\rangle$ are considered, since in each order $G(E)$ contains the same operators V, and corresponding pairings of creation and annihilation operators can be made in the two cases. Therefore, we write

$$\langle F|\hat{U}(\beta)|F\rangle_c = \frac{1}{2\pi i}\int_C e^{\beta(E_F-E)}\langle F|G(E)|F\rangle_c dE\,. \tag{41.7}$$

Now using (40.46) for $G(E)$ we get

$$\langle F|\hat{U}(\beta)|F\rangle_c = \frac{1}{2\pi i}\int_C e^{\beta(E_F-E)}\left\{\frac{1}{E-E_F}+\frac{\mathfrak{F}(E)}{(E-E_F)^2}\right\}dE\,, \tag{41.8}$$

where $\mathfrak{F}(E) = \langle F|T(E)|F\rangle_c$.

The integrand in (41.8) has poles at $E = E_F$ and at higher values of E, the latter coming from $\mathfrak{F}(E)$. $\mathfrak{F}(E)$ has no singularity at $E = E_F$ because no connected diagram can involve an energy as low as E_F, which is the energy of the state with no lines present, $|F\rangle$. For large β, the residues of the poles at higher energies become exponentially small relative to the residue of the pole at $E = E_F$. Thus,

$$\langle F|\hat{U}(\beta)|F\rangle_c = 1 + \mathfrak{F}'(E_F) - \beta\mathfrak{F}(E_F)\,. \tag{41.9}$$

This is of the desired form and yields

$$\begin{aligned}\Delta E_0 &= \mathfrak{F}(E_F)\\ &= \langle F|V + V\frac{1}{E_0 - H_0}V + \cdots + |F\rangle_c\,,\end{aligned} \tag{41.10}$$

which is known as the Goldstone expansion. The terms independent of β have to do with the value of $|\langle F|0\rangle|^2$.

The Goldstone expansion is complete only when there is an energy gap between the ground state and the higher states. If the spectrum is continuous, the sequence of poles spoken of above becomes a cut in the E-plane, and there are other contributions to ΔE_0.

The mathematical trick used to calculate ΔE_0, that of replacing t by $-i\beta$, has profound physical significance. Making the replacement in (41.1) yields

$$\hat{U}(\beta) = e^{\beta H_0}\sum_n |n\rangle e^{-\beta E_n}\langle n|\,. \tag{41.11}$$

Taking the trace gives

$$\begin{aligned}\mathrm{Tr}\, e^{-\beta H_0}\hat{U}(\beta) &= \sum_n \langle n|e^{-\beta H_0}\hat{U}(\beta)|n\rangle\\ &= \sum_n e^{-\beta E_n}\,.\end{aligned} \tag{41.12}$$

The function on the right depends on various parameters of the system such as its volume or density, and is known as the *partition function* of the system. It has the standard form of a partition function if β is replaced by $1/kT$, the inverse temperature of the system. The limit $\beta = \infty$ is the low temperature limit of the system. In this way, the methods of quantum mechanical perturbation theory can be applied to the problems of statistical mechanics.

APPENDIX. THE DENSITY OPERATOR

Even when a system is in a well-defined quantum mechanical state, there is a statistical element which enters when one predicts the value of an observable as measured in that state. If the observable does not commute with the observables which define the state, only a probability distribution with a non-vanishing dispersion can be predicted. This type of statistical element has been thoroughly discussed earlier in this book. Another type of statistical element enters when the state of the system is not specified with complete precision. This lack of precision can also occur in classical mechanics. In both cases it leads to the subject of statistical mechanics. In this appendix we wish merely to introduce a quantity, the density operator, which is basic to quantum statistical mechanics, and to apply it to some simple cases of polarized particles.

If a system is in the quantum state $|\alpha'\rangle$, the expectation value of an observable f associated with the system is $\langle\alpha'|f|\alpha'\rangle$. If the state is not specified completely, but if a probability, $\mathcal{P}_{\alpha'}$, is given for finding the system in the state $|\alpha'\rangle$, we may define an *average expectation value* of f by

$$\bar{f} = \sum_{\alpha'} \mathcal{P}_{\alpha'}\langle\alpha'|f|\alpha'\rangle. \tag{I.1}$$

Under these circumstances the system is said to be in a *mixture* of states. A mixture differs from a superposition because the relative phases of the states in a mixture are not specified, while in a superposition they are. A superposition of states is a state. A mixture of states is not a state.

In order to describe this situation simply, it is convenient to write the expectation value of an observable in a way such that the state vector itself does not appear. To accomplish this we introduce the projection operator onto the state $|\alpha'\rangle$, denoted by $P_{\alpha'}$, through the definition

$$P_{\alpha'}|\alpha'\rangle = |\alpha'\rangle$$
$$P_{\alpha'}|\beta'\rangle = 0 \text{ if } \langle\beta'|\alpha'\rangle = 0\,. \tag{I.2}$$

It follows from these that

$$P_{\alpha'}{}^2 = P_{\alpha'}\,, \tag{I.3}$$

which shows that $P_{\alpha'}$ has eigenvalues unity and zero, and that only one state has eigenvalue unity. With the help of $P_{\alpha'}$, the expectation value of an observable f can be written as a trace:

$$\begin{aligned}\langle\alpha'|f|\alpha'\rangle &= \sum_{\alpha''}\langle\alpha''|P_{\alpha'}f|\alpha''\rangle \\ &= \text{tr}\, P_{\alpha'}f\,,\end{aligned} \tag{I.4}$$

where the sum is over a complete set of orthonormal states. Any such set of states can be used to evaluate the trace.

The above holds for a pure state, $|\alpha'\rangle$. It is easily generalized to hold for a mixture. If the mixture consists of states $|\alpha'\rangle, |\alpha''\rangle, \ldots$, which occur with probabilities $\mathcal{P}_{\alpha'}, \mathcal{P}_{\alpha''}, \ldots$, we define the *density matrix* in the α representation by

$$\langle\alpha''|\rho|\alpha'\rangle = \mathcal{P}_{\alpha'}\,\delta_{\alpha''\alpha'}\,. \tag{I.5}$$

This matrix is diagonal with the probabilities as eigenvalues. From this definition we see that the trace of the density matrix is unity, and that all its eigenvalues are non-negative. The average expectation value of f can now be written as

$$\begin{aligned}\bar{f} &= \sum_{\alpha'}\mathcal{P}_{\alpha'}\langle\alpha'|f|\alpha'\rangle \\ &= \sum_{\alpha',\alpha''}\langle\alpha''|\rho|\alpha'\rangle\langle\alpha'|f|\alpha''\rangle \\ &= \sum_{\alpha''}\langle\alpha''|\rho f|\alpha''\rangle \\ &= \text{tr}\,\rho f\,.\end{aligned} \tag{I.6}$$

It is the trace of the product of the *density operator*, ρ, and f.

The density operator is defined in a certain representation, here that defined by $|\alpha'\rangle$, as having a diagonal matrix in that representation. In another representation the matrix of ρ will in general not be diagonal, but its diagonal elements still give the probabilities of finding the corresponding states in the mixture. When ρ is not diagonal the states in the mixture are correlated. To show the probability meaning of the diagonal elements of ρ, we use the f representation to evaluate (I.6).

$$\bar{f} = \sum_{f'} \langle f' | \rho f | f' \rangle$$

(I.7)

$$= \sum_{f'} f' \langle f' | \rho | f' \rangle.$$

This shows that $\bar{f}$ is the weighted sum of eigenvalues of f with the diagonal elements of ρ as weights, which is consistent with their being probabilities.

Let us apply these ideas to polarization states. If a particle of spin $\frac{1}{2}$ is polarized in the $+z$ direction, it is in an eigenstate of s_z with eigenvalue $\frac{1}{2}$ (in units such that $\hbar = 1$). In the s_z representation, then, the density matrix is given by

(I.8)
$$(\rho) = \begin{pmatrix} 1 & 0 \\ 0 & 0 \end{pmatrix},$$

which clearly corresponds to a projection operator. Had the particle been polarized in the $+y$ direction instead, the corresponding matrix in the s_z representation would have been

(I.9)
$$\frac{1}{2} + s_y = \begin{pmatrix} \frac{1}{2} & \frac{-i}{2} \\ \frac{i}{2} & \frac{1}{2} \end{pmatrix},$$

which is not so obviously a projection operator. In this representation the density matrix is not diagonal, but it nonetheless represents a pure state.

If the particle were unpolarized, we would have

(I.10)
$$(\rho) = \begin{pmatrix} \frac{1}{2} & 0 \\ 0 & \frac{1}{2} \end{pmatrix}$$

in this same representation. This is a multiple of the unit matrix and is the same in all representations. A completely unpolarized beam is completely unpolarized no matter what direction of polarization is referred to. In general for particles of spin $\frac{1}{2}$, if the diagonal density matrix is

$$\begin{pmatrix} \frac{1+\lambda}{2} & 0 \\ 0 & \frac{1-\lambda}{2} \end{pmatrix},$$

the polarization is defined to be λ. In a different representation, ρ is no longer diagonal and the polarization can no longer be inferred from the diagonal elements alone, but it depends on the correlations between the states of the mixture as given by the off-diagonal elements. The matrix, written in the s_z representation,

$$\begin{pmatrix} \frac{1}{2} & -\frac{i\lambda}{2} \\ \frac{i\lambda}{2} & \frac{1}{2} \end{pmatrix},$$

for example, represents a particle with polarization λ along the y direction. The probabilities of the two possible values of s_z are equal, but the particle is not unpolarized.

When more than two eigenvalues of s_z occur, the situation is more complicated. Consider $S = 1$, $S_z = \pm 1, 0$. An unpolarized particle has a density matrix

$$\tfrac{1}{3}\begin{pmatrix} 1 & 0 & 0 \\ 0 & 1 & 0 \\ 0 & 0 & 1 \end{pmatrix}$$

which is the same in all representations. The density matrix

$$\begin{pmatrix} \frac{1}{2} & 0 & 0 \\ 0 & 0 & 0 \\ 0 & 0 & \frac{1}{2} \end{pmatrix}$$

also gives zero average expectation value for S_z, but does not treat all directions alike because the state $S_z = 0$ is not present in the mixture. If one looks at this in the representation with S_y diagonal, obtained by rotating the coordinates through $\pi/2$ about the x axis, one obtains

$$\begin{pmatrix} \frac{1}{4} & 0 & -\frac{1}{4} \\ 0 & \frac{1}{2} & 0 \\ -\frac{1}{4} & 0 & \frac{1}{4} \end{pmatrix}.$$

The probability of finding $S_y = 0$ is $\frac{1}{2}$, which is greater than the value $\frac{1}{3}$ corresponding to zero polarization. A state such as this is called *aligned.*

As a last example we take two particles of spin $\frac{1}{2}$, a neutron and a proton, say. Let the proton be unpolarized so that its density matrix is

$$(\rho_p) = \begin{pmatrix} \frac{1}{2} & 0 \\ 0 & \frac{1}{2} \end{pmatrix}$$

and let the neutron be polarized in the $+z$ direction.

$$(\rho_n) = \begin{pmatrix} 1 & 0 \\ 0 & 0 \end{pmatrix}$$

In the representation given by s_{nz} and s_{pz} diagonal, the density matrix of the system is the 4×4 matrix obtained by multiplying each element of (ρ_n) by the matrix (ρ_p).

$$\begin{matrix} S_{nz} = & \frac{1}{2} & \frac{1}{2} & -\frac{1}{2} & -\frac{1}{2} \\ S_{pz} = & \frac{1}{2} & -\frac{1}{2} & \frac{1}{2} & -\frac{1}{2} \end{matrix}$$
$$\begin{pmatrix} \frac{1}{2} & 0 & 0 & 0 \\ 0 & \frac{1}{2} & 0 & 0 \\ 0 & 0 & 0 & 0 \\ 0 & 0 & 0 & 0 \end{pmatrix}.$$

The column labels are shown. This can be transformed to the representation with total $\mathbf{S}^2$ and total S_z diagonal, a representation in terms of the singlet and the three triplet states. The result is

$$\begin{matrix} S = & 0 & 1 & 1 & 1 \\ S_z = & 0 & 1 & 0 & -1 \end{matrix}$$
$$\begin{pmatrix} \frac{1}{4} & 0 & \frac{1}{4} & 0 \\ 0 & \frac{1}{2} & 0 & 0 \\ \frac{1}{4} & 0 & \frac{1}{4} & 0 \\ 0 & 0 & 0 & 0 \end{pmatrix}.$$

The total probability of finding the triplet state is $\frac{3}{4}$, just what it would be if the neutron were also unpolarized.

The average expectation value of f may change with time. When f does not contain the time explicitly, we have

$$i\hbar \frac{d}{dt} \langle\, |f|\, \rangle = \langle\, |[f, H]|\, \rangle\,. \tag{I.11}$$

This holds for each state in a mixture, so for the average expectation value we require

$$i\hbar \frac{d}{dt} \operatorname{tr} \rho f = \operatorname{tr} \rho [f, H]. \tag{I.12}$$

In the Schrödinger picture, $\dot{f} = 0$, so that (I.12) becomes

$$\begin{aligned} i\hbar \operatorname{tr} \dot{\rho} f &= \operatorname{tr} (\rho f H - \rho H f) \\ &= \operatorname{tr} (f H \rho - f \rho H) \\ &= \operatorname{tr} f [H, \rho]. \end{aligned} \tag{I.13}$$

Since this is true for every f, we see that

$$i\hbar \dot{\rho} = -[\rho, H]. \tag{I.14}$$

This looks like a Heisenberg equation of motion except for the sign. ρ is not an observable of the system, however, but describes the state of the system, so that (I.14) is equivalent to the Schrödinger equation. In the Heisenberg picture we get

$$i\hbar \operatorname{tr} (\dot{\rho} f + \rho \dot{f}) = \operatorname{tr} \rho [f, H],$$

but in this picture $i\hbar \dot{f} = [f, H]$ so that here

$$\dot{\rho} = 0. \tag{I.15}$$

This is to be expected since in the Heisenberg picture the state does not change with the time. The transformation from the Schrödinger to the Heisenberg picture gives all operators, including ρ, an additional time dependence described by $i\hbar\dot{\mathcal{O}} = [\mathcal{O}, H]$. For $\mathcal{O} = \rho$, this just cancels the time dependence in the Schrödinger picture. For observables it gives the Heisenberg time dependence, there being none in the Schrödinger picture.

Index